Air-Age Education Series

AIR-AGE EDUCATION SERIES

WINGS FOR YOU

(A Book About Aviation)

BY

E. A. CROSS

Head of English Department
Colorado State College of Education
Greeley, Colorado

Member of

AVIATION EDUCATION
RESEARCH GROUP

Teachers College, Columbia University

Prepared with the Coöperation of the
Civil Aeronautics Administration

NEW YORK • 1943

THE MACMILLAN COMPANY

FOREWORD

The revolutionary influence of aviation on military strategy is now recognized by laymen as well as by military authorities. It is also apparent that the influences of aviation on civilian life are equally revolutionary and perhaps more important from the long-term viewpoint. Wide seas, dangerous reefs, precipitous mountains, frozen wastes, and jungle depths, all barriers to earthbound generations, have become features of the landscape below the global sweep of the airplane travelers in the ocean of air which is now the third dimension for an air-free people. No aspect of human ecology will remain unaltered by this new instrumentality which not only abolishes distances but also reshapes basic human geography and remolds the internal and external relationships of national and continental population groups. City, state, national, and even continental boundaries vanish or become curious anachronisms to the stratospheric travelers on great-circle routes which wheel around a planet bereft of topographical restrictions.

Our educational leaders and the schools and colleges which they represent have made it clear that they will not only contribute directly to the paramount task of winning the war by helping to train the young men who will give air supremacy to the United Nations but will also help prepare the American people for constructive living as world citizens in the air age. The War Department, the Navy Department, the Civil Aeronautics Administration, the United States Office of Education, and state and local educators are advocates of this type of education.

The AIR-AGE EDUCATION SERIES represents a major step in providing our schools with teaching materials for these purposes.

This series has two objectives. First, it seeks to provide text and teaching materials for older students in high schools in the field of pre-flight aeronautics. Second, it seeks to provide pertinent aviation materials which may be woven into existing courses in the curricula of the secondary schools and, wherever feasible, of the elementary schools.

To name all the men, women, schools, aviation industries and authorities, publishers, representatives of colleges, universities, school systems, non-profit institutions and agencies of State and Federal Governments who made possible the AIR-AGE EDUCATION SERIES would be a difficult task. In individual books, authors have acknowledged assistance and advice from many sources. Yet the series owes its existence more particularly to a few individuals and organizations.

Special acknowledgments are due to Mr. Robert H. Hinckley, who, as Assistant Secretary of Commerce for Air, was the pioneer advocate of "air-conditioning" America; to Mr. C. I. Stanton, Administrator of the Civil Aeronautics Administration, who gave essential support to a program of aviation-education research; to Mr. Bruce Uthus of the Civil Aeronautics Administration, whose encouragement, resourcefulness, and ability so largely account for the development of the AIR-AGE EDUCATION SERIES; to Dr. John W. Studebaker, United States Commissioner of Education, who has done much to prepare American education to meet the challenge of the air age; to Professor N. L. Engelhardt, Teachers College, Columbia University, and his colleagues, who guided the development of materials reflected in this book and related teaching materials; and, finally, to Teachers College, Columbia University, for the provision of indispensable office space, library, and other research facilities.

So then, the Civil Aeronautics Administration, Teachers College, Columbia University, the University of Nebraska, the publishers, and many especially qualified authors have co-operated in producing the AIR-AGE EDUCATION SERIES in the belief that it will aid American education to eliminate the hiatus between technical aeronautical advances and popular understanding of aviation as a revolutionary world force today and tomorrow.

BEN D. WOOD
Chairman, Education Committee,
The Institute of the Aeronautical Sciences

TABLE OF CONTENTS

vii

Index of Authors

THEY WANTED WINGS

By E. A. Cross

HUMAN beings are animals adapted by nature to live upon the surface of the earth, the land surface at that. But nature endowed man with curiosity and longings. We want to know things and go places and see sights. Our curiosity has made us inventive and resourceful. We learned to swim and thus to abandon for an hour the land where we belong and to cross narrow rivers and lakes. We have explored caves. We have excavated mines and gone into the depths of the earth. Our curiosity led us to skies and to wish to leave the surface of the earth. We built towers and climbed mountains. We sent up balloons. But these were not enough.

In submarines we learned to go down into the sea three or possibly four hundred feet. Then the bathysphere was devised and man went a half mile below the surface of the ocean. The French built Eiffel Tower nearly a thousand feet high. Then the Americans erected business buildings as high and higher. Men made balloons and soared at dizzy heights; and that was not enough. They wanted wings.

Their wants got into poetry and song. About the time men are said to have built the Tower of Babel so high that it was thought God feared it would reach up into his heaven and man would thus learn his secret, Icarus, the son of Daedalus, made himself wings of eagle feathers with which to follow the sun across the sky. But Icarus, who is supposed to have had godlike wisdom, knew nothing of brass and steel and duralumin. He had never gone to a welding school. He fastened his wings to his body with beeswax, and when he soared too close to the sun, the wax melted, poor Icarus lost his wings and hurtled through the sky and crashed as tragically as a modern airplane crashes when a wing is ripped off by storm and strain. He had no parachute to open and let him gently down to earth.

One of the Hebrew poets a thousand years ago longed to

1

soar aloft as on the wings of an eagle, and one of our Christian Church hymns has man yearning for the wings of a dove. We think of Leonardo da Vinci as an old, old bearded man, as a great painter, he who painted "The Last Supper" and the "Mona Lisa." He was a restless spirit with many talents besides painting. He was, to mention two of his accomplishments, a sanitary and a military engineer—and he had a great ambition to fly. Leonardo gave much time to the problem of flight. He designed wings. We have the drawings he made for sets of wings. He actually made the wings, and one of his apprentices tried them in actual flight. The poor fellow crashed, of course, and that was the end of Leonardo's attempt to construct a pair of flapping wings by means of which a man might fly. Late in the nineteenth century, when we were upon the very eve of success, John T. Trowbridge, an American poet, wrote a hilariously funny ballad about a visionary boy who made a fool of himself by trying to fly. The poem is one you doubtless have read, "Darius Green and His Flying Machine."

Two sure ways of proving yourself a fool or downright crazy, after "Darius Green" was written, were to try to invent a perpetual motion machine or a flying machine. It could be proved by the laws of physics that neither could be done. To lift 150 pounds of man off the ground requires more power than a man's muscles can produce. And up to the twentieth century no engine had been devised that could lift its own weight, the weight of a flying machine, and that of a man to operate it.

The flapping-winged machine has not yet been devised and probably will never be constructed; but modern parachutes and gliders have positively shown that Leonardo and Darius Green were not as foolish as those who laughed at them. Men watching buzzards, hawks, and eagles discovered how to use rising air currents to keep themselves aloft for hours at a time without flapping their wings. They also calculated how many square feet of wing surface were needed to support 150 pounds. From such data modern gliders are constructed. These are launched into the air by means of automobiles or airplanes and then released. In them aviators have been able to soar for hours.

After the mathematics and mechanics of flight had been

The Boeing Flying Fortress banks to the left to reveal the U. S. Army Air Force's insignia and its four powerful engines

worked out, it was only a question of time until the rigid-wing, power-driven airplane would be built by somebody. The first problem was the engine. Before 1900, steam and electricity were the possible sources of power. A steam engine was necessarily heavy, water was heavy, and gas, coal, or oil to heat the water were the possibilities. Storage batteries to provide electric power were impossibly heavy.

Then experimenters in petroleum products learned to refine benzine and gasoline as well as kerosene out of crude oil. Next the mechanics invented an engine operated by direct explosions of gas within the cylinders. After that the world was ready for the right man to mount an internal combustion engine inside a rigid-wing machine. The right man turned out to be two men—the Wright brothers.

A short time before their success, Professor Langley in Washington built a small high-pressure steam engine and a plane that in a trial flew a few yards before crashing into the Potomac. Then came success, but after how many centuries of waiting! The painter-engineer Leonardo had believed flight possible. The English philosopher-scientist, Roger Bacon, regarded in his lifetime as a wizard in league with the devil, predicted six hundred years ago that men some day would fly. "We will be able," he said, "to construct machines which will propel ships with greater speed than a whole garrison of rowers, and which will need only one pilot to guide them. We will be able to propel carriages with incredible speed without the assistance of an animal. And we will be able to make machines which by means of wings will enable us to fly like birds." And finally the poet Tennyson added his word to that of engineer and scientist, and in the last quarter of the nineteenth century confidently predicted "argosies of the air."

All these desires of men, these predictions, and these failures, failures that paved the way to success, waited for the right men and the day when all was ready. The day was December 17, 1903. The men were Wilbur and Orville Wright of Dayton, Ohio. These young men were not visionary. They were so realistic that at one time after trials and failures Wilbur made the pessimistic remark: "Men will sometime fly, but it will not be in our lifetime." For their story turn to David Masters' account of the progress of flying from 1903 to 1925.

MAN'S FIRST FLIGHT[1]

By David Masters

THE passing years will weave their legends around the Wrights, with fact and fiction so intertwined that it will be difficult to disentangle one from the other. The fact that they once made cycles * "in some one-horse American village," as I have heard it described, has given rise among many to the impression that the Wrights were two illiterates from the backwoods, a couple of ordinary mechanics who solved the problem of flight by some lucky accident.

Let me scotch that false impression straight away. Nothing could be farther from the truth and nothing do them a greater injustice. Instead of being the sons of a village blacksmith or backwoodsman who could not read or sign his name, they were the sons of a preacher, Milton Wright, who was the head of a religious body in Dayton. The local school gave them a good groundwork of education; but in the science of flying they were self-taught. When men do what no man has ever done before, they have to be self-taught, for no living man knows how to teach them to do what they want to do; so it needs a touch of genius to find the way.

There is indeed no need to bedeck the Wrights with legends, for the truth itself is romantic enough. Born near Newcastle in Indiana on April 16, 1867, Wilbur Wright moved with his parents to Dayton in Ohio, where Orville came into the world on August 19, 1871. There was no humbug about their father, nothing about him of the stern Covenanters who turned their Scottish manses into prisons of gloom. He preached, as he was bound to do, but he was a human being as well as a minister, and practised the good deed as well as speaking the good word.

---

[1] From *On the Wing*, by David Masters, Henry Holt & Co., 1934. Copyright by Eyre & Spotteswood, Ltd., London.

* *cycles:* bicycles. Since the author of this selection is British, the reader will encounter many words and expressions which differ slightly from American usage.

Some families pull together, others draw apart. The Wrights were a happy family. As well as Wilbur and Orville, there were two elder brothers, Lorin and Rechlin, with a sister, Katharine, to give the boys an insight into the mind of femininity. They were quite united. Their father jollied them and watched them grow. He gave them all many a pleasant surprise, but the surprise that made the most impression on the minds of Wilbur and Orville came very unexpectedly one evening. They were together in a room in their wooden house when their father walked in at dusk. Boy-like, their eyes at once detected that he had something in his hands, something which he was trying to conceal from them. Before they could get to him to ask him what it was, he threw one hand upward in the air, and an object whirred away across the room, touched the ceiling and fell to the floor.

They dashed after it. "What is it, father?" said one.

"It's a bat," said the other.

It was one of those French toys known as a helicopter that are carried through the air by a whirring screw, but to them ever after it was a bat. They never forgot it. Years later their interest was stimulated by birds on the wing, and as they went into the fields together they would watch the feathered songsters flying. They were very much interested, but it was just the interest of boys whose minds were expanding to the wonders around them.

The kite-flying craze took hold of them, as it has intrigued most boys who could get into the open spaces. I also flew my kites and made them of brown paper, kites much bigger than myself, which I decorated with a human face whose large eyes and laughing mouth full of big teeth used to grin down on me from above. I gloried in the length of tail I could make them carry, and got much fun out of slipping a piece of paper on the string and seeing it slide upwards in the air to carry my message to the kite.

I was very young, but there used to be three men who flew kites that bore no resemblance to mine. Theirs were like boxes, which they flew to great heights. And continually I saw the men writing in a little black book.

"The big fools! Pity they ain't got nothing better to do," I remember one working woman saying to another.

Those young men were undoubtedly trying to work out the effect of various winds on their kites, but to the ignorant they were merely fools.

Orville and Wilbur Wright suffered similar disparaging remarks. They enjoyed sending their kites in the air until people began to laugh at them, whereupon they concluded they were too old for kite-flying and gave it up. Making a model of the helicopter their father had given them, they found it flew quite well. Not content, they decided to make something bigger, which they did, thinking if the little one flew well, the bigger one would fly even better. Instead of which, the bigger they made them the worse they flew. Baffled and puzzled, they gave it up and turned their attention to other things.

It was Orville who began to dabble in letters. He wrote and edited a four-page paper for boys. He did more than write it, for he printed it on a printing press tied together with bits of string and pieces of wood that would have made Heath Robinson chortle with joy. Caxton himself could not have made it work, nor could anyone else who saw it, but somehow Orville got it to go. He had the magic touch that could persuade the crude machine to do its job, and when it struck work, owing to the string breaking or bits of wood falling out, they had to fetch Orville to tie it together again.

At the age of seventeen Orville launched out seriously as Editor and Publisher of the *West Side News,* a new four-page weekly with which he sought to coax the dimes from the pockets of his townsmen. He was young and stout-hearted, but the day was only twenty-four hours long, and he found that editing, printing and publishing a local paper all by himself was a little too much, even for him. So he brought in Wilbur as editor, and confined himself to the job of publishing, with the task of running about to try to get advertisements and any printing that was going.

Now Orville thought he saw an opening for an evening paper, and the *Evening Item* made its appearance. Lorin took a hand in this venture, but it was not the success the brothers hoped it would be. They made the paper as bright as they could, yet the townspeople were not enthusiastic enough to support it, and it died after running four months.

For the next year or two they were occupied in the printing

works, but the journalistic urge did not succumb with the *West Side News*. It broke out again in October, 1894, in the form of a weekly magazine called *Snap-Shots* which was launched by Wilbur and Orville. They were probably unaware of it, but running at the same time in London was a weekly with a similar title. The London weekly was one of the early comic papers, a contemporary of *Ally Sloper*, that enjoyed a wide popularity. The Dayton paper was of a different type with a different aim. It was not designed to make people laugh, but to make them think, and Wilbur enjoyed wielding a pretty trenchant pen on local affairs.

Snap-Shots and the printing business kept them busy until they detected in the growing cycle boom their big opportunity. Backing their opinion by deeds, they formed the Wright Cycle Company, took a small building opposite their printing works and started to manufacture the Van Cleve cycles. If their journalistic ventures had not been wholly successful, they now felt sure of a certain livelihood in their cycle business. The Van Cleve cycles began to run about the streets, and the demand provided work for their hands.

Ever since they had watched birds on the wing and flown their kites and made their model helicopters they had taken an interest in flying. I doubt, however, whether their interest was much greater than that taken by tens of thousands of other boys who have watched birds and flown kites, not only in the western hemisphere, but in the east, where kite-flying used to be the national sport. Yet throughout these years something was probably working subconsciously, and it needed the death of Lilienthal * in 1896 to focus their attention on the problem of flight.

There was nothing haphazard in the way they began. Being extremely sensible, they decided that the best thing to do was to read all that had been written on the subject to discover the true position. Finding the facilities in Dayton rather limited, they wrote to the Smithsonian Institution in Washington to inquire the names of the best books.

Then they started to read and study one book after another. Much had been written about machines which, in the words of

---

* Otto Lilienthal was killed experimenting with gliders.

Wilbur Wright, were guilty of everything except flying. But the books that mattered were not numerous, and the most important from their point of view was one by Lilienthal in which he gave a series of tables that were worked out from his many glides. Here was no theory, but fact, the results of practical experience in the air, and they concluded that they might accept Lilienthal's tables as being accurate and make them the basis of their own experiments.

Little was known. There was so much to learn. The death of the German warned them of the danger confronting them if they should strive to emulate him. They took it into account, but they did not let it worry them unduly. Their common sense warned them to exercise all the care they could. They were not out to commit suicide, but to fly.

Lilienthal had ridden the winds. What he had done they might do. They might even surpass him. They read of Langley's belief in human flight and they never doubted its possibility. What the rest of the world thought could never be accomplished, Wilbur and Orville Wright, studying their books quietly of an evening after toiling hard with their hands in their workshop, concluded could be done.

The men who agreed with them might have been numbered on the fingers of both hands. They were so very, very rare. Humanity in the mass was earth-bound, as it had been since the beginning. Man had never flown and could never fly. This opinion was so deep-seated that nothing could dislodge it. Just as the opposition to smoking was summed up by the old lady who averred that if man had been intended to smoke, the Almighty would have installed a chimney-pot on his head, so the opposition to flying might be summed up in the remark that if man was intended to fly, the Almighty would have given him wings.

It is comical today, but it was rather tragic then. All sane people regarded flying as utterly impossible, and the man who considered it possible and said so was thought to be qualifying for the nearest lunatic asylum.

Fortunately, popular opinion did not weigh much with the Wrights. They built a glider to start their troubles! Requiring a constant wind if their experiments were to be carried on successfully, they had the sense to pick on the men who ought to know where to find it. So they wrote to the Weather Bureau in Washington to inquire about a locality in the United States where the winds blew fairly constantly in one direction, and were informed that Kitty Hawk, on the Atlantic seaboard of North Carolina, seemed to provide the conditions they sought. It is typical of the men who learned to fly that they took nothing for granted. Instead of rushing off to Kitty Hawk straight away, they decided to get local confirmation that the Weather Bureau had made no mistake. A polite note was dropped into the post for the Postmaster of Kitty Hawk, who told them that the winds certainly blew there and that the sand-dunes seemed a pretty safe place for the boys to play on!

It was good enough. Packing their glider, they took a tent and a few necessaries and started out for Kitty Hawk. It would have been difficult for them to select a more inaccessible place. In the beginning was a long railway journey, with one change after another, that even at the best, when all connections were caught, took over twenty-four hours; and when connections were lost it took very much longer. Then came a tiresome trip in a sailing vessel up the coast, a stretch that was often most unpleasant, after which they had to pull four miles in a rowing-boat to their destination.

Six days it took them to make that first trip. They arrived in a land of desolation, nothing but sand-dunes in every direction, where even the tough grass could not hold its own in the face of the salt-laden winds. Other men would have gone stark mad at the sight of the place; they would have cursed the perpetual winds; but the Wrights were happy to pitch a tent there and live like nomads for the sake of their hobby.

They regarded their experiments as a sport. There was no thought at all of making money out of them. They had their cycle and printing works, from which they gained a living, with the problem of flight to occupy their analytical minds when their hands were idle of an evening. The very difficulties seemed to act as a spur.

They found three sand-hills facing just right for their purpose, the lowest only thirty feet high, while the Kill Devil Hill, the tallest of the three, was but a hundred feet—quite high enough for an unlucky man to break his neck on! The Wrights did not want to break their necks. Life may not have been perfect, but it was worth living, despite the disappointments which met them at every turn.

At home, they had worked out that they had only to find a hill resembling the Kill Devil in order to send their glider aloft like a kite with a man in it, and when he reached a decent height he would be able to cast off the ropes and glide to the ground.

Alas for fond hopes! They attached two ropes to the glider; one of the brothers sat in it, but it refused to leave the sand and fly like a kite. It lacked sufficient lift. Theoretically it should have flown, but practice confounded all their ideas. They had gone to any amount of trouble to work out their lifting surfaces accurately, according to Lilienthal's tables, but their glider would not do what they designed it to do. They knew they had made no mistake, so the error must lie in Lilienthal's tables. That was the beginning of their disillusionment concerning the printed word. In later years they wrote:

> Having set out with absolute faith in the existing scientific data, we were driven to doubt one thing after another, till finally, after two years of experiments, we cast it all aside and decided to rely only on our own investigations.

They found that the words of the men they regarded as teachers were as unreliable as the winds.

Their intention of spending hours in the air hovering like a kite while they learned to control their glider was thus frustrated at the very beginning. Too sensible and courageous to fold their tent like the Arabs and silently steal away, they simply altered their glider out there among the sand-hills and began to make glides in the teeth of the wind down the smallest hill, keeping as near the earth as possible so that if they fell there would be little risk. Their glider landed safely on its skids, and they made a beginning of gaining actual experience in the air. The distance of each glide was carefully noted, the time the glider was in the air was marked down. At the end of their holiday they added all the seconds together and found they had been up a little more than two minutes! They succeeded in breaking the gliding record, yet they came away from Kill Devil Hill so very disappointed that Wilbur was prompted to make his pessimistic prophecy that man would fly sometime, but not in their lifetime.

Their quest at Kitty Hawk taught them the falsity of certain things that were accepted. Spending their spare time in the next few months working out further calculations and making another glider with their own hands, they again journeyed to Kitty Hawk and dumped all their stuff on the sands. Being practical men, who could braze a cycle frame and handle a saw with the best, they set about building a little wooden hut in which to live while they experimented. It was just a shack to shelter them and their belongings, a place in which to sit to make up the record of their day's work when darkness came, something that kept out the persistent wind much better than their tent had done the previous year. It did not keep out the mosquitoes, however, and these winged pests did their best to drive the brothers home. Wilbur and Orville spent some nights in their little hut when the temperature stood at over 90 degrees and the mosquitoes with their lust for blood nearly drove them mad. Yet they managed to survive and keep their tempers unimpaired for the new day's experiments. Many an hour they spent watching the way the buzzards altered the angle of their wings to soar in the upward currents from the hills. There was never a day passed but they learned some little thing that helped them forward to the final triumph.

At the end of the second season, concluding that the textbooks were useless, they decided to work things out for themselves. They built a wind tunnel in which they tested wings of various shapes, placing an electric fan at one end to provide the necessary current of air. They cut their tiny sheets of metal and bent them into many different curving forms to discover the best wing curvature, and so amazed were they at some of the results that they were inclined to doubt their own observations. In the case of an experiment with a square plane they felt sure they must be wrong, despite the care they both exercised. Then they hit on a method of testing whether their experimental result was right or wrong by fitting two of these planes to the pointer of a wind vane. It proved the accuracy of their observations.

Thousands of experiments were carried out by them. Each

one was recorded in a little note-book. In 1902, as a result of a sudden gust tending to overturn the glider, they arrived at the discovery which gave them the conquest of the air. It was derived straight from nature, from the wings of the birds which they watched so closely. They had noticed how birds alter the tips of their wings in order to maintain their balance in gusts of wind.

"If we could alter the tips of the wings of our glider in the same way we should be able to achieve similar results," they thought.

They talked it over, altered the edges of the planes so that they could warp them, conceived the idea of connecting up the warping of the wings with the movements of the rudder, and tested it out to find they had a machine they could control. In September and October of 1902 they had made nearly a thousand glides; they went up in winds of thirty-six miles an hour without crashing; in some cases they travelled a distance of 200 yards. They had practically solved the problem.

"If only you fitted it with feathers, she'd fly," one of the helpers from the nearest village remarked one day. The man meant it too. If birds could not fly without feathers, it surely needed feathers to make a machine fly.

It was not feathers they needed, however, but an engine, and this they set about fashioning with their own hands, just as they had built their gliders. There was no doubt in their minds as to what the result would be when their engine was fitted. They knew they could fly. They had worked out everything in the most scientific way. It was no lucky chance which gave them their triumph. It was hard work, a genius for taking pains, the laborious method of trial and error which compelled them to make thousands of experiments in their home-made wind tunnel to test the lift and curvature and shape of planes, the risking of their lives hundreds of times in the air while gliding. As Orville Wright wrote in a paper to the Royal Aeronautical Society of Great Britain:

It is much nicer to sit before a pleasant fire and speculate than work out, at the risk of limb and life, the combinations necessary to reduce speculation to practical invention.

These extraordinary brothers, who remained single because they "could not support a wife and a flying machine at the same time," attained such a degree of perfection that they were able by calculations to make their first propeller twice as efficient as any then in use.

In 1903 they arrived at Kitty Hawk once more and began to assemble the machine. It was what we should term today an ordinary biplane, although it was actually the most marvellous machine the world had ever known. They fixed their fifteen horsepower motor, which weighed 240 pounds, into it, fitted the two screws which were geared to the engine by cycle chains, and made everything ready. So sure were they of success that they issued an invitation to the local people to come to see them start.

The local people, like the rest of the world, thought that pigs might fly if they had wings, but man certainly could not. To add to their excuses for ignoring the invitation and staying at home was a bitter wind on that day of December 17, 1903, when the Wright brothers prepared to take the air. Their own description of that historic event from the *Century Magazine* is worth recording:

> The first flights with the power machine were made on December 17, 1903. Only five persons besides ourselves were present. . . . Although a general invitation had been extended to the people living within five or six miles, not many were willing to face the rigors of a cold December wind in order to see, as they no doubt thought, another flying machine not fly. The first flight lasted only twelve seconds, a flight very modest compared with that of birds, but it was, nevertheless, the first in the history of the world in which a machine carrying a man had raised itself by its own power into the air in free flight, had sailed forward on a level course without a reduction of speed and had finally landed without being wrecked. The second and third flights lasted a little longer, and the fourth lasted 59 seconds, covering a distance of 852 feet over the ground against a 20-mile wind.

So the first men flew. Their speed was barely thirty-six miles an hour, just sufficient to take them into the air. And as their biplane was mounted on skids, like those of a sledge, they could not work up to top speed by letting the machine run forward over the ground. They solved the problem of launching their machine by building a wooden slipway. Attaching a rope from the machine to a ring in the end of the slipway to hold the aeroplane back, they set the propellers whirring to work up speed, and when they had attained the necessary speed they gave the signal, the man in charge of the rope cast it off and raced behind to steady the machine as it rushed forward. In a little distance it was moving too fast for him and was in the air before it reached the end of the slipway, leaving the runner lying breathless on the ground!

Directly the biplane alighted, the seven men lugged the machine, weighing nearly half a ton, back to the slipway. It was no easy task tugging it on its skids over the shifting sand, but they hauled away gaily, unmindful of the cold wind, their minds full of the flights.

At the moment of triumph came disaster. They had brought the machine back after the fourth flight and were standing discussing the events when a sudden gust caught the wings and started to tilt up the biplane. Instantly Daniels, the nearest member of the party, a giant of a man, rushed to the machine and tried to hold it down. He was quite powerless. The machine overturned, tipped Daniels between the wings, shook him about as though he were a dice in a box, and shot him out with a few bruises, but otherwise uninjured, on the sands. The damage was such that the Wrights, instead of trying to repair it, packed the machine and took it home.

In seven years these two gifted men from that small cycle shop in Dayton solved the problem of flight. They gave it all their attention; any thought of marriage was sedulously pushed aside, every penny they could spare was devoted to the difficult task; their sister, who was a school-teacher, even lent them her savings to help them on. The brothers pooled all their resources and all their intelligence on the common aim.

They worked in absolute harmony. At first it used to be thought that the greatest credit was due to Wilbur. Even Mr. Griffith Brewer, who was the first Englishman to fly in their machine and who became their lifelong friend, thought this was so, but found as the years went on that he was mistaken. It was their joint achievement. They worked out everything together. Each difficulty that arose was argued out, often from standpoints diametrically opposed. It became almost customary for one to oppose the other whenever a difficulty cropped up so that they could work out the problem to a logical solution. Now and again, indeed, the brothers found that they had each persuaded the other to adopt their original viewpoint and that each had finished holding the opinion formerly held by his brother.

In my mind I picture the little model of an aeroplane in the South Kensington Museum * which would have flown had the power been available—a model made as long ago as 1842 by James Stringfellow, one of the founders of the Royal Aeronautical Society of Great Britain. I recall that Hargrave, an Australian, invented the form of the box kite, on which the biplane is based, and gave it to the world while refusing to patent it; I do not forget that Horatio Phillips was wise enough to study nature and patent a wing form which led to Lilienthal's success in his gliders. So important was this discovery of Phillips that every aeroplane built since has used it, although the Englishman has received too little credit for his brilliant work. All these men added a little to the knowledge of the world. But the Wrights watching the buzzards on the dunes, found the key to flight when they learned how to warp the wings of their gliders to control a machine in the air.

They arrived home to spend the happiest Christmas they had ever known, with the wreck of their machine in their workshop and little money in their pockets.

Realizing that Kitty Hawk was too far distant for them to carry out the work that lay before them, they hired a ninety-acre field called Huffman's Prairie about eight miles from Dayton in which to develop their machine.

Building an improved biplane, they invited the local reporters to see it fly. To the disgust of the fifty on-lookers and the disappointment of the brothers it failed to rise from the ground, for it lacked the help of the strong winds they had found at Kitty Hawk. The next day they tried again and made

---

* The South Kensington Museum is in London.

a twenty-yard hop, which the reporters regarded as rather a joke, so they trekked home and left the Wright brothers to play with their gadgets in peace.

Wilbur and Orville had no doubts about their achievement. They had flown, could fly, and were going on flying. They were not much concerned about what people thought. On the other hand, they were not anxious to be interrupted by crowds of sightseers, so they timed their flights to take place during the intervals when the tram * from Dayton, which arrived every half hour, was not passing along the road bordering their field.

They started to go round and round. Flights of ten miles were placed to their credit. The remarkable thing is that the sight of the machine in the air became so common to one or two farmers that they hardly took any notice of it. A flock of crows settling on their seed corn to devour it would have aroused their ire, but they were not excited by the thought of men flying!

On October 5, 1905, the machine flew round and round and covered a distance of twenty-four and a quarter miles. Farmer Stauffer, from whom the Wrights rented their field, was harvesting in the next field when the machine rose in the air.

"Well, the boys are at it again," he said to his farmhand, and they both went on cutting corn, giving an occasional glance at the white machine roaring round the field about sixty feet in the air.

When Mr. Weaver was afterwards asked by Captain Ferber, the French aeronaut, to find out if there was any truth in the rumours that the Wrights had flown, he saw Farmer Stauffer, who told him what he had witnessed that day. "I just went on shocking corn," he said, "until I got down to the fence, and the durned thing was still going round. I thought it would never stop."

The easy way in which this American farmer accepted the miracle of flight was rather amusing.

The Wrights brought out a friend of theirs, Mr. Foust, a chemist in Dayton, to time this flight, and made him vow not to tell anyone of what he had seen. No doubt Mr. Foust did

---

* *tram:* streetcar.

his best, but he was only human, and this incredible piece of news somehow slipped off his tongue and got about.

Next day the privacy in which the Wrights had worked for two years was gone. The whole fence by the side of the road was lined with an inquisitive mass of people armed with cameras.

The sight was too much for Wilbur and Orville. They just dismantled their machine and went back to Dayton.

It was not to ensure secrecy, but to get the help of the constant winds that the Wrights went to Kitty Hawk. Yet the very remoteness of Kitty Hawk sufficed to prevent the news of their first flight from reaching the world. When the news of what they had done began to filter through at the end of 1905 hardly any one would believe it. The Americans smiled at the story which the newspapers served up to them. The people of Europe thought it was a pack of sensational lies, that America, the land of tall stories, had excelled itself and let loose the tallest story of all, a yarn which no one but a credulous fool would swallow.

The Wrights, immersed in their work of improving their machine, let tongues wag. They were men of simple habits and kindly ways, with a natural gift for the great work they undertook, as well as the patience and determination to carry it through. It did not occur to them that people might persist in denying the facts, still less did they imagine that anyone would seek to deprive them of the honour that was their due. They were the first men to fly. They knew it, and they thought the world would accept it.

They themselves were just men, living in an unjust world. They heard with amazement the claim that Ader, a Frenchman subsidized by the French Government, had flown in a heavier-than-air-machine long before they did. It was some years before the French Government could be induced to publish the report which proved that Ader's machine had never left the ground. The Wrights saw with disgust the nations rob them of their financial reward by taking their patents and using them without payment.

There was one exception. The British Government has had many crimes laid to its door, so let it be said in favour of Great Britain that it was honourable enough to recognize that the

Wright brothers were the conquerors of the air, that their patents, which they had worked out at the risk of their lives, were valid. It was arranged that the British Government should be sued so that the findings could be placed on legal record; but before the case could be brought the war came, and in the end Orville Wright magnanimously agreed to give the British Government the use of his master patents for the nominal sum of £15,000. It was Orville Wright's great gesture to Britain for receiving fair play.

Before that came to pass Wilbur Wright was dead. Since his earliest years he had suffered from ill-health, which made a life in the open air practically essential to him. While working happily on their experiments he was able to keep reasonably well. But the worry of the patent litigation in which the brothers were compelled to embark in order to justify their achievement affected his health greatly, and when he was smitten with an attack of typhoid in 1912, he had not the strength to pull through.

In May, 1933, the pilots of the Royal Air Force broke the long-distance flying record by flying over 5300 miles without a stop, a flight beaten by the Frenchmen Codos and Rossi, who flew 6558 miles in August, 1933. These were magnificent achievements in every way. But the most wonderful flight the world has ever known, a flight which nothing can ever surpass, was that first short flight of fifty-six yards which the Wrights made at Kitty Hawk, in North Carolina, on December 17, 1903.

That day Wilbur and Orville Wright made Man the Master of the Air.

Suggested Film

Conquest of the Air, an excellent film illustrating the development of aviation, includes scenes of the Wright brothers' experiments at Kitty Hawk. A 16mm. print of this film, which takes forty-five minutes to show, can be rented from Films Incorporated, 330 West 42th Street, New York.

PROFESSOR S. P. LANGLEY AND THE WRIGHT BROTHERS[1]

By Selden Rodman

A NARRATIVE poem, *The Airmen*, relates all the classic attempts at flying. Its four parts are constructed around the most prominent of the pioneers—Icarus, Leonardo, the Wright brothers, and Lauro de Bosis.

In Part III we have the story of Professor S. P. Langley's *almost* successful attempt to launch a power-driven man-carrying machine on the Potomac river near Washington only a few days before the success of the Wrights at Kitty Hawk, North Carolina, on December 17, 1903. Professor Langley was a very able scientist and president of our national Smithsonian Institution. The selection below opens with the headlines of the *Washington Post* on the day following his attempted flight.

*　　*　　*　　*　　*

"Read all about it! Get your copy of The Post! Read how

AERODROME DID A FLOP HOW PROFESSOR MANLY * GOT DUCKED

Any boy could have skimmed an oyster-shell farther. . . .
The buzzard is a bust; that is all there is about it."

That was all there was about Professor S. P. Langley
As he stood that afternoon with Mr. A. G. Bell
On the deck of the houseboat in the Potomac,
Watching the tangled guy-wires upset the plane and spill
Mr. Manly, the Government's $50,000,† the hopes of twenty years
And the salvation of a scholar into the water's lap.

---

[1] From *The Airmen*, by Selden Rodman, Random House, New York. Copyright 1941 by the author.

* Manly was to fly the plane.

† *$50,000:* an appropriation by the United States Government to finance Langley's experiment.

The modern "Mars," largest of the flying boats, is capable of sustained flight to Europe and back

As famous as the "Mars" in its day was this DH-4 De Haviland which flew the first night mail in 1921

The public was delighted. What does the public, he thought,
    care
If Dr. Langley draws sunspots, determines the temperature of
    the moon,
Invents the spectro-balometer, by whose heat-curves the eye
    can trail
The passage of spiral nebulae, read magnitudes baffling the
    brain?—
The public, he thinks, wants to see man fly
—But better than that, it wants to see him fall.

"When all was ready, Mr. Manly nodded to a helper who fired
A skyrocket, warning the battery of photographers: Get
    SET . . . GO!
There was a roaring, grinding noise,
And from the houseboat toward the river sixty feet below
It simply slid into the water
Like a handful of mortar . . ."

But it could have flown! he says over and over. It could have
    flown;
It had everything but the method of launching necessary to
    flight;
Did I fail to wait because afraid to be one among the rank?
Will that Fame for which I risked so much consider everything
    I did,
My whirling-tables, measurements of bird in flight, an old
    man's prank?
My God, why have I cared so much . . . despising and yet
    caring . . . they will say
This is the scholar who tried to act, the professor who wanted
    to be a man,
Who, instead of being remembered as the inventor of the first
    machine that flew,
Will go down the ages as a crank . . .

"As for the rest of the Smithsonian staff, the stuffers
Of birds and rabbits, who have nothing to do with airships,
    they see
Through field-glasses and a telescope specially mounted on a
    tower
The debacle of 'Langley's Folly' " . . .

And the testers of teeth and of crank splines know nothing of
    airships,
The dusters of diaphragms, the welders of bailwire know
    nothing,
Nor the nameless inspectors whose eyes under mercury lamps
Check breathers; nor designers at drafting-boards; the regular
    trips
All forgotten, only the crossing of continents is remembered;
Not the movers but the shakers; not the dreams but the dates
    touch the lips,
Nor the date * of the trial on the premature 8th of December
Nineteen Hundred and Three.

*   *   *   *   *

Otto Lilienthal in Germany had built and successfully used
a man-carrying glider a few years before the Wrights achieved
success at Kitty Hawk. The Wrights first built and sailed gliders without any power but the wind and rising air currents.
They were the first to install an engine in a machine heavier
than air and to make it carry a man. On December 17, 1903,
after long and disheartening trials, failures, and alterations of
the wings, they asked each other: Can it be done? Are we ready
for the attempt?

*   *   *   *   *

Brother to brother, against the sea's roaring, cried Yes!
It has come: peoples and countries will have in common—the
    air . . .
But voices are not heard by those unwilling to hear
Even when carried around the earth by wires or blasted at the
    sky . . .
Paid telegram † for Bishop Wright from Kitty Hawk:

"SUCCESS

LEVEL WITH ENGINE POWER FIFTY SEVEN SECONDS INFORM
PRESS"

---

* *Nor the date:* Not even the date of Langley's attempt will be remembered.

† *Paid telegram:* This was the wire the brothers sent to their father announcing their flight of fifty-seven seconds.

"If it read 'minutes'," said the reporter, "there'd be an item
    there."
Only a bee-keeper's journal carried the story completely
But it leaked out little by little. Though the city of cash-
    registers * slept
Day and night, while crossing its tramlines, outlying pastures,
    sky,
The brothers studied maneuvers, learned to lower the nose on
    a turn,
The secret of power that it promised was too big to be kept.

The gamblers, the founders of fortunes, the amateur sports-
    man, the spy,
The scouters for exclusive weapons, the seekers of quick return
Began to maneuver at the crossroads, their faces at the fences
    pressed;
Their questions roar above the motor; and in the mail their
    offers burn.
And why not? Can the knowledge be hidden though the hand
    of the receiver is unclean?
It's the kind of a world we live in, and if it must be paid for,
    best
That we take a share to shape the future (thought the broth-
    ers, dismantling their machine)
But they looked at each other and smiled a little grimly. "It
    may not be so easy to learn . . ."

TOPICS AND ACTIVITIES

1. Is the public eye so fixed upon success that it does not
see and value the many experiments that lead up to success
and make it possible?

2. In spite of Langley's many significant contributions to
science, especially astronomy, is he remembered today only as
a crank who failed?

3. What did the Wrights think of Langley's machine?

4. Is the poet cynical when he points out that the significance of the success was not seen by the regular newspapers?

---

* *city of cash registers:* Dayton, Ohio. The experiments after Kitty Hawk
were made on a farm near Dayton.

The bee-keeper's journal referred to was edited by a minister, Rev. A. I. Root, of Medina, Ohio.

5. What is it in the last line of the poem that the Wrights thought "might not be so easy to learn"?

6. Franklin was ridiculed about his "kite-and-string" study of lightning. Can you think of other explorers, inventors, and discoverers who have been ridiculed, neglected, and forgotten?

7. Is such neglect the outcome of ignorance, indifference, carelessness, or what?

8. Someone should find out about Otto Lilienthal and report the facts to the class.

9. Why have large helicopters failed to be successful? How does the modern autogyro resemble a helicopter? How does it differ? On what principle does its flight depend? What can it do that a regular airplane cannot do? Is it likely to supersede or supplement the airplane—or to be abandoned as impractical? Give reasons for all your opinions.

10. Let someone find out about Langley's first flying machine and report to the class. Should the credit for constructing the first successful flying machine go to Langley or to the Wrights? Why?

11. Can the first successful heavier-than-air flying machines be seen anywhere? If so, where?

12. In what year did Langley make his almost successful flight? Find out about the kind of engine and fuel he used and compare his engine with that of the Wrights.

13. The Wright engine weighted sixteen pounds per horsepower. How much weight per horsepower has a modern airplane engine? Does that have much importance in building an airplane? Explain.

TEST DIVE[1]

By John J. Floherty

I WAS but a cub in a group of seasoned newspaper men assembled on a bleak Long Island plain about twenty miles from New York City. A tent such as a circus might use for sideshows stood silhouetted against a pink evening sky. Two earnest looking young men shuttled between the tent and a slender wooden tower that stood a hundred yards away. They were Orville and Wilbur Wright.

We were about to witness their first flight in the vicinity of New York. Within the tent the plane stood carefully guarded against curious visitors. The gentle evening breeze had almost died out. There was but the faintest drift to the smoke from the chimneys in the village at the edge of the plain.

After what seemed an endless wait one of the two young men, Orville, now without hat or coat and quite bald, threw aside the tent flap and stepped outside. He had a short stump of a candle in his hand. Holding it slightly above the level of his face he studied the effect of the zephyr-like breeze on the blaze. He held it toward the four points of the compass. Then with a decisive gesture he blew it out and curtly remarked to the newspaper men: "Too much wind; there will be no flight today, gentlemen." With that he disappeared into the tent.

As we plodded back to the railroad station every man felt that while human flight was an accomplished fact, it could hardly be considered a contribution to transportation as evidently it could be practiced only in the stillest air.

Quite recently I flew from New York to Washington on a luxurious air liner. The weather was bad. A forty mile southeast wind kicked rainsoaked clouds into our path. The earth was hidden in a storm tossed murk. We landed at Washington only a little behind time.

Later that day as I sat over coffee with our pilot and discussed planes, motors, "props," instruments and test pilots, my thoughts flew back to the evening on Hempstead plains, when I saw Orville Wright gauge the force of the wind with a lighted candle. Although I did not know it then, I had seen the first of the test pilots at work.

The modern test pilot is a consulting engineer of broad experience in design, construction and flying. He is usually called in before pencil is put to paper in the draughting room to discuss the many phases of the design. When the plane is placed in construction he follows every step. Not a detail escapes him. Like the specialist in medicine, his broad experience enables him to detect symptoms that may have escaped the family physician.

As construction progresses, the test pilot's visits become more frequent and more critical, for many vital parts will soon be concealed within the covering of wing and fusilage. Each of them must be inspected by him personally. He takes no one else's word for their staunchness and workmanship.

His eye for balance is often uncanny. Although the distribution of weight is worked out on paper to a mathematical nicety, often only a glance at the new ship tells him that certain readjustments are necessary. Occasionally a shop engineer who has spent long hours on his calculations will declare hotly that figures do not lie. But the test pilot, a diplomat among his other accomplishments, has his way. When the last rivet is headed up, and the last instrument installed, the testing period is close at hand. The test pilot surveys his ship from nose to tail, from wing tip to wing tip. He spends hours in inspection of her operating parts. By this time he knows her so thoroughly in all her details that she becomes a part of him.

As the ship is rolled out of the shop she is followed by the hopes and fears of her builders. There is nothing more they can do. Her fate now rests in the hands of the test pilot.

The tests begin. The pilot climbs aboard and starts his motors and listens with the concentration of an orchestra conductor.

He opens the throttle gently at first, and then in a succession of blasts that cause the plane to strain at the impeding wheel-blocks he "revs" her up from dead slow to flying speed. Meanwhile he notices the recordings of her instruments; he tests the variable pitch of the propellers as well as oil pressure, temperature, fuel flow; he tests the "stick" which operates the ailerons and elevators and the foot bars that operate the rudder. In fact, he operates and tests every device within the cockpit without putting the ship into motion. This may take many hours. When he leaves the plane he has a sheaf of notations that record the behavior or performance of each part or device. This static testing may continue for days before the ship is moved under her own power.

When he is satisfied that the motor is functioning properly he signals to have the blocks removed. At the touch of the throttle the new ship gets under way. Slowly at first and then with increasing speed the pilot taxis her down the runway. Then he crosses and recrosses the field steering her here and there sometimes in a straight course and again in curves and circles. He is testing her rudder and her response to it. As the ship feels the bite of her propeller in the air she begins to develop individual characteristics as if she were a living thing. No matter how carefully the builders strive for uniformity, planes built from the same plans and specifications will function differently. This behaviorism must be studied, and corrected if necessary.

When the great day arrives that is to see the plane take to the air, tension runs high among the men who built her. While they have the utmost confidence in her ability to stand up to the many strains to which she is to be subjected, they cannot help but remember the planes that ended their first venture in the air as masses of twisted wreckage.

The least concerned outwardly about the outcome of the flight is the test pilot. Cool and unhurried he walks around the throbbing plane while her motors are warming up. No detail on the ship's exterior is overlooked by him, every sound has a meaning of its own.

Slipping into his parachute the test pilot climbs aboard, signals to have the blocks withdrawn, and is off without a moment's delay. As he gathers speed on the runway, he prepares for the momentous instant of take-off. The first few moments after a plane leaves the ground on her initial flight are perhaps the most critical in her career. She may prove to be gentle and tractable or she may develop treacherous tricks that need close watching every minute.

In spite of the greatest care in design and construction, she may develop vibrations and tremors that mean danger. Beset by the natural forces of drag, thrust and gravity, her conflict with each is studied and recorded, and so, the test pilot flies her back and forth and around in every known maneuver from spins to stalls, to wingovers and side slips. Not until this stage does the test pilot's dual personality manifest itself. Still the scientist and engineer bent on fact finding, he gradually assumes the role of daredevil. Strains and faults, structural and otherwise, can be brought to light only by actual test under actual flying conditions. From this point the test pilot gambles with death.

When a large transport or army bomber is tested, she prepares for her initial flight in the same manner as a fledgling that has just left the nest. She is taxied back and forth across the field for an even longer period than the smaller planes, while every part and device is tested and adjusted. Not until her mechanical components are deemed in perfect working order is she lifted from the ground, and then only in short hops. The length of the hops and the altitude are greatly increased until the ship finds herself in full flight. Then come banking and turning and climbing and gliding and landing under varying conditions. The whole process of testing a large plane is one of extreme deliberation and precision; until she has proven herself, each flight is a hazard.

In testing the smaller army or navy planes, a shorter period of ground testing is the customary procedure. When the day arrives for the pilot to go aloft, he must be in perfect physical condition. Furthermore he must possess an inherent strength and resistance to injury due to strain on his vital organs. His must be a super brand of courage. He must have a sublime confidence in his subconscious self, as it is not unlikely that in some of the tests he will wholly or partly lose consciousness while hurtling to earth with the speed of a bullet.

Take the case of Eddie Allen: While testing a small pursuit ship, he was required to fly her to the highest altitude she could obtain. But even her builders did not believe she would make a ceiling of more than twenty to twenty-two thousand feet. For this reason Allen decided to fly her without oxygen equipment as he had flown to that height more than once without experiencing more than shortness of breath and a rapid heart.

As he took off, he thrilled at the performance of the motor. The roar of the exhaust sounded like a sustained note on a fine organ. As he reached an altitude of twenty thousand feet diminishing oxygen made it difficult to get a full breath; his heart hammered at his ribs; a thick feeling was in his inner ears. He had experienced all these before; he could stand a lot more.

As he spiralled still higher he noticed that the rarefied air did not seem to decrease either the motor power or propeller traction. The needle on the altimeter registered 25,000 feet. The sky was a translucent blue-black, blending to steel gray toward the earth which was now merely a dark, hazy circle without defined horizon or detail. Breathing now became difficult. He had forcibly to pump enough air into his lungs to give him sufficient oxygen to sustain life. He gasped for each breath like a runner at the end of a sprint. A reddish haze before his eyes blurred his instruments. Still the plane spiralled upward unfalteringly. It took all his strength to write his notations on the pad strapped to his knee.

A numbness began to set in all over his body, partly from the intense cold and partly from the oxygen starvation. At 27,000 feet he could scarcely hold the stick. He could tell that his feet were on the rudder bar only by the perfect behavior of the plane. Great bursts of sound crashed within his head. A million pins and needles pricked deeply all over his body.

The altimeter indicator, now a hazy streak, steadily moved on a dial that had lost its outline. His mind wandered and he babbled all manner of nonsense. He was to all intents physically unconscious. His subconscious self, however, stuck doggedly to the task of keeping the plane climbing until she could climb no more. The altimeter read 28,000. Allen laughed crazily at the joke the ship had played on all of them.

A darkness, streaked by flashes of spectral fireworks, had closed in on him. The exhaust of his motor was drowned by a turmoil of noises that filled his brain. Drowsiness soothed him but he fought it off. The plane was still climbing. Then, as from a great distance, he heard his motor cough. He felt the laboring propeller send a shivering through his ship. He could dimly see his inclinometer through a red darkness. It indicated that he was on a level keel. His swollen eyes strained at the altimeter and gropingly read 29,000 feet! He had reached ceiling!

Even in his dazed condition, he managed to scrawl his last reading on his knee pad. Then the dreaded oxygen starvation seized him. His right hand dropped powerless beside him, with his left he pushed the stick forward and slumped into his thickly padded seat. The plane teetered crazily on her nose and fell off into a series of wild gyrations like a leaf in a high wind. As gravity gripped her, she went hurtling down a five mile slide of imminent death. Allen's body slumped forward on the stick, holding the ship's nose to the earth. With a roaring motor and screaming flying wires, she dived for nearly a mile and a half straight as a plumb-line, while Allen hung limp in his seat, held in by his safety belt.

As oxygen increased in the lower altitude, life came slowly back to his paralyzed limbs. Still dazed, he straightened up and grasped the stick. A glance at the altimeter told him he had dropped sixteen thousand feet. Thirteen thousand feet were between him and the ground. That was ample. He swiftly surveyed each instrument and made a quick notation. The rapidly changing altitude made his ears crack, and caused a feeling of pressure in his head and chest. The air-speed dial showed 450 miles an hour but what of it? He could breathe, hear and see. Filling his lungs, he let out yell after yell. This eased his head and ears and braced the stomach muscles. The ship was intact and doing well. The big ordeal, however, lay ahead. With such momentum would she stand straightening out?

He felt the bandages and pads, which test pilots sometimes wear around lungs, liver and kidneys, grow tighter. What a shock they were going to get in a few moments when he changed the direction of the plane from the vertical to the horizontal! If he had not been unconscious so long, he could have retarded speed by opening the throttle, for when gravity is pulling a plane down faster than her propeller will drive her, engine speed has a retarding rather than an accelerating effect. It was too late now.

He would pull her out at 2000 and give the boys on the

ground a thrill. If she crumpled, he could still bail out and depend on his 'chute to take him down safely. As the altimeter needle neared the two thousand mark, he braced himself for the most critical moment of the flight. He tightened his grip on the stick and waited. At 2000 feet he pulled it back. With a roar and a mad swoop the plane changed her course. As her propeller bit into solid air again, she roared her defiance at gravity.

Allen's body was crushed down into his seat as if by the hand of a giant. In an instant his weight had changed from one hundred and fifty to thirteen hundred and fifty pounds. Frustrated gravity had increased his weight nine times. Legs, arms and every organ were weighted by nine gravities, or 9 Gs in the parlance of the test pilot.

As the plane rocketed round the curve between the vertical and horizontal, the overwhelming downward pull was supplemented by centrifugal force which strove to fling Allen off at a tangent to the curve with a sickening violence. As the wings took up the weight of the plane, Allen could feel them tremble under the strain. They were supporting nine times the weight of the ship and pilot. This is the only moment when the test pilot must depend entirely on the skill of the builders and the inherent strength of the plane. Half conscious, he can only wait. No device nor instrument can help him. His numbed ears listen for the first crack of a breaking member. He is still many times his own weight. To leave the ship would be impossible. At this critical time many a wing has been torn off as if it were tissue paper.

Firmly but gently, Allen pulled back on the stick as the ship reached the horizontal. The depressing weight lifted from arms, legs and body. He took a long deep breath and continued to make notations. The sky had again assumed its translucent blue, and the earth became a smooth green carpet dappled with the mellow brown of ploughed fields.

With joy in his heart he kicked his rudder bar and threw his stick sharply over, putting his ship into a steep right bank, then opening his motor he streaked back to the landing field. So gently did he lay the wheels on the ground, the plane seemed to be without weight. He came to a stop near the anxious group that had witnessed the test. Cutting off his motor, Allen climbed out, and slipping the parachute harness from his shoulders surveyed the plane from one end to the other. When his pad was consulted in the draughting room, it read like a hospital chart. Symptoms, temperatures, reactions and behavior were discussed. Diagnoses and prognoses were made with terse finality. A sound bill of health was given to the plane. The test was ended.

Problems to be Considered

1. A great plane used for such a dive as Mr. Floherty describes here may cost a quarter of a million dollars. A crash would destroy it absolutely and kill a very highly trained man. Are the results worth the risk?

2. What is meant by "9 Gs"? Suppose you were sitting on a pair of scales in a plane that was going through a "3 Gs pull-out"? What would the scales show your weight to be at that moment? What at "9 Gs"? Could you jump up, run to the door, open it, and make a parachute jump? Explain.

AIR BASE[1]

By Boone T. Guyton

AIR BASE is a book designed to give its readers a picture of the training of Navy pilots at North Island, San Diego, California. Pilots are moved to North Island after preliminary training at Pensacola, Florida. The author is a Lieutenant in the Naval Reserve, but at the time his book was published in 1941, he was a test pilot for Vought-Sikorsky Aircraft and had just completed the tests for the then fastest single-engined fighting plane in the world, the XF4U1.

Reading *Air Base* will give you a very clear narrative account of the activities and the training at a modern naval aviation training base. It is not fiction. The following chapter has been selected from the book to show the activity through any typical day.

*   *   *   *   *

A typical North Island day for the whole station is long and noisy. At about seven each morning the duty sections push the planes from the hangars to the parking places on the operating line. Just about this time the weather plane takes off for its long climb to high altitudes. At eight planes start taxiing down the line to the take-off area, and from then on an unceasing procession of take-offs and landings is made.

All day long the fighters, scouts, and bombers roar up and away to their practice areas or to any of the numerous auxiliary fields. Planes circle the island, towing their sleeve-gunnery targets behind them, drop the targets clear of the landing mats, and then come in to pick up new ones. On the bay seaplanes and flying boats dodge the shipping as they take off and land amid wallowing tugs, maneuvering destroyers, and anchored cruisers. In a less spectacular manner the overhaul shops are working at full speed to keep up with the pace the operat-

---

[1] Copyright by Whittlesey House, New York.

ing units are setting. About four-thirty, all activity seems to stop as operations are secured until night flying.

Those who fly again that night shove off from their respective squadrons to have an early dinner and report back for flights that start at sundown. The shops close until the next day, though in the present emergency lights burn also until the night flights return. From sunset until ten the roar of powerful Cyclones and Wasps again abounds in the air as planes practice formation flying or make night-practice carrier landings on the field. Then, as the dead line approaches, the last pair of twinkling red and green lights comes swiftly down the bight, turns toward the mat, and presently the dim outline of a plane is silhouetted in the brilliant glare of the floodlights.

Its motor cut, the plane is quickly pushed into a hangar, the floodlights are extinguished, and quiet has again settled on America's busiest flying field. If four carriers are operating their squadrons at once from the base, business is extremely good. When these are out for cruises in and around the islands, up north to San Francisco, or down south along the Mexican coast, you find the Marine squadrons and utility groups taking over.

This morning, as the five of us lifted our wheels from the already warming tar to fly out to the carrier, we beat the usual rush by minutes.

"Take it easy, and bring them all back," Noz had pleaded as we left. "The cruise is too close to go hunting up new airplanes now. Save the crackups for the war games if you can, and don't forget," he added, "we were only joking about 'new bloods' cracking up the other day."

A hot sun had burned the ground fog off the island by eight o'clock, leaving a cloudless sky with perfect visibility. We were all excited about our first trip from the air station to land at sea aboard the Lexington, and I could almost have hummed a good song through the engine roar.

Gazing out past the clean silver fuselages and yellow wings that made up our V formation, I picked up the small nubs of land to the south that were known as the Coronados Islands. We often flew close to these crests of rock and scrub brush when going out to sea to fire fixed or free machine guns at target sleeves. The largest of these islands wasn't over a mile long and poked up out of the blue ocean some fifteen miles off the coast as though dropped there and forgotten. We were told that these islands were used by the Mexicans, to whom they belonged, for fishing retreats, but you could never spot any sign of habitation or any life except a few wild goats. Most early mornings, fog covered these "forgotten sea marks," but today they were sharp and clear outlines that broke an otherwise unmarred horizon.

Now, as we rounded Point Loma over the old lighthouse and headed out to sea, I felt that exaltation a man can feel on a cloudless day in a good plane. The radio cracked even as I made out the long white wake, trailing away in the blue Pacific behind the Lexington, miles out at sea.

"Two Baker Ten from Lexington—the ship is ready to land you aboard. Acknowledge!"

Lieutenant Stuart answered, "Aye, aye, from Two Baker Ten." I could now see the two planeguard destroyers knifing along through the easy swells astern of the carrier on either side of the wake. Their purpose is exactly what their name implies. If a pilot lands in the "drink" near the carrier, one of these fast "guards" spurts out to give aid. They seldom miss, and in foul weather, with a heavy sea running, they literally plow through the rollers.

"Lexington from Two Baker Ten—we have the ship in sight and are waiting instructions," Stuart radioed.

Then he signaled, and we slid over into right echelon, ready to get down into the landing circle. As we passed over the carrier I could see the long, narrow deck alive with the men of the plane-handling crew. Black smoke was pouring out of her stacks on the superstructure. Aft at the stern I could just make out Sperry Clark getting squared away to signal us aboard. The ship piped up.

"Bombing Two planes from Lexington—land aboard!" I felt the tingle of something new and untried coming up as Stuart rolled away and headed out in a circle for the stern of the ship.

"Land aboard!"

That is the order you'll hear from Panama to Sitka, from Guam to San Pedro, from "Dago" to the Philippines when you start flying from the deck of a carrier. No matter how often those two words pipe up in your earphones, they will always give you a slight thrill. Land aboard! After hours of patrolling over unbroken sea or doing battle with the "enemy" in mock warfare, you get that order.

At once you unconsciously see the long sliver of a deck, the belching smoke, the scrambling crew, the long, trailing wake, flanked by the two whippet-like destroyers. At once you vision the steaming coffee in the wardroom, the soft leather cushion in your customary chair, the cribbage board and magazines, waiting down there after a long grueling flight.

Land aboard! I've heard it for days around Honolulu, Maui, Molokai, Lanai, Wake Island, and always with the same anticipation. It means put your wheels down—over the water, then over the deck, then on it. It means watch Sperry, try for a good smooth landing, see how straight and easy you can set her on the teakwood. It also implies that you can land aboard with no more than that short order, and subconsciously you are proud that it is taken for granted.

I watched over the side as our first plane went aboard and then, passing alongside the ship toward the bow, waited for Kane to break off. There he went! Out to the left in a wide circle, wheels down, flaps down, and hook down. I dropped my wheels, watched Kane. Then down went the hook and flaps, and I was in the circle heading for the groove. As I reached the destroyers behind the carrier, Kane hit the deck, and I slowed the plane down, got into the groove, and leaned over the left side of the cockpit to pick up Sperry. He was there, all right, his coat flapping against him in the man-made breeze blowing back across the deck. I was too fast. There. Gosh, that deck looked narrow! It felt as if we were moving pretty fast to land into some arresting gear and stop short. The stern heaved about a little in slow but firm oscillations, and I began to think about what the chief had said the other night at security watch.

"If the deck is coming up at you when you get the cut, ease it down. Don't push the nose over to duck into it."

Sperry had the come-on signal showing, so I must have been doing O.K. My left hand gripped the throttle as though even the pulsations in my wrist might change the angle of the arm in its quadrant. Almost to the stern now. The throbbing yel-

low ramp looked suddenly very large, and the signal officer was
almost under the left wing. Below, the white-chopped wake
from the ship's screws had become a scrambled and wider
break in the blue sea. As I crossed the ramp I could make out
two men behind Sperry, ducked low beneath the deck guard,
watching and waiting, with microphones hooked around their
chins. More deck crew was hunched over the side up forward,
peering at the plane from the safety net some five feet beneath
the landing platform.

There was the cut! Sperry jerked the paddle across his
throat, and I could just catch a quick smile on his lips and
nod as we flashed by. Pulling off the throttle, I eased the nose
forward, then up a little, and we were on the deck. The arresting gear took hold immediately as the plane plumped to a
sudden stop. I sank back away from the belt and swallowed
my heart. Someone motioned hurriedly, "Taxi forward, taxi
forward," as I sat there for a brief moment trying to gather
my wits.

We were aboard. Only a few short minutes ago I was air-
borne, circling above a blue ocean, attached to nothing. Now
the throb of the straining ship's engines came up through the
landing gear from the deck, up through the seat to nudge the
parachute I sat on, as if to say, "Move on, boy, move on.
There is someone who wants to sit down coming up the
groove behind you." I was completely tickled, and taxiing up
the deck past the rows of odd-colored sweaters of the deck
landing crew, I masked a stern face to hide my childish glee.
I thought to myself, "You made it O.K., you old son of a gun.
Now you're a full-fledged carrier flier with one landing to your
credit. Hurray!"

In the ready room below the bridge at the forward end of
the superstructure, we sat around on the long leather bench
seats, admiring our newly acquired "living room." Up against
the wall on one side was the roll of names below the plaque
that stated that these officers and men had negotiated thousandth landings aboard the carrier. The list was impressive,
and I noticed the names of several of my old instructors at
Pensacola sprinkled through the list. Bright brass, shined to
high heaven, formed most of the fixtures, ash trays, cotton
holders, and so on, that lined the walls. The deck was spot-

less, and I began to know what made Uncle Sam's Navy ships
the cleanest in the world. It took a lot of swabbing to make
that deck look like my mother's kitchen!

Outside on the wind-swept landing deck the handling crew
was rushing about, spotting our planes for take-off, gassing,
and oiling the last few aboard. Sperry stepped into the gang-
way as we somewhat excitedly reflew our landing for the bene-
fit of any "unfortunate" individual who might not have witnessed the feat. Not a mishap in the group. We felt kinda
proud.

"O.K., fellows," Sperry said. We crowded around him to get
the news. "Stuart, you were too slow obeying the signals. Speed
it up, and don't go to sleep in the groove. Ewers, you were far
too close to the right-hand side of the deck. Get lined up when
you turn in at the destroyers, and then follow a straight flight
path to the ramp. You'll end up in the stacks someday, sliding
over there. Watch it on your next landings."

Sperry paused to flip the pages in his little notebook and
then finished off the remaining qualifiers. He had mistakes
for all of us to correct, and it brought us back to earth again
after the elation that had blossomed in our bosoms while
crawling out of our planes. Still, we were pretty happy about
the successful qualifications and were anxious to get back to
Alex and the squadron to tell them we hadn't scratched a
plane and had all done O.K.

After a cup of coffee and a sandwich, thoughtfully brought
up by the mess boy, the ship's loudspeaker sounded. "Pilots,
man your planes! Pilots, man your planes!" We crawled back
into our cockpits, warmed up against the chocks, and waited
for the ship to swing back into the wind. Up forward the
wave-off man was unfurling his checkered flag and scanning
the deck to see that all was clear.

"Turn it up and hold your brakes!" The wave-off man
signals his orders by flag. "Open your throttle wide." There.
He puts a cupped hand to his ear and then looks at you.
That means, "Your engine sounds O.K. to me. How about it?
Are you satisfied for take-off?" Quickly you take a last look
at oil temperature, pressure, manifold, tachometer readings.
O.K.

A quick nod back to him, and he swings his starter flag.

That's you! Off go the brakes, and the plane literally jumps forward. Down past the nose the end of the deck looks awfully close. Good God, do I have to get into the air in that space? you think to yourself. Over the end you can see the white-caps flying spray from the ocean fifty feet below the bow. Straight down the yellow lines for the end of the deck. Then the wheels leave the deck as you ease back on the stick, with upturned faces flashing by and guns, nets, and bow drifting back and away. Then the ocean is under you. The deck falls away and gets play size as you pick up your wheels and turn out for the rendezvous.

What a thrill! It was worth all those hard, trying days back in training and then some to know that you could fly a fast fighting plane aboard an aircraft carrier far at sea, pick up fuel, bombs, ammunition, or what you needed, and then take off again to "go get the enemy." In the following years that I spent aboard the air station at North Island, I can picture time after time the qualifying groups of fliers returning from their first crack at deck landing at sea. They would gather around the lounge that night, as we did, and go over their "big moment"—their first carrier landing. You soon learn, even on cruises, long or short, that this type of gossip never grows old. You can't talk about it enough.

"Did anybody crack up?" was the first question Bud asked when we sat down at the lounge that night.

"How many wave-offs did you get? Was the ship pitching any?" We answered all questions and by using hand motions explained just what happened and how we did it—needless to say, to the joy of some of the older pilots.

"Boy, did I drop in on the second one! I think old Sperry was trying to see how slow he could bring me in. I'll bet I didn't fly twenty feet forward after the cut. The old bus took it, though it sure jarred my backbone when we hit."

"Well, you know," Kane put in, "on my first two I had a hell of a time seeing the signals over the cowl flaps. My engine was heating up, and let me tell you, it's a job to peep around those open flaps without flying up the groove in a skid."

Before we ended our little hangar session half the new bloods in the lounge were gathered around listening in and, with a casual awareness, were picking up pointers on what can and does happen on landing aboard. Several nights before we had done the same thing, but it was quite pleasing now to act a little nonchalant about the whole thing and be the proverbial veteran aviators.

Throughout the next two days other squadron groups took off from the base to fly out to sea and land aboard in preparation for embarkation on the cruise. Big three-place torpedo planes, moderate-sized bombers, tiny, stubby fighters roared away from the field in groups and headed for the carrier. In the evening we would get the news.

"Stinky Davis sure put one away today. Hit the ramp coming aboard, and Stinky and one-half the plane slid on up the deck while the other half hung over the stern. Wasn't even scratched, the lucky rascal! Imagine!"

"Hear about Charlie? He must have doped off on his second landing and ended up minus landing gear and propeller. He's O.K. except for a big shiner and four stitches in his chops where the instrument panel didn't give."

We listened to the tales with avid interest and were just a little proud all the while that our outfit had come through unmarred. Ewers had made the thousandth landing and would receive the cake when we got aboard the next week to start the big cruise. Of course, he had to write home about that, and you couldn't blame him. We were a part of a big force of men, all pulling together like some huge football team, and though this was no longer play, it was still much like a game in which you put out your level best to make the whole team better.

He usually doesn't like to admit it, but the pilot flying a fighting plane with his formation in the service, the bomber or fighter pilot going aboard the carrier still has his little tales to "write home about." There is still something about this flying game that holds it, as a profession, just a bit apart from others and allows all those who make flying their business to see eye to eye on a certain "something." In the service that "something" is known as *esprit de corps,* and although a member of a squadron may not detect this at first, he will soon recognize the existence of the unpopularized "think of your shipmate" phrase.

Probably the best illustration of loyalty up and loyalty down, so to speak, was brought out when Ensign Gil Brown, a reserve in the class behind us, stayed with his plane one day over the desert to give the enlisted man in the back seat a chance to bale out. Gil was ferrying a JF-2 Grumman Amphibian back to San Diego from Tucson, Arizona, with a third-class mechanic riding in the rear seat. Over the rugged, copper-colored Mohawk Mountain Range near Yuma, Arizona, where houses are still some forty miles apart, the engine suddenly became very rough. Before Gil could pull the throttle completely off, the propeller let go and pulled off of the crankshaft. Within a short second or two the whole engine vibrated itself out of the plane and fell away. It all happened in a flash.

Gil jammed the stick forward to try to keep the now nose-light airplane in normal flight, at the same time yelling to the mechanic to bale out. After a few seconds more Gil pulled himself half out of the cockpit and started over the side, when he noticed the mechanic still struggling to get free of the plane. He dropped back down in the seat and grabbed the controls shortly thereafter, feeling the ship pitch as the mechanic got free and successfully opened his big silk umbrella. Then Gil started out again.

But he had waited too long. The ground was only a few hundred feet below now, and there wasn't a prayer of getting a chute to open fully in that space. He slid back into the seat, maneuvering the engineless ship as best he could until it crashed into the sandy desert to fold up like an accordion. That crash, by the laws of physics or what have you, should have cost Gil his life—and it almost did. He went through the subinstrument board, the half-intact part of the fire wall, and carried rudder bar and stick with him.

When the mechanic, who had landed some half a mile away, dragged himself to the plane over sand and cactus with a broken leg, he finally managed to get Gil out of the tangled wire and instruments, stretch him out on his unused parachute to render what first aid he could under the circumstances. On top of that, he dragged himself to the highway, another mile and a half north, stopped a car, and got some help. I talked to the mechanic a few days later, when they let us in at the hospital.

"That last quarter of a mile was sure long," he said. "I

didn't think I could go another inch through that hot sand, but I guess we can do a lot of things that look impossible when we have to. I just remembered that I kept a thinkin' to myself about the title to a story I read somewhere—'The Long Haul.' Seemed like all I could think of was 'the long haul, the long haul.' "

Gil was all messed up. His right elbow is now such that he can bend his arm only enough to get the hand in his pants pocket. One ankle is likewise stiff for keeps, and Gil has flown his last airplane for Uncle Sam. I believe the Navy sent him to a Reserve base for duty not involving flying, but I remember his words when he came over to the lounge for a chat with the boys after the hospital let him out for the first evening. We were all tickled to see him, though it was a shock to observe the drawn face, lined with stitches, the stiff arm in a cast, and the hop-hop as he carefully maneuvered across the linoleum on a pair of crutches.

"Listen, you guys," he said, "I know what you're thinking, and don't give me any of that stuff. I don't need sympathy or pity—so stuff it, will you?"

We all knew he meant it, too, undramatically and definitely, and we listened to his story of how it all happened until the officer of the day came around to take him back to the hospital. Gil lauded the enlisted man's sheer guts to high heaven and credits him with saving his life, which he certainly did. We all remembered, too, that Gil stayed with his plane to give his passenger the first chance. The boys at North Island won't forget soon the time the officer and the enlisted man saved each other's lives out there in the broiling sun and barren desert.

TOPICS FOR DISCUSSION

1. Talk about things you have learned in the chapter. Compare your new knowledge with that of others.

2. Explain the meaning of these words and phrases: Night-practice carrier landings on the field; bight; turns toward the mat; silhouetted; already warming tar; nubs of land; slid over into right echelon; teakwood; reflew our landing; chocks; tachometer; cowl flaps; ferrying a Grumman Amphibian.

Suggested Film

Eyes of the Navy, a 16mm. film which can be borrowed from your nearest Navy Recruiting Station, illustrates clearly the activities and the training at a modern naval aviation training base.

USING THE STARS AS GUIDES[1]

By Harry M. Davis

EVERYONE knows that he can guide himself by the sun or the North Star if he loses his sense of direction by day or night. That is quite simple. Face the sun in the morning, and north will be on your left. In the afternoon it will be on the right. When you face the North Star at night, the east will be on your right and the west on your left. This is the principle used by navigators on ships and planes to establish their positions at sea, but the navigator's problem is much more complex than that. He needs to know not only north, south, east, and west but exactly where his ship is on the sea at the time the bearings are taken. He must know, for example, how far north of the equator the ship is and how far west of the Greenwich meridian it is. (The meridians run north and south, the parallels east and west.) After the navigator has calculated those two positions he can draw the line for north and south and the line for east and west. Where the lines cross is the exact position of the ship at that moment. He can then report, say, that his latitude is 38° 46′ and longitude 27° 11′, and any sailor or pilot could look on the map and locate the exact spot.

But the North Star is not always visible. It is not visible in the southern hemisphere. Navigators learn to recognize many stars, and through their books and tables they are able to establish their positions.

*   *   *   *   *

How do the stars serve to determine position on the earth? Well, suppose you were lucky enough to get a seat on a southbound plane. On leaving New York, if you were astronomically minded, you might notice that Polaris, the North Star, stood somewhat less than halfway up the northern skies from the horizon.

[1] From *New York Times Magazine*, April 26, 1942.

At Miami, where you whiled away an evening waiting for a clipper to South America, you would see Polaris distinctly lower. As your pilot took you across the Equator, you might see the same star dip below the horizon. From then on that familiar beacon of the northern sky would be invisible—but the Southern Cross and other strange constellations would appear ahead.

Thus, in an approximate way, you could estimate your latitude north of the Equator by the height of a single star. The navigator measures that height exactly with the sextant—precise instrument of lenses and mirrors that permits him to get an accurate measure of the altitude above the horizon of a star, a planet, the moon or the sun. The altitude of the North Star gives him his latitude.

Longitude can be obtained by ascertaining the time difference between the point in question and Greenwich, a suburb of London. The navigator knows his Greenwich time from the chronometer on his ship or the watch on his wrist—both of which are checked by radio time signals. It remains to determine the local time.

On a clear day any one can determine local time in an approximate way by noticing when the sun reaches its highest point. Since all the celestial bodies—sun, moon, planets and stars—make a similar passage across the heavens in the course of each day or night, the navigator can use any one of them to determine his local time.

If he already knows the latitude, the navigator doesn't have to wait for the body to reach its highest point in the heavens as it crosses meridian; he can tell how far along it is by measuring its height above the horizon with a sextant. A comparison of local time with Greenwich time gives the degrees of longitude east or west.

This has been an oversimplified example, assuming that the navigator can first determine his latitude and then his longitude. In most cases the navigator sights the sextant successively at any two bright stars that are not too near each other in the sky. He must then consult his nautical almanac or air almanac, with its pages and pages of timetables for the motions of Venus, Jupiter and the other planets; of Aldebaran, Arcturus, Betelgeuse, Capella, Deneb, Fomalhaut, Sirius, Vega and the other bright stars; of the sun and the moon. There is mathematical computation, and the drawing of lines upon a chart. Those lines must cross, and the "X" thereby formed marks the ship's spot on the map.

The point is, as far as the constellations are concerned, that the navigator must be able to identify the star on which he is sighting his sextant as the same star whose name and timetable appear on a certain line of his almanac. To recognize the star he is guiding the ship by, the navigator must know his constellations. He can count on the stars to tell him just where on earth he is.

UNSUNG AIR HEROES[1]

By Harvey E. Valentine

YOU don't read much about the navigator, but he is indispensable to the striking force of the air arm, charting, with unbelievable accuracy, the course which enables a raiding bomber to reach its objective in the shortest time and then insuring, as far as it is humanly possible, its safe return.

In the by-guess-by-gosh-I-hope-I-get-there days of aviation, a pilot used to follow roads, railways, rivers and other such objects. If he encountered bad weather and poor visibility it was just too bad, for then it was impossible to distinguish objects. Today there is no guesswork in navigating a plane.

Our own air services are now training hundreds of men to navigate the large number of heavy and medium bombers rolling off our production lines.

To assure an adequate number of skilled crew men, the Army has relaxed the qualifications for prospective navigators. A young man will be accepted for the forty-five-week training course if he is a high school graduate and can pass an Air Corps intelligence test.

In the initial training period alone, the navigator takes eighteen hours in the duties of junior officers; eleven hours in squadron duties; seven hours in military law; fifty-five hours in Morse code; eight hours in map and chart reading; twelve hours in a study of ground forces; six hours in anti-aircraft defense; forty-nine hours in a course concerning the air force; fourteen hours study of naval forces; 106 hours of signal communications of various kinds; eight hours of photography; twenty-two hours of mathematics; forty-eight hours of military drill; forty-eight hours of supervised athletics and many other subjects.

Aerial navigation is the science of piloting a plane from one point to another on the earth's surface and establishing its

[1] From *New York Times Magazine*, April 26, 1942. Copyright by the publishers.

position at any time. The four methods of air navigation are pilotage, dead reckoning, celestial observations and radio aids.

Pilotage is the method of conducting an aircraft along a course by determining its position by observation of landmarks, either previously known or recognized from a map.

Dead reckoning is the method of determining the geographical position of an aircraft by the distance and direction from a known position.

Celestial navigation is the method of determining the geographical position of an aircraft by observation of stars and planets in the sky.

Radio navigation is the method of conducting an aircraft along a course by radio aids, such as the radio beacon.

The Army navigator does not rely upon any one method. Conditions often arise on an extended flight when all four methods must be used.

By determining ground speed, drift and course, the navigator can accurately tell when the bomber will reach its objective. Charts are indispensable to him, as they provide the only reliable means of determining the distance and direction to be flown to a desired destination. Airports, beacons, and radio ranges are shown on sectional and regional charts. Besides the charts and the navigating instruments installed in the plane —compass, air speed indicator, etc.—his only other aids are the common protractor and divider.

In wartime it is the pilot who receives the glory for a successful raiding mission. But some also should go to the "young man with the protractor and the divider."

TOPICS FOR DISCUSSION

1. It has been said that it takes thirty men on the ground to keep one pilot in the air. Does that seem possible? Name all the ground jobs in connection with aviation you can think of, omitting those connected with building planes in factories. Which jobs seem most important? Which require the most school preparation?

2. If you could not be a flier, which ground job would be most attractive to you? Why?

3. Find out all you can about what a navigator does in a plane that carries a pilot, copilot, navigator, and mechanic. Report to the class.

WIDER WINGS[1]

By Patricia O'Malley

A VERY pleasant way to get information about a new vocation is through a story. If a girl wishes to become a hostess on an airliner, there are serious, technical books she can read to acquaint herself with the requirements and duties and to get help in making up her mind; but through a story she can get her first picture of the job, if the story is written by someone who really knows. To many girls employment as an air hostess looks glamorous. They see only the spectacular, romantic side of it without realizing that the job is serious and exacting work.

Patricia O'Malley, author of the following selection, has been a writer for more than fifteen years. Since 1929 her work has been connected with commercial airlines. In her novel of 1941, *Wings for Carol,* Miss O'Malley tells the story of Carol Rogers, an airline hostess. In *Wider Wings* she continues Carol's experiences as a hostess and also her romance. Carol has become chief hostess for an inter-American airline with planes going from the United States to Mexico, Central America, and South America. The two chapters we have here from *Wider Wings* will not satisfy you. But they will prompt you to read the whole of the two books. By doing so you will learn, from a writer who knows, a great deal about the qualifications for this service, and about the duties connected with the job itself—and you will be delightfully entertained as you read.

* * * * *

The laboratory ship stood at the end of the runway, its propellers stilled, its engines silent. While Carol waited, the door opened and the crew got off. Grant was nowhere to be seen, and the two men who stood talking in the entrance were unfamiliar to her.

---

[1] Copyright 1942 by Patricia O'Malley. Published by Greystone Press, New York.

Modern airliners at a commercial field preparatory to the take-off

While she waited, the men walked slowly away and continued their conversation, leaning against the treadway on a wing. Several others, also unknown to her, left the ship and joined them.

Still no Grant.

She felt a sharp flood of disappointment. Suppose he was not on board? She waited a few more seconds and was turning to go when she heard him call. She spun around quickly and there he was, filling the entire door space, ducking his head to come down the gangplank to join her. She walked toward him.

"I've seen you before somewhere." He placed both his hands on her shoulders, looking down at her steadily. "You're more than vaguely familiar. You seem to be my best gal."

"If you put it that way, I've got to admit it." Carol's smile matched his own. "Eric Benton told me you'd be here soon and I've been looking for you."

"Benton was ever a friend." Grant's smile seemed a little less blithe. "Have you been seeing much of him?"

"I've seen him once, by actual count. But I left a friend of his in the hangar chasing a monkey with my assistant, just a few minutes ago."

Grant laughed. "A monkey might be slightly superior in mentality to any friend of Benton's. Of course I wouldn't know about your assistant."

"How long are you going to stay here?"

"Not long," said Grant. "Unfortunately."

They followed the narrow cement walk around the Administration Building toward the place where the cars drove in to disembark passengers. Grant looked down at her again.

"What are your plans for this evening, Beautiful? Big date, I suppose."

"I have just one plan," smiled Carol. "What would you like to do?"

"What I'd like to do and what I've got to do are so different, there's no point in even thinking about it."

Carol remained silent.

"What I'd like to do is go somewhere and eat and dance until the dawn came up like thunder over Dallas. But what I've got to do is eat and then go looking for weather to give my direction finder a final test before the Los Angeles show."

Looking for weather! The first time he had ever taken her flying was on a murky Sunday afternoon in Chicago and they had gone looking for weather over Lake Michigan. Carol remembered that flight vividly. He had perfected his static-remover that day and Foster had suffered an attack of claustrophobia which had nearly ruined her career before it had started. How long ago it seemed! And how many things had happened since that day to shape their lives—to weld them together and to separate them again. Mildred in England. Jack in the Canal Zone. Foster in New York. She in the Southwest, and Grant, as always, here, there and everywhere in his endless hunt for things to make flying safer.

Suddenly she spoke. "I'm surprised you aren't in the Army yet."

"Is it so odd?" There was an edge in his tone.

"Well, everybody else seems to be going into active service, or else joining the Ferry Command," said Carol.

"Do you think I should? And which do you think would suit me better?"

"Well, you're a reserve officer, aren't you?"

"That's no answer to my question," replied Grant. "Would I be more attractive in olive drab or as a dashing transatlantic pilot?"

"I don't know. Which would you rather do?"

"As long as you want to know, I'll tell you," Grant said. "I'd rather be in the Army, but the Army thinks I'm doing them more good on the outside carrying on my experiments."

"Well, then, I suppose you are."

They stood looking at each other doubtfully. "How pretty she is," thought Grant, "and why do I always manage to make her uncomfortable?" He began to laugh.

"I'm the world's most awkward Romeo," he said. "All the way down here I've been practicing fancy speeches and rehearsing what I'd say when I'd see you again and here I am, as usual, tongue-tied."

It cleared the air immediately. "Me, too," admitted Carol. "I've been trying to figure out what's wrong with us. I've been wanting to see you ever since I left New York, and now that you're here I can only think of stupid things to say."

"Let's begin all over again." He linked his arm through hers. "There must be some place in this town that has music with its meals. That storm I'm looking for isn't due here for three hours yet."

"Will you take me with you?" asked Carol.

"Of course, if you'd like. There's a cold front on its way down here from the Dakotas. It's moving fast and shouldn't last long, but I'm warning you, it won't be comfortable."

"Storms don't bother me."

"This might be a little rougher than you're used to," Grant said. "I'm deliberately going to lose my way and do some testing."

"If that direction finder's as good as it's supposed to be, I won't worry," declared Carol. "Besides, we can't get very lost."

"Your confidence touches me, madam, and seems to have restored my appetite. Let me make one last weather check before we start on the fatted calf."

While she waited for Grant to return, Jim Hathaway and Maggie came around the corner of the waiting room, headed, like themselves, for the bus terminal.

"Did you catch the monkey?" called Carol.

"Mr. Field did," replied Marguerite. "He had an awful time, but he finally cornered the brat."

"That was a fine idea of Pete's, but it certainly raised Cain with poor Rosa."

Maggie giggled. "Imagine her believing Mr. Field was throwing things at her."

Carol smiled broadly. "So she'd stay away from the hangar, when he's so crazy about her! By the way, does she know yet?"

"Yes. He called her himself and explained the whole thing. He had to do some fast talking, but I heard him say he'd be over at eight o'clock."

"What made you run away from us?" asked Lieutenant Hathaway. "Did we suddenly break out with the measles?"

"I saw Grant's ship landing," Carol explained, "and I wanted to be on hand to meet him."

"More than he deserves. Where is the lucky pup now?"

"Getting the weather. He's going to do some flying later on."

"Not if we can talk him out of it," said Lieutenant Hathaway. "What does he mean, wanting to fly when the material for one of the best foursomes in Texas is gathered right here?"

"Well, he wants to make sure that direction finder's right before he demonstrates it to all those big scientists," explained Carol.

Just then Grant joined them. The two men shook hands and were genuinely glad to see each other. Carol presented Marguerite.

"Well, what are we waiting for?" asked Grant. "Hasn't anybody got any ideas?"

"Miss Beauregard and I were going to dinner and the movies," said Lientenant Hathaway. "Why don't you two join us?"

"Dinner's okay," said Grant, "but Carol and I will pass up the movies. We're going flying."

"Go tomorrow," suggested the Lieutenant.

Grant shook his head. "Sorry, but tomorrow won't do me any good. It's got to be tonight."

"Why don't we all go with you?" said Marguerite.

Lieutenant Hathaway growled. "What a break that will be!"

"It won't be dull, I'll guarantee that," said Grant. "And if you get airsick easily, I'll advise you to stay on the ground. The stuff is moving in here with a push and it's anything but gentle."

Hathaway grinned. "Might as well count me in, then," he said in a resigned tone. "I can see from the faces of the ladies that you've won."

The bus came along and they all piled in.

"Drive on, Magellan," said Hathaway sadly; "the condemned will have at least one good meal before the axe falls."

The sidewalks were reflecting the gleam of the street lamps and a fine mist was falling when they left the brightly lighted restaurant where they had dined.

"A walk wouldn't do us any harm," said Grant, "but I suppose everyone'd melt in this downpour."

"Not at all," Marguerite Beauregard spoke up quickly. "I love rain when it's like this. Cool, and sort of comforting."

"So do I," said Carol. "I like to feel it against my face, it's so fresh, and, well, caressing."

"We've a couple of romantic maidens here, Lowrie. For my

part a nice warm living-room is the ideal place for people to be on a rainy night. Inside, looking out, that's me."

"I'll take it either way," said Grant. To Carol he said, "It's up to you where we take the rain. Just let me know where you want it and I'll have it there."

They walked slowly down the almost deserted thoroughfare, looking in store windows and commenting on everything they saw. People turned to look at them—two tall, clean young men and two attractive and well-turned-out young girls, strolling along, oblivious to the rain which was gradually getting heavier, wet faces smiling at each other, high spirited and happy laughter echoing against the noises of the city.

"This has gone far enough," declared Lieutenant Hathaway, stopping suddenly before a window display of hospital furniture. "We'll be spending time among these dreary things if we get another drop wetter. If we're really going on this crazy expedition, let's get there and get it over with."

He waved at a cruising taxicab and opened its door as the driver eased it against the street curbing.

"Get in," he ordered. "Rain may be soft and cool and caressing, and all that, but sniffles have been known to blight love's young dream in its very bud. You, too, Lowrie. Of all the clucks," he continued. "Suppose you get pneumonia and pass out on us, what then? What would happen to all those high-flown notions of yours about getting the man in the street into the air? You don't want to run out on him at this stage of the game, do you? You wouldn't desert him after all those years of devotion, would you?"

"You talk too much, my lad." Grant climbed into one of the small jump seats, sitting sideways so his long legs had more room to stretch in the crowded taxi.

"Airport," he said to the driver, and with a loud scraping of shifts and gears they sped east in the direction of the flying field.

The ship was ready when they got there, engines warmed up and propellers revolving slowly in their arcs of silvery mist. The co-pilot and engineers from several airplane manufacturing companies were already seated and waiting.

Grant took his place in the Captain's seat of the pilot's compartment.

"Strap your belts securely," he called back. "And keep them strapped, because it's going to be rough. When we're high enough, I'll come back and explain this gadget to you."

They raced down the field along the path of gold cut through the darkness by the floodlights. The cabin was strange and bare-looking and filled with the sound of the powerful motors. Grant sat easily at the controls, his strong brown fingers handling the wheel with the complete confidence of the experienced pilot.

The laboratory ship was a standard transport model, stripped of half its seats and filled with instruments and experimental equipment. It did not have the refinements of the passenger-carrying airplanes. It was a workshop and looked what it was—to be used to develop and carry out some of the most important work in all the science of aeronautics.

They were aloft now, circling the field in a climbing turn. The running lights on the wing tips could barely be seen. Higher they went, and higher, shrouded momentarily by soggy, broken clouds, now completely submerged, now quickly shaking the sticky tentacles from their wings and body, flying head-on into the storm.

Everybody was prepared for turbulence but even so, when it came, it was with a terrifying suddenness as they were tossed upward a thousand feet, shaken and gasping. They all looked self-consciously at each other and grinned. Not very happily, however—rather pale, sickly grins and not too assured. This type of flying is not pleasant for anybody, pilot or passengers. Carol watched Grant's feet work hard at the rudders. His face was set and it looked drawn in the half light of the instrument board. But she knew it was because he was in the shadow, as they had not been flying long enough for him to be under any strain, regardless of the going.

The airplane was tossed about like a cork in an angry sea, twenty thousand pounds of metal guided by the hands and hearts of two men, matching their strength and brains against the fury of the elements.

One of the cabinet doors swung open with a jerk and a box of tools fell to the floor, making a loud, sharp noise, wrenches and hammers clattering away in all directions. Twice they were thrown forward with such violence that Carol thought surely the seat belts would not hold. She looked at her watch. Less than ten minutes! It seemed an hour.

By degrees the turbulence subsided. Grant removed his earphones and turning the controls over to the co-pilot, came back into the cabin.

"Worse than I thought," he said cheerfully, "but most of it's over. It'll still be a bit squally though, so you'd better hang on." He motioned to the railing which runs close to the ceiling of an airplane and serves to hold magazines, newspapers, brief cases and other odd articles which are not placed in with the regular baggage.

"Was that cord wood you ran into?" asked Jim Hathaway. "Or was it just a blast from the Polar region, and are we above it or below it?—and whichever it is let's keep out of it."

"You're a fine soldier," jeered Grant, "grousing about a gentle spring breeze. I'll show you some real weather if you'd like. My forecast says there's plenty of it around."

"I'm a soldier all right," was the answer, "and when I fly in storms I want to handle the airplane myself."

Grant understood. It is always difficult for a pilot to sit idly by when there is work to be done. Many experienced flyers become nervous when anyone else is in command of the ship. He had felt that way himself many times.

"Well, are we going to see that brain child of yours work, or did we come up here to have our palms read? Get going, young Mr. Edison."

They crowded around the stand on which the direction finder had been mounted. Marguerite and Carol sat on the arm of a chair close to the cabin wall, making themselves as inconspicuous as possible. Everyone was given a set of headphones and Grant busied himself with switches and needles.

"Were you scared?" whispered Carol.

"Green. Positively green," Maggie replied. "I thought we were going to fall to pieces. Is it like that very often?"

"Not often. And we'd never take passengers up in anything like it."

The explanation of the direction finder was involved and well over Marguerite's head, and though for the first few moments Grant included her in his remarks, the discussion soon became so technical that she had to give up trying to under-

stand. She knew, however, that something important was going
on. The concentration on the faces of the men, the gravity of
their expressions and the repetition after repetition of the
same problem told her that.

For more than an hour they bumped back and forth across
a hundred-mile stretch of Texas night, losing themselves time
after time and finding their proper position in the uncharted
sky simply by turning in on any of the commercial stations
within range of their radio sets.

Oklahoma City, Houston, El Paso, Baton Rouge, New Or-
leans, and any number of others came in loud and clear, or
scratchy with static, sometimes muffled, sometimes plainly, but
always with sufficient force to enable them to know the direction in which they were flying.

One of the engineers spoke. "You have something here,
Lowrie," he said. "My company will be definitely interested
in the production of this instrument."

"Not to mention the Army," said Hathaway. "Can't you see
what this would mean to a combat pilot? With one of these he
could reach his objective in any kind of weather, by day or by
night."

"I wish I understood it." Marguerite leaned forward in her
seat and spoke to Carol as they came in for a landing. "I hate
being such a dumbbell when everybody else is so intelligent."

Carol laughed. "Give yourself time," she said. "Nobody ever
understands what engineers are talking about. I happen to
know because Grant's been telling me about it for a year. It's
this way: Think of the air being a great big ocean, full of
waves and currents and tides and everything just like the real
ocean—after that tossing around we got, you shouldn't find
it difficult—well, there you have this great big space and you
want to get somewhere in it. You tune in your direction finder
and you hear a symphony orchestra broadcasting, or maybe
it's a bedtime story, or somebody selling toothpaste. Anyway,
you listen and when the station makes the announcement, you
find that place on your map and you just fly on that course
until you get there. That isn't the proper explanation, of
course, but it's the idea."

Marguerite nodded. "I see."

The wind was blowing straight from the north and sheets of

rain swept the field in almost solid formation when Grant brought them to a standstill before one of the loading gates.

"Can't let you go outside in that," he said. "You'd drown. I'll taxi right inside the hangar and then borrow someone's car to take you home.

"Did you enjoy the ride?" he asked.

Carol answered and Marguerite echoed. "We loved it. It was fun."

"I'll bet it was."

"Does Dallas offer any night life?" Jim Hathaway wanted to know on the way back to town. "I'm all for keeping this going."

"I imagine plenty," said Carol, "but we've got to pass it up tonight in favor of sleep."

"Sleep tomorrow; it's Sunday."

"I'll sleep when Monday's over and not before. Hostess service starts Monday and we've a million things to do between now and then."

"You going to work all day tomorrow?" Jim Hathaway expressed his disappointment. "I thought we might do things. You promised me once, you know."

"We've got too many things to do. A dress rehearsal in the afternoon, for one thing, and that's important."

"Well, save the evening for me. That's important too. I'll drive you around town for relaxation."

Carol looked questioningly at Grant.

"Perhaps you wouldn't mind if Marguerite and I joined you?" There was nothing in his voice to indicate how he felt other than complete friendliness.

"I'm afraid you'll have to count me out," said Maggie. "I've already made other plans."

"In that case I'll come by myself," declared Grant. "I'm hanged if I'm going to let any kiwi beat my time . . . while I'm around to watch, anyway."

*　　*　　*　　*　　*

More than a year later, Carol, on a flight from Brownsville to Dallas, met Señora de Garmo, an American woman whose husband was a government official in Guatemala and a very wealthy coffee-grower. Elizabeth de Garmo had been a girlhood friend of Carol's mother. On her flight to the Canal Zone to act as bridesmaid at the wedding of an air-hostess friend, Carol promised to spend two days with the de Garmos in Guatemala City.

* * * * *

The spectacular beauty of the flight to Guatemala City stamped itself indelibly on Carol's memory. The stars were crystal clear above the prairies when the Captain lifted the B-Liner into the wind and toward the Border, but before long the orange glow of the rising sun heralded the coming of another day, and the darkness receded before the dove-gray light that turned first to pink, then to orchid, and then to fiery gold and blue.

They flew high above a parade of gray-green cactus, cedar brakes and spiny bush, swollen streams and cattle fences, and miles and miles of sand—veritable proof of the old timers' saying that "Texas is a land of more rivers and less waters, more cows and less milk, and where you can look farther and see less than in any other State in the Union."

Out of Corpus Christi, however, brown open spaces gave way to the green, cultivated fields of the Rio Grande Valley, while across a stretch of shallow green Gulf water strewn with yellowish islands, Tampico lay, its narrow harbor crowded with tai.kers. Out of Tampico the earth grew into thick ridges, which got higher and higher until they joined the mountain range that is the backbone of the Americas.

The counterpane of the earth unfolded in a pattern unfamiliar to Carol. The hills were covered with winding trails, but there were no signs of habitation, no clustered villages, no thatched huts—nothing but the barren historic ground where once the conquistadores scourged a trail through a morass of blood and tears.

Gradually the scene changed. To the westward clouds began to gather in massive, churning formation. Occasional raindrops spattered against the cabin windows and the sky was overcast and dismal before the airplane came to rest on the lofty plateau where brooding mountains stand in silent and perpetual watch over Mexico City.

The stop was brief, barely long enough to refuel and exchange passengers before the ship was off again. From the air the Mexican capital presents a spectacle unlike any other city in the world. It lies flat and drawn against the immensity of a broad, brown valley, encircled in the eternal embrace of stately Popocatepetl and his white Sleeping Lady.

At five thousand feet a fair wind split the steel gray clouds asunder and a flaming bolt of sunshine struck radiance from the icy slopes of Ixtacihuatl. Shafts of light poured down in widening spaces between the moving masses, straight down in cascades of gold that made a filmy curtain across the cordillera toward the far horizon and infinity.

Such beauty was almost unendurable. Carol closed her eyes and bowed her head in gratitude and wonder, feeling the insignificance, the impermanence of creature things, humble indeed in the presence of the Lord.

When she opened her eyes again she looked down on the crazy quilt layout of the lower inclines of the Sierras, little villages clinging against their sides, or nestling in what looked like miniature valleys. There was snow in the gullies and some of the mountains bore the bitter scars that molten lava had carved deeply into their dark faces. A dry river bed cut through the rocky sides of Malintzi and a road, straight as a string, went from nowhere to nowhere.

They climbed through scattered clouds, above mountain peaks strewn across the mesa, beyond the black majesty of Orizaba, formidable and timeless, the lesser hills clustering as if in homage at his feet.

Here was a lonely rancho. There a few dwellings lay along a narrow stretch of lowland. A single row of trees marched like a column of twisted men along the knife edge of a cliff, etched against a motionless bank of cloud hung like a shroud in back of them.

To the left was the sea, dashing against a broken shore. There was not a level space the size of a man's hand between the mountains and its rocky coast. Only the rough, broken face of mother earth, serried and pitted.

It was getting warmer in the plane, and the country was getting greener. Clouds like massive plumes were floating in a cobalt sky. Cultivated patches appeared below, and a murky winding stream meandered across the land. A row of volcanoes

paraded by the wing tip, separated by deep and narrow valleys. And then they were circling the town of Tapachula where
a little river sings its way around the city, and banana trees
stand in orderly rows on all sides. This was Carol's first ac-
quaintance with the tropics. The airport station here is simply a palm-thatched roof set on poles, wide open to whatever
breezes come that way.

The ticketing procedure was all very casual and friendly.
The immigration official sat under a lattice covered with a
riot of yellow trumpet vine; to the back of him a curved walk
was outlined with pineapple plants, and over the heads of the
captain and the crew, as they discussed their flight plan with
the airport manager, scarlet and purple bougainvillea hung in
colorful riot.

"How long before we get to Guatemala City?" asked someone.

"Oh, we're almost there. It's only two hours now and clear
weather all the way in."

It was a smiling, friendly country the rest of the way. Even
the volcanoes looked less formidable. Out of Tapachula the
sun was on the wings, and the distant Pacific was softly
blurred. There was a speck of white sail against the blue water. Beyond its marshy edges the breakers rolled and spread
themselves in long, foamy ridges along a curving line.

Again they were flying high and again the jagged mountains
accepted the airplane's challenge and poked their bleak heads
defiantly through the stretches of the cloud layer.

The clouds had taken on fantastic shapes, expanding in
rows of cold cliffs across snowy antarctic wastes. Here a giant
camel lay in sleep. There a herd of buffalo galloped in fantastic panorama. Now in this cloud country of mountains, craters and plains, a phantom city came into view. A weird city,
laid out in proper order—houses, buildings, streets, a frozen
lake, a fortress.

They were out of the clouds now, and the mountains were
turning purple, the distant valleys holding the long shadows
of the afternoon on their slanting sides. There was a waterfall
below and a winding road that twisted through the timber
and the thorny underbrush, and looked like nothing else but
a length of molasses candy.

The big ship flew serenely over ground where four centuries ago Spanish soldiers fought and conquered in the name of the Cross and the Crown. Over the same wild and dreary wastes where the fair-skinned Alvarado struggled to wrest the kingdom of the Quiches, the Cakechiqueles, and the Tzutohiles from the hands of its rulers and add it up to the glory of Spain. White men, bearing destruction in their hands, were preserved by their gods from the javelins and darts, slugs and arrows of the native whose gods equipped his naked bronze body with no such armor. Small wonder that his simple soul found it easy to believe that these blond giants were Children of the Sun.

Actually seeing this country made the story of the conquest far more astonishing than it could ever appear on the printed pages of a history book. How was it possible for a few men to subjugate an empire? By what superhuman standard were they able to force themselves through stagnant marshes, up and down the steep sides of the Sierras, over the crests of the cordillera and across the plateau to the very stronghold of the Emperor?

Red rooftops proclaimed the approach to Guatemala City. Parks and church spires stood out from the mosaic with definite clarity. To the right appeared the twin volcanoes of fire and water, the cone-shaped heads of Agua and Fuego, and it was then only a matter of seconds before the steps were rolled against the airplane's door and Carol was held close against the motherly bosom of Elizabeth de Garmo.

SPOT LANDING[1]

By Blaine and Dupont Miller

THE authors of this story have already made Bob Wake-field known to all readers of stories of aviation. Blaine Miller is a Lieutenant Commander in the U. S. Naval Air Force. The co-author is Mrs. Jean Dupont Miller, his wife. You can readily see that they know about flying from actually doing it, not by reading about it and hearing pilots tell about it. Often in their stories they are showing something about character-making, human nature, problems of living, and the motives back of action.

As you read "Spot Landing" see if there is some such human problem in it and ask yourself if the story shows us people as they are.

*   *   *   *   *

In the vicinity of Corry Field at the Naval Air Station, Pensacola, Florida, the air was alive with chrome-colored training planes. Like an unbroken column of yellow-jackets, the aircraft circled the edge of the field over the scrub blackjack. Then, as each one reached the downwind side of the field, the engines were idled and, in succession, the biplanes darted for the landing mat to level off and then slowly settled to the earth. After a short roll the engines would roar to life and the planes skimmed on to continue their merry-go-round.

Below the Operations Tower stood Lieutenant Bob Wakefield. It was his first visit to Pensacola since he had graduated and departed to an exciting life in the Fleet. Now, as memories of student days came back to him, he turned to Tom Baker, the Chief Flight Instructor, "Tom, I almost wish I were coming back to instruct students instead of going on to Jacksonville to join up with a patrol plane squadron."

---

[1] From *Boys' Life*, May, 1941. Reprinted through the courtesy of the authors and *Boys' Life*, published by the Boy Scouts of America. Copyright 1941 by the authors.

"Instructing has its interesting points," agreed Tom, "rarely does a day go by that we don't have some excitement. Our biggest difficulty is in holding our students down. If they'd only be contented to learn more slowly! But a fellow comes down here believing aviators are supermen and he wants to be one as soon as possible."

Bob laughed, "We felt the same way!"

"True, but once we got out into the Fleet we soon learned that being a pilot was only the beginning of a naval aviator's education. The easiest part, too!"

"Yes, and what a rude awakening that was!"

The conversation was interrupted as the whining blast of the field siren split their ears. The crash bell began its alarming call. All ground personnel stopped their work to look up. The bluejacket in the Control Tower above called down through a megaphone, "Mr. Baker, that fighting plane is coming in for a landing with its wheels up!"

"Flash the danger light on him!"

The flight surgeon ran by and swung aboard the ambulance as it got underway with a roar. Its siren screamed a frantic alarm as it dashed out onto the flying field. But, as quickly as the first-aid equipment moved into action, one of the training planes was even faster. It darted from its position in the landing circle and flew straight across the path of the fast-gliding fighting plane.

Instinctively, Bob cried, "Collision!"

For a second it appeared as though he was going to be correct. But, at the last moment the pilot of the single-seater zoomed his machine upward to clear the trainer by inches.

Except for the straining engines of the two planes, the field was silent. All hands breathed a sigh of relief, their eyes turned to follow the flight of the planes which now were circling the field. Once more, the fighter cut in for a landing, the wheels of the tiny plane still retracted within its fuselage.

Baker muttered to himself, helpless to avert the impending crash. But, as the fighter leveled off, the trainer once more dove at him, passing ahead just close enough to throw the full blast of his slipstream on the settling single-seater. Bob could see the fighter pilot struggling against the violent propeller wash, his wings wobbling abruptly from side to side. To save himself, he was forced to open his throttle wide and go around once more. This time he obviously realized what the trainer was trying to tell him, for his wheels were extended as the fighter glided in for the third pass. The trainer followed for a landing well clear of the Operations Building.

Baker called up to the Tower, "Who are the pilots in those planes?"

The lookout checked the Flight Board, "Ensign Whitehead in the single-seater and Machinist's Mate Ajax in the trainer."

Bob's eyes lighted with recognition as he heard the familiar name of Ajax. But, as he started to speak, Baker cut in.

"Now there Bob you have a perfect example of student psychology. Whitehead very stupidly forgot to lower his wheels o he has appeared in a poor light before the other students. It is probable that never again will he forget his wheels. He has gained from this experience."

"Seems to me it presents Ajax in a highly favorable light, too," said Wakefield.

Baker sighed, "There's a case that has me completely baffled. In an emergency he's the first one in the air. He saves Whitehead from possible injuries and he saves us a complete overhaul job on the fighter. Yet he isn't doing so well in his regular flight work. In fact, he isn't doing well at all."

Bob was distressed. "I'm sorry to hear that. I know Ajax very well. We've been shipmates for years and he's the best mechanic I ever saw. What's the trouble?"

"He doesn't seem to be able to get his small-field landings. I gave him his flight check the other day on that phase and I was forced to bust him. He persisted in using a nose-high slip and that is dangerous for a student."

"What is his status now, Tom?" asked Wakefield.

"He has been given five extra hours solo and two hours dual instruction in this stage, after which I will check him again to see if he is able to qualify. Some make it after busting a check, and others don't. If they fail, they are dropped from flight training and are sent back to the Fleet."

By now the trainer had swung into the space allotted it in the long line of planes and the whirling prop came to a stop. Bob excused himself and walked the short distance to the plane. With painful deliberateness, the pilot climbed down from the cockpit and removed his parachute. Straightening up he glanced toward the officer who was approaching and his tense face relaxed into a broad grin. He ran around the wing crying, "Mr. Wakefield! When did you get down here?"

They had parted only a few months before when Ajax had received orders for flight training, but they shook hands as if they had been separated for years.

"It's good to see you, Ajax! I find you up to your old tricks of saving pilots and planes!"

The mechanic smiled deprecatingly. "I was already in the air."

"It was a job well done, anyway."

Ajax asked eagerly, "How is the *Denver*? Is Captain Rumble still the Skipper?"

"You sound as though you might be homesick for heavy cruisers."

"Indeed I have been—especially lately."

"Why do you say 'especially lately'?" inquired Wakefield.

"Because," admitted Ajax, "it looks as though I'll be going back to the ship before very long."

Bob smiled. "Let's get down to business. How are you getting along with your flight training?"

"Not so well. I busted my small-field check the other day. Mr. Baker was more than fair. He gave me every chance, but they make you land an airplane on a dime."

Bob remembered that in his time he and his fellow students had made the same complaint. "You've been connected with aviation long enough to know that the deck of a carrier in the middle of the ocean will look even smaller than a dime if you're afraid of it.

"I know. But they don't seem to land the way you did. I didn't help myself the other day, either, when I told my instructor how you used nose-high slips when you wanted to get into the middle of a field."

Bob was dismayed. Out in the Fleet, many times, he had let Ajax take the stick of the plane they were in and had given him perfunctory instructions. He had enjoyed doing it because Ajax was so enthusiastic about aviation. But he saw now that the little bit Ajax had known before he came to Pensacola was very bad for him. It kept him from mastering basic flight rules. Many things that he, Bob, was able to do, like making nose-high slips into a small field, he could do because he had been flying for so long. But, for a student, they might be disastrous.

"How much time have you left before your final check?"

"One hour of instruction, then an hour of solo. After that a check and all of it will probably come tomorrow. Frankly, Mr. Wakefield, I don't think I have learned much since the last check. I haven't a chance of passing, I know."

In all the years since he had known him, Bob had never seen Ajax so discouraged. Now, Wakefield felt guilty as well as unhappy for his friend. His ill-advised instruction of Ajax in the Fleet might well be responsible for most of his friend's troubles.

"I don't shove off for Jacksonville until tomorrow. We'll get together tonight and discuss small field work. In the meantime, I must go over and pay my respects to the Commandant." Bob turned to go, "Keep your chin up, I'll see you tonight."

On the way over to the Administration Building, Bob turned Ajax's problem over in his mind. Undoubtedly small field landings were the mechanic's present stumbling block, but that was too general a statement. Something definite, something specific must have happened to put him badly off the track, for Ajax was excellent aviation material, he knew. What was it? Bob felt that if he could put his finger on this hidden difficulty, he might be able to save Ajax.

By this time, Bob was so anxious for his former shipmate to win his wings, that he felt he would gladly give up his assignment to patrol planes rather than go off and leave Ajax to his fate. But he had worked hard to obtain the orders and he knew he couldn't ask for a change every time something extraordinary arose. But if he could just help Ajax through this bad slump in his flying career, he would be happy.

As the Aide took Bob into the Commandant's office, the Admiral held up a dispatch, "Glad to see you, Wakefield. You must have informed the Bureau of Navigation you were stopping off here. I have some news from the Bureau which I'm afraid you will consider bad."

Bob felt excited and curious, but not particularly apprehensive. He took the message and read:

PRESENT ORDERS LIEUTENANT ROBERT WAKEFIELD MODIFIED REPORT NAVAL AIR STATION PENSACOLA FOR TEMPORARY DUTY INVOLVING FLYING PENDING DELIVERY NEW PLANES TO PATROL SQUADRON NINETY ONE

For a moment, a feeling of having been let down came over Bob. For so long he had been working toward Big Boats. Then, as the full realization of the orders reached him, he smiled. Why, they were just what he had been wishing for! They were only temporary and he would be certain to go on to big boats later. Here was his opportunity to help Ajax.

The Commandant questioned him, "Well, what do you think of them?"

Bob smiled, "Why, I think they're almost perfect, Admiral. I couldn't have asked for better."

They shook hands and the Commandant said, "I'm delighted to have you with us, Wakefield. We are woefully short of instructors and you will be of tremendous assistance to the Training Department. Do you have any preference of duty?"

"Yes, sir. I should like to instruct in primary land-planes. From what I saw over there this morning there is always some excitement at Corry Field."

"That's right. But, we don't care for that sort of excitement down here. We want you to teach your students to fly safely, not spectacularly. You will report to Lieutenant Baker over at Squadron Two who will assign you to your new duties. Good luck!"

Back at Corry Field, Tom Baker laughed as Bob walked into the office, "So you thought you were to go through a career of naval aviation without a tour of instructing? The Aide telephoned me the news and I'll assign you eight students right away. They'll keep you busy. I can vouch for that fact!"

"Could I have that mechanic, Ajax, by any chance?"

"All right. Perhaps a change of instructors might help him."

Wakefield sent word to Ajax concerning the change, and cancelled out the mere talk they were going to have, in favor of the instruction hop the following morning. When he reached Corry Field, Ajax was waiting for him with the engine of their trainer warmed up and ready to go.

Bob called his student aside. "Ajax, we have only a short time before you check and we must make the most of it. I want to ask you several questions and you must answer me as fully as you can."

"I'll do the best I can, sir."

"First of all, do you like this idea of becoming a pilot? Does it bother you to discover yourself up in the air alone? Are you comfortable?"

"Being in the air doesn't bother me, Mr. Wakefield."

"I didn't think it would after all the flying we've done together. And yet, for some reason you've permitted yourself to be buffaloed by small field landings. Can you account for that?"

Ajax looked long at the toe of his shoe before replying. Then, he said, "Yes, I think I can."

Bob regarded his student with interest. Perhaps this would be the key to his student's difficulty, which he must discover in order to help him. "Come on, then, tell me," he encouraged. "Time is important to us right now. Every minute must count."

"Well, sir, it's the landings themselves. During the first hour solo after my dual instruction in side slips, I practised small field work using slips to landings. Twice I lost speed and stalled just before I reached the ground. I came down hard both times, although the landing gear took it without any trouble. Once I landed on one wheel and one wingtip. I patched up the damaged wingtip and the Station never knew about it. But, I'll admit to you that those two attempts scared me plenty. After that I didn't do much work on sideslips. And I didn't sleep much that night, either. Every time I dozed off I would suddenly awaken thinking I was about to crash. I almost turned in my student's resignation right then."

This was bad. This was worse than Bob had expected. Ajax had acquired a fear complex about this particular phase of his work. He knew from past experience that Ajax had the ability to fly, but to wipe out from his mind fear of crashing when side-slipping close to earth was something else again. So much would depend on Ajax himself. Some men could be talked out of fear. Some could be laughed out of it. Only actual flight would show him what could help his old shipmate.

Bob jumped to his feet, "Come on, Ajax," he called, "we're going out to learn how to shoot small fields. Remember, though, a check flight covers all phases you've been taught up to the time of the check. So, give me a good takeoff and smooth airwork so I can judge how you are doing. We'll make a landing or two at the Old Barn, then we'll really go to work."

The plane taxied out to the mat and Bob signaled for a takeoff, watching closely every move his student made. Obviously, Ajax was nervous, but he made a fair takeoff. Once in the air, he steadied down and flew as smoothly as any student with his number of hours in the air could be expected to do. The landing at the Old Barn Field, a normal landing area, was good. So far, Ajax had demonstrated, just as Bob had expected him to do, that he had the ability to fly. Discouragingly, he had affirmed the fact that his trouble with small field work was a mental fear condition.

There was no point in wasting further time over the ordinary work. Bob turned around, "Your elementary flying is passing, Ajax. We'll waste no time on that."

The student was encouraged, "There's a lot of difference between flying for you and flying for a check instructor."

"Not if you really can fly." Bob turned around in the cockpit, his knees on his parachute. "Now, we'll get down to sideslips. There are times when you must get into very short fields with an approach over trees or telephone poles. Obviously, the necessity for a high approach means that you will have wasted a portion of your already short landing area. As a result you will overshoot the field and roll into a fence or a ditch."

"It's the same in a deadstick landing?" queried the student.

"Exactly. If you have a dead engine, you don't dare undershoot your field for fear of ploughing into a powerline or some other obstacle. Consequently, you must come in with extra altitude. But, again, if your field is short, you must lose your altitude quickly without picking up speed, or you will overshoot with the probability of cracking up your plane at the far end of the field."

Bob blimped the throttle to clear the cylinders, then continued, "What you do is to drop one wing and kick high rud-

der. This will cause your plane to slip sideways toward the
lowered wing. Now, if you keep your nose up level, you won't
pick up speed. As a result, you lose your excess altitude in a
short distance without converting the energy into forward
speed. This means you will be able to set your plane down
very short."

He went on, "The secret of this maneuver is to level your
wings just before the lower one hits the ground. But, under no
condition lose flying speed. This is dangerous at such a low
altitude."

"I found that out," said Ajax ruefully.

Bob turned around again and buckled his safety belt. "Stay
on the controls with me and see how I do it."

The trainer took off and flew to Swamp Field where the approach was over a line of tall pines. As the plane came around
in a gentle turn, Bob suddenly dropped the inboard wing and
kicked high rudder. The machine went into a sickening slip
toward the ground, the slipstream almost blowing them from
the cockpits. Then, just as it appeared to the student that
surely they must crash, the instructor pulled the wing up,
leveled off and set the plane on the ground.

Ajax turned around to gaze in amazement at the short landing after coming in over such a high obstacle.

Bob said, "That's all there is to it, Ajax. Go ahead and try
it a few times."

The student made his first pass at the field. But, though he
dropped his wing, he also dropped the nose and the plane
picked up forward speed. By the time the trainer was slow
enough to land, they had reached the opposite end of the
field. The throttle shot forward and they circled the field
again. On the following approach, Ajax held the nose too high
and Bob was forced to use full gun to keep the plane from
stalling. Turning around, he saw the worried look on Ajax's
face and he said, "That's all right. I'm in here to keep you out
of trouble. Let's try it again!"

Again and again the trainer shot the field, but rarely was it
able to make a successful landing. Bob was discouraged. He
knew that Ajax could fly better than this exhibition would
manifest. But there was no further time to correct his spot
landings, for their hour was up. Now, Ajax had an hour of

solo practice before his check and unless he did better than he had been doing during the instruction period, he didn't stand a chance of passing.

Back at Corry Field Bob told him, "Go on out, now. Remember what I have just told you and work hard. Your career as a pilot depends upon what you do in the next hour."

Standing on the ground, Bob watched Ajax's plane disappear from view on its way back to Stump Field where he must work out his own destiny. Then, Tom Baker would take him out for his check. Bob was sick at heart. He had so hoped that he would be able to get Ajax over the hurdle in his mind—this fear of side-slipping. Perhaps he could have done it if he'd had more than an hour. As it was, only a miracle could save Ajax.

A half hour later, Bob was at his desk working on his students' jackets—their flight records from the time they started training—when Tom Baker rushed down from the Control Tower. "Bob, there's a line squall moving in fast from the northwest. It's a nasty one with buckets of rain in the windshift. We've got about twelve primary students working over east of Pensacola. If we don't round them up quickly, we're liable to lose some of them. The rest of the instructors have gone to lunch. Jump in a plane and find as many as you can. Have them follow you back. Try to go around the squall, if you can. I'll follow as soon as I can get a plane."

Bob jumped into the warmed up plane and took off downwind. Already the line squall, its low black line flecked with vertical lines as torrents of rain fell, was almost on Corry Field. Bob thought of the students, scarcely able to solo. They wouldn't know what to do. He must find as many of them as he could, quickly.

He was fortunate to find a half dozen planes circling Stump Field. It was apparent that the pilots had seen the oncoming storm. But, already they were cut off from Corry, and they were huddling close, as though to provide comfort for one another. Bob zoomed his plane violently and flew close to the circle. Nothing happened. He zoomed again, and he felt like cheering when the trainers began to close up on him. He patted the side of his fuselage to indicate that they must close up.

It was a grim business, he knew. None of them had ever flown formation. Yet, here they were forced to stick in close, if they were to get through the violent front. On he went parallel to the line squall gathering up an occasional grateful student. But, there was fear in Bob's heart, for now the storm had pushed them further and further to the southeast and they were nearly over the Gulf. They'd have to push their way blindly through the opaque blanket of rain, for they couldn't get around it.

He turned to look back. All of his charges were doing a beautiful job of follow-the-leader. The pilot of the closest plane waved to him. He looked again. It was Ajax!

Now, they were out over water. There was no time to lose. They swung back over land again, so low that they were barely over the sharp pine trees. Now there was nothing for it but a gradual turn headed into the storm. The splash of water struck Bob's plane as though it were a waterfall. The rain was like lead pellets on his unprotected face. Two minutes went by and his goggles became so fogged he threw them over his head as useless. The cockpit was soaked. He fully expected his engine to drown out, so heavy was the storm.

He glanced backward. He could see no further than three planes, but the students were still there and he prayed that the remainder of the column were hanging on. Below was nothing but swamp and trees. Visibility ahead was still practically zero. On he flew by compass.

Suddenly a yellow object below caught his eye. In spite of the slicing rain, he leaned out of the cockpit and saw the object more clearly. A yellow training plane hanging in a tree on its back! Bob placed his plane in a slow circle to hold his position on the crash. As he circled, again, it was apparent that the pilot down below was in desperate need of assistance. It was clear what had happened. Because of an engine failure the pilot had attempted to land in the small clearing. He had overshot and crashed in the trees.

Wakefield turned the situation over in his mind. He looked back at his column of students. He didn't dare leave them, even though this other pilot needed help badly. If he did, he'd lose one of the students. What he needed was another instructor. Someone to go down and render assistance. As he struggled with the problem, he suddenly realized that Ajax had flown up very close to him. He was making violent gestures, pointing first to himself and then to the crash. Bob looked again. Surely Ajax wasn't proposing that he go down into that impossibly small field? But, he was!

Bob's first reaction was to signal an emphatic "No." But wait. This Ajax, using the sign language they had developed together on the *Denver*, was like the old Ajax he knew. He was alert, eager for an emergency, with never the shadow of a doubt about what he was going to do. Bob decided to follow his hunch.

He held the control stick between his knees and clapped his hands over his head. Ajax nodded in acknowledgment and pulled out of the formation. The third pilot, not knowing what was going on, joined up on the leader and kept the formation intact. Scarcely able to breathe from anxiety, Bob continued to circle.

He could see his student begin a slow approach. He knew it was painful, for Ajax, too, had thrown off his goggles. He would be forced to peer over the side, his face on fire. As he eased in over the pines, Bob could see him drop his left wing sharply. The plane made a quick dart for the ground but at the last possible instant, the student ruddered into the slip. The nose must have been held to perfection, for as the wings leveled off, the plane sat down short to roll to a stop in the muddy ground.

"Good boy, Ajax!" shouted Bob. He felt the blood rush back to his heart from relief. Ajax had licked his bugaboo! When he had someone else's plight to think about, he forgot his own fear entirely.

Bob turned away and pushed on through the front. It was ten minutes before the lightening sky foretold the clearing weather beyond. As he broke into the clear, he turned around to see his students also emerge from the storm.

Back at the Operations Building, Bob dispatched the ambulance to the general location of the crashed plane. "I'll fly over as soon as the squall has passed that point and lead you to the exact spot," he directed.

It was another fifteen minutes before another plane was ready for him, and as he started to taxi from the line, the me-

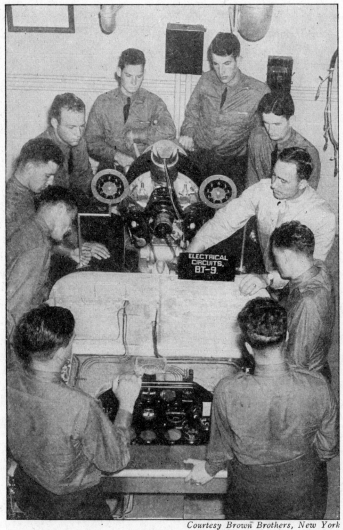

Courtesy Brown Brothers, New York

**Army cadets attending a lecture on the operation of the BT-9
training plane**

chanic on his wing shook the aileron. Following his out-
stretched arm, Bob saw a trainer coming in for a landing. He
swung back into the line, and as he reached the late arrival,
he found several bluejackets removing Tom Baker from the
front cockpit. Ajax was unbuckling his parachute.

Tom's face was gripped in pain, but he called, "Thanks,
Bob, for flying over me on your way home. I was caught in the
plane, hanging by my leg. Broke it pretty badly. Had a cut gun
and tried to make the field, but overshot."

They placed Baker on a stretcher and were just about to
carry him away, when, stopping the stretcher-bearers, he held
up his thumb, calling, "By the way, Ajax, when a student gets
into a small field that a check instructor can't, I always give
him an up check."

TOPICS FOR DISCUSSION

1. If you do not know what these words and expressions
mean in the sentences in which they occur, exchange information with other members of your group. Use the dictionary
for pronunciations and meanings about which none of you
are sure: operations tower; biplane; field siren; crash bell;
ground personnel; coming in for a landing with its wheels up;
fuselage; propeller wash; small-field landings; nose-high slip;
prop; deprecatingly; perfunctory; apprehensive; buffaloed;
dual instruction in side slips; stalled; fear complex; taxied
out to the mat; dead-stick landing; blimped the throttle; kick
high rudder; lose flying speed; safety belt; stay on the controls; use full gun; line squall; zoomed; had a cut gun; an up
check.

2. Find out all you can about the Naval Training School at
Pensacola and report to the class.

3. "We soon learned that being a pilot is only the beginning of a naval aviator's education." Why does Tom Baker
say that? What else is there to learn?

4. How did the trainer warn the incoming student pilot
that his landing wheels were up.

5. This story seems to say that one can overcome a fear by
action. Have you ever had a "fear complex" and conquered it

in any such way as Ajax conquered his? Does such a fear stay conquered?

SUGGESTED FILM

Navy Wings of Gold is a film which will give you an excellent picture of the activities and training at the Naval Training School at Pensacola. This film can be obtained from your nearest Navy Recruiting Station.

WINGS.[1]

To T. F. T.

By William Rose Benét

1914

The bay was bronzed with sunset, and so light
The ripples idled on the gentle tide
That we who swam in silence side by side
Paused; shifted poise; and floating, lost our sight
In a vast well of blue, benign and bright,
Just ere it faded and the clouds were dyed
Saffron and crimson. With one gasp we cried,
"Thus eagles float, through heavens of pure delight!'

Then with the splendor of a falling star,
Great wings swept down; a muffled engine whirred;
And iridescent as a humming-bird,
A biplane swooped upon us, veered, and fled
Chanting Man's realized dream . . . Yet higher far
We soared, upbuoyed on waters sunset-red!

1939

A quarter-century, and again the guns
Unheard when that was written, even unguessed;
And still one heart is beating in the breast,
One mind again confronts a change that stuns.
O bride and comrade, past the farthest suns
Or where nor space nor time are manifest
You still are near, who were the glorious west,
The dawning east, and all between them, once.

Now wings we never imagined swarm the skies
Where darkened cities shudder at those in dust,
Or those like torches to the heavens upthrust
Show in their glare how Man's dark mind has made
An assassin of his dream. Far otherwise
These rhymes would praise the dream that does not fade.

---

[1] From *With Wings as Eagles,* copyright by Dodd, Mead & Co., New York, 1940.

SAILBOATS IN THE SKY[1]

By E. F. McDonald, Jr.

MANY young people are experimenting with model airplanes. Most of these planes either soar in the breeze
or are carried for short flights by a small propeller
driven by a rubber band. Some older boys have had the courage to imitate Darius Green, but with more knowledge than
either Icarus or Darius had, and have constructed gliders. Gliding and soaring have both become major sports. The author
of this selection believes that there is no sport equal to that of
soaring. In his enthusiasm he has written a very entertaining
book about the construction and operation of gliders, of
which the following is a sample.

* * * * *

Not until he experiences the thrill and grandeur of thermal
soaring does man know the reality of pure flight at its finest.
Straight gliding, marvelous though it is, cannot compare with
it. Even slope soaring, riding for hours on the updrafts over
ridge or dune, lacks the supreme finesse required for this finest
and most exhilarating of sports. Any attempt to describe it in
words must necessarily damn it with faint praise; the best I
can do is attempt to tell how it is done.

Technically, soaring is used to describe motorless flight
which carries the ship higher than the point at which it was
launched or released from the towrope as distinguished from
gliding, a long slide downhill through the air. Soaring was
discovered by early gliding experimenters who on occasion
were able to hover a few moments in the updrafts above the
face of the slope from which they were launched. The first
known soaring flight of more than a few seconds' duration was
made in 1911 when Orville Wright hung poised in a strong

---

[1] From *Youth Must Fly*, copyright 1942 by Harper and Brothers, New
York.

wind for nearly ten minutes over a dune at Kitty Hawk, North Carolina.

Soaring is possible only when the glider flies into a current of air rising more rapidly than the glider sinks; it is like walking backward through a train that is moving forward faster than the passenger walks, or sailing a boat at three miles an hour against a current moving five miles an hour in the opposite direction. The net result in either case is to travel in the direction the train or current is moving. The glider, flying free in the air, is always going down, down, down through the air in which it flies, but if the air is rising more rapidly than the glider sinks, the ship will gain altitude.

When wind strikes the face of a cliff or ridge it is deflected upward. If the wind is swift enough, say ten or fifteen miles an hour, the resultant updraft will be strong enough to support and lift a glider which has a normal sinking speed through still air of from three to five feet a second.

Soaring pilots of the early 1920's discovered that if their glider was launched into this updraft they could maintain and, within certain limits, increase their altitude by cruising back and forth through the area of lift, and that they could keep their ship aloft as long as the wind blew from the proper direction. They were launched into the wind usually by a shock cord, from a point well up the slope, and flew straight ahead until the updraft supported them. Then they turned to right or left and continued flying back and forth.

That is about all there is to slope or ridge soaring today. The glider or sailplane is launched by winch or automobile tow and flies into the area of lift. Then it maneuvers along the face of the slope in great figure eights which usually extend the full length of the ridge, planning the flight so that the turn at each end of the "eight" is into the wind. This keeps the ship from drifting downwind into the area of turbulence and downdraft usually found on the lee side of the hill.

As the ship gains altitude, the area of lift broadens out like a giant V, making it possible for a good pilot to perform maneuvers of considerable extent. At Frankfort, Michigan, where the dunes provide excellent sites for ridge soaring, I have seen high-flying gliders well out over the lake, and others almost as far inland; at lower altitudes they could not possibly stay up over either of these positions.

All our early soaring was of this type, which explains the location of most of our well-known, long-established soaring sites. It also explains the misconception, still rather widespread, that hilly country is needed for gliding and soaring.

Ridge soaring is good practice for beginners because it permits flights of long duration in smooth air, since the ship will stay up as long as the wind continues to blow and it is kept in the relatively large area of lift. Should the student miscalculate his position in the air a few hundred feet while making his turns, he can always fly back into the updraft again, because he knows for certain where it is. Many an embryo pilot, with many things yet to learn, has completed his duration flight qualifications for a high-ranking glider license by riding the updraft on the face of a friendly hillside.

However, this method of flight soon becomes rather mechanical, since the pilot is pinned to a definite area limited by the length of the ridge. It is true that there are a few regions where ranges extending for many miles make cross-country flight possible, and where rough country jumbled in just the right way makes it possible to hop from ridge to ridge. Cross-country flights of more than one hundred miles have been made through the Appalachians by pilots who depended almost entirely on ridge currents, and a convenient ridge current at just the right time has proved highly welcome on many a cross-country soaring flight. But it is thermal soaring that has really made the art what it is today, and that has brought this magnificent sport within the reach of people no matter where they live.

A thermal is a great bubble of heated air rising through the cooler air around it.* The atmosphere lies over the earth like a layer of great blankets, the upper layers pressing on the lower to increase their density, and hence their temperature. When it is perfectly stable it is in equilibrium; although the lower air is warmer, it is also denser than that above. There is

---

* We have much to learn about the formation and character of thermal currents. The explanation and description given here makes no pretense of having 100 per cent scientific accuracy.—Author's footnote.

balance between the combined effects of temperature and pressure at different levels.

When the sun's rays strike the earth, the air near the surface is heated much more than that even a few feet above, until the temperature right on the surface may be far higher than that a few feet higher. The amount that the air is heated varies with the heat-absorbing and heat-retaining properties of the earth; black dirt, for example, will absorb more of the sun's energy and retain it as heat than a reflecting surface like water.

This heated air expands and tends to rise, but is held down by the blanket of air above. On certain days, when conditions are otherwise favorable, something happens to cause a breakthrough at some one point: a tiny difference in topography, a difference in temperature at two adjacent points, a quick gust of wind. The heated air rises through the break; hot surface air near by flows along the surface and up, pressed on by the pressure of the colder blanket of air around. This continues until the warm air in the immediate vicinity has been drawn off in the thermal bubble. Then the new air on the surface is heated by the sun's energy, and the process is repeated, with another "thermal" breaking loose, perhaps at the same point, and perhaps at one some distance away. Thermals usually start forming on favorable summer days along in midmorning, and continue until close to sunset.

As the thermal rises it goes faster and faster, expanding and growing cooler as the pressure decreases, continuing to rise until it reaches a level where its temperature and density is the same as that around it. If it goes far enough and carries enough moisture it will reach a point where its moisture begins to condense. Condensation releases heat, causing the air to expand even more, and it rises much more rapidly. Cumulus clouds of summer days are formed in this manner; the straight line at their base occurs at the point where the rising thermal reaches its dew point. The great, puffy, billowing mounts result from the way the expanding air continues racing upward until it reaches thermal stability.

The art of thermal soaring is the art of finding one of these rising, expanding bubbles of buoyant air and staying within it until you have reached the altitude you wish, or until the thermal has dissipated. Then you cruise around, steadily losing altitude, until you find another thermal. It sounds simple, but it actually demands the finest kind of flying technic, a thorough working knowledge of atmospheric movements, and a considerable degree of luck. Two pilots of nearly identical skill, in identical ships, may be launched within a few seconds or minutes of each other; one may hook onto a good thermal right away and get off for a 200-mile cross-country flight, while the other glides ingloriously back to earth and has to try again. It is like two fishermen with equal skill, fishing the same pool with similar tackle; one man may fill his creel while the other never gets a strike. It is a case of being in exactly the right place at exactly the right time, and then using every bit of skill and bird brains that you have.

Thermal soaring is an art that has few rules; on one day you will find a system that works to perfection, and that you think has universal application, and on the next good soaring day it will not work at all. Today you will find thermals as low as one or two hundred feet; tomorrow there will not be the least bit of lift at any altitude you can reach by winch or auto tow. There will be cloudless days with thermals popping all over the place; days when the sky is filled with cumuli and you have a terrible time getting up there. On some windy days the thermals will be dissipated so rapidly that you can't get enough altitude to leave the field safely until you have drifted as far as you dare go; on others every thermal you find is strong and well defined. All you can do is take things as you find them and go to it. Assume that you start your soaring flight from a winch tow. You are out just for the sport of it, and have no desire to go cross-country, chiefly because you don't wish to land fifty or a hundred miles away and sit by the ship until a crew comes out for you with a tow car and trailer.

It is nearly noon. The summer day is bright and sunshiny; a few small clouds are beginning to form above you. There is a gentle southwest wind, perhaps ten miles per hour. You have had two or three flights earlier in the day; you were towed to about a thousand feet, found a weak thermal or two that you lost before gaining additional altitude, and had to land.

You get into the ship, fasten your safety belt, set your altimeter, tap the variometer to see if its zero reading is actually at zero. A helper hooks on the tow wire and then lifts the low wing until the ship is level. The winch operator at the other end of the field sees the ship level off and starts reeling in wire. When the slack is taken up your helper dips the wing as a signal and raises it quickly; the winch operator opens his throttle, and you start moving. You put your left hand on the release lever, where the throttle would be on a powerplane, and your right on the stick. You leave the ground, wait a moment, and pull gently back on the stick. Up you go, steeper and steeper, getting every inch of altitude you can. Near the top of the climb you feel a sudden surge; are you being towed through a thermal? The tow slackens, you ease the stick forward, pull back on the release lever. Then you give it left stick and rudder and double back to investigate the thermal through which you were towed. It's not there, so you continue flying downwind, slowly so that your rate of sink will be at a minimum, but fast enough to eliminate danger of stalling.

You go the length of the field, losing altitude at nearly three feet a second. You go to the right in a slow, sweeping circle, applying right rudder and stick gently and simultaneously. You sink a little faster on the turn, straighten out smoothly, and fly upwind. Your shadow on the ground moves perceptibly slower than on your downwind hop.

Then you feel it, a gentle surging upward. Something tells you to circle to the left; perhaps it is just a hunch, perhaps you felt an almost imperceptible tendency of the ship to fall away to the right. You fly through half a circle and the surge continues; with one hand you tap your variometer while the needle swings up to zero and then higher. Then the buoyancy disappears; you have left the thermal.

You turn more sharply, and are back in it. You continue your circle; this time your lift continues all the way around, but is much stronger on one side of the circle than on the other. This you know by the feel of the ship; the variometer lags a trifle despite your tapping.

You continue spiraling, gradually working toward the side of greatest lift, cutting a course much like the path of a pen in the old Palmer Method exercise of continuous ovals, feeling your way along as you gradually form a mental map of this particular thermal. Your luck and judgment are good this time; after two or three spirals you maintain a steady lift of three feet a second. You and your thermal are drifting slowly with the wind, but you are gaining altitude, you can fly back to the landing field easily. Gradually you tighten up your spirals, and your rate of climb increases. It is a combination of two things, you believe: the thermal is building up with altitude, and you are working toward the core. Your variometer reading continues to go up, to five, six, seven, and finally ten feet a second. The landscape beneath you widens, the altimeter needle creeps past the 2000-foot mark.

You have drifted a short distance away from the field. You look back and see the winch operator get into the retrieving car with the rest of the ground crew and head in for lunch. You see tiny clouds forming here, there, and everywhere, and know that you have an afternoon of soaring ahead of you if you wish.

The old urge to go cross-country comes up. It's only noon; you have six or seven hours before you have to land; the wind is probably at least fifteen or twenty m.p.h. if you get to six or seven thousand; the cloud formation shows that you can make that with little difficulty. You can go a hundred miles easily; maybe a lot more. Perhaps you can establish a record. Why not try it? But you remember that tomorrow is a day of work. There is no ground crew ready to follow in the general direction you are going. If you land at six or seven and call in, it will take them several hours to reach you. Then you'll have to take down the ship, stow it on the trailer, and drive back. Probably an all-night job. So you decide against it.

What to do? There is an air show this afternoon at the municipal airport, ten miles away from your soaring field. Why not go see it? You have been drifting directly away from it in the southwest wind. By now you have four thousand feet, so you leave the thermal and fly upwind. You consider the flying characteristics of your particular ship. It is rather heavy, very efficient, with high cruising range. While feeling for your thermal and in the first few broad spirals you flew it slowly, just under forty miles per hour, only a few miles above its stalling speed, to give you a sink of less than three feet per second. Now you have places to go against a ten- or fifteen-mile wind, so you push the stick forward gently. The nose drops a trifle, the song of your wings takes on a higher tone, and the air speed goes up to sixty miles per hour. Your rate of sink increases too, to more than eight feet, but as you ease slowly back on the stick it gradually diminishes to about four, while the air speed continues to hover over sixty. This is a swell ship, you think; a gliding ratio of twenty-two to one while cruising along at a mile a minute.

Suddenly the sink increases. The nose is not heavy; just that the whole ship settles as you fly. You are losing seven and eight feet a second, then ten. The altimeter needle falls below three thousand feet, but you are not worried. You know that when you hit downdrafts like that you are going to find another thermal pretty soon. With that much altitude you don't even bother flattening out. Why should you? Straight ahead a mile or so is a grass fire; the smoke is going straight up. You head in that direction, suddenly feel the surge of a strong thermal. Once more you spiral, flying again at about forty, knowing that your ship is going down at the rate of nearly three feet per second within the thermal, but that the thermal is carrying you upward at better than seven feet. Soon you reach six thousand.

Then you loaf around the sky. You fly a straight course toward the municipal airport. Off to your left you see a thermal. Yes, you actually see it; a place where the haze is a little denser than that around you. You fly into it, begin to spiral. This time you have company; you see, of all things, a swallow. Swallows are not soaring birds, but this little fellow has the time of his life. He darts ahead with quick flutters of his wings; then coasts around in sharp, tiny spirals that make you envious. He follows with another fluttering dash; again he coasts. Apparently he is perfectly willing to do his own work, but when a quick dash carries him out of the thermal he jumps back in.

You see other things that have no business being five or six thousand feet in the air. A piece of paper swings past your wingtip, and you watch it fall away as you climb from it. You almost crush a butterfly, and you know very well it didn't fly that high.

You aren't paying much attention to your instruments now, but when you begin to feel chilly you look at the altimeter. Six thousand feet; twenty or thirty degrees cooler than the eighty-five you left on the surface. You fly out of that thermal and watch the air show for a while. Powerplanes with stunt pilots roar across the field, barrel rolling and leaving a trail of smoke behind them. They can have it; you're having your own fun.

You see a cloud a mile or so away, and head for it. You fly beneath it at about four thousand feet, and get a strong lift. From force of habit you work toward the center of the thermal, and your lift increases from five to ten and then twelve feet a second. You look up and watch the cloud; it's a small one, but you don't want to take a chance of getting sucked up inside. The rate of climb increases to more than fifteen feet a second, and you start flying away at sixty miles per hour. In spite of the eight feet per second sink of your ship at this flying altitude, your rapid climb continues. Then you fly out into the sunshine at about seven thousand feet and hit a downdraft. The cloud is behind and a few hundred feet above you. You know that if you had continued up into it your rate of climb would have jumped still higher as a result of the heat liberated by condensation. Within the cloud there might have been turbulence enough to throw you on your back; with no blind-flying instruments or experience you would have no way of knowing when you were right side up and when you were upside down. Pilots have been known to come out of clouds looping the loop when they believed they were spiraling. Others have been flopped on their backs, and picked up dangerous air speed as they came out in a spiral dive. Your sailplane is rugged, but it is designed for operation at eighty miles per hour or less, and even with its liberal safety factor 120 to 125 miles per hour might cause dangerous strain.

Some pilots, seeking records, go in for cloud soaring, but this compares to normal soaring much as driving in an Indianapolis Speedway race does with motoring. If you are going to do any cloud flying you had better have instruments for it, and earn an instrument rating. Otherwise, being a bold pilot may keep you from ever becoming an old pilot.

You decide to go home. You have several thousand feet more altitude than you need, so you fly a straightaway course, circle your own airport to let them know you intend to land, and then go just downwind from it and fly figure eights to lose altitude. You pick this path for a definite reason; your sharp turns at top and bottom of the eight are always toward the field, and your diagonal swipes only slightly away. In this way you are never in a position where you can't duck right into the field in case a downdraft should come along and cause you to lose altitude rapidly.

On a day like this you can stay up until sunset if you wish. You fly over the city, watch a bathing beach far below, see the wide V made in the water by a speedboat towing a surfboard. You go over a steel mill and ride the powerful thermals it creates up to six or seven thousand feet. There seems no limit to what you can do.

But you encounter days that should be good soaring when you find it difficult to stay up. Sometimes the thermals peter out as fast as you find them. Sometimes they are so narrow that you have to tighten up your spirals almost to the limit of human endurance; centrifugal force in a tight spiral has the effect of increasing your weight several times.

There are absolutely no rules that you can follow for sure; each flight brings something new. You will encounter thermals of irregular shapes; you get in and out of them half a dozen times in your first circle and have to feel your way along until you find some part of it with enough lift to carry you up. You will encounter others that are long, narrow ovals; you can fly straight away for a mile or two or three, constantly getting lift, but if you try to spiral you will fly in and out on every turn. There are days when large areas seem to be characterized by tiny puffy thermals; you can fly right through the area with a constant lift of one or two feet per second, but can't find a single strong updraft.

On some days you will tease along for hours with "ground bumps," little teasers that you strike at low altitudes, work up a few hundred feet, and then lose. You swear at yourself for sloppy flying, crisscross the field a time or two in vain search for the missing thermal, then find another teaser. They seem to form low, rise a short distance, and then melt away.

Sometimes thermals appear to occur in patterns like the dia mond defense of a football team; at others they form in columns parallel to the wind direction. You will work one for a while and then fly straight up- or downwind right into another. The nearest one to right or left may be a mile or more away with nothing but sink between, but as long as you stay in line you are all right. A similar condition is found when long chains of cumulus clouds appear in a straight line downwind, to form a "cloud street." These are usually found downwind from a large source of heat, such as steel mills or a large city. The heat released by their moisture condensation is enough to maintain almost constant lift along the street, so that a pilot can fly straight along at steady altitude without stopping to spiral. Cloud streets have been used by American pilots on several record distance flights.

You may bite your fingernails trying to get away on a day when the pilots who go off just before or just after your futile attempts catch free rides right from the winch. You start your stop watch; change take-off intervals from ten to fifteen minutes. Perhaps it works; again it may not.

There will be days when you get started, rise to two or three thousand feet, and hover over the field for hours, finding thermals at every turn, while down below you see pilots taking off in ships as good as yours and vainly seeking some means of getting up with you. On other days you are the one who is unable to find anything under a thousand feet, while a luckier man has squeezed one for a few hundred feet until it built up into a good strong current.

An unusual condition occasionally encountered is a broad area of gentle lift, punctuated by a few weak thermals. You manage to cruise around with zero sink at from one thousand to fifteen hundred feet, but you encounter nothing to take you any higher. This may be caused by the approach of a very weak storm front; it usually disappears suddenly after an hour or so, and leaves you with nothing to do but glide in to a landing.

On cross-country flights your technic will vary with your objective. If you are out for distance you will strike a course as straight downwind as you possibly can, since the addition of ten to twenty miles an hour can make the difference between a record-breaking and an average flight. By the same token, you will pick a day with little wind, or you will go cross-wind, if the objective is a goal flight and return.

If you have a "super-whooper" day with strong thermals, you will scorn weak ones, make altitude as rapidly as you can in currents with strong lift, and then fly as fast as your ship will cruise and still maintain a gliding ratio of about twenty to one or better. If the day is one when thermals are weak at low altitudes but strong at high, you will stay as high as you can, and start looking for new thermals whenever you get down to about three thousand feet. On other days you can safely continue distance-devouring straight flight for another few miles.

You may get so low that the flight seems near an end and then spot a ridge where a handy slope current will keep you aloft until a thermal comes along. Always you keep an eye on the ground within gliding radius for a possible landing spot. If you begin to get down pretty close, two thousand feet or under, you will have several picked out, depending on topography. At these low altitudes you will avoid rough country, and areas such as large plots of timber or large bodies of water where thermals are unlikely. Sometimes it will seem that your flight is over, and you will be as low as one hundred feet heading for a landing when something, perhaps the disturbance of your own passage, will break loose a thermal that will carry you back up and set you on your way.

You will keep a constant check on surface wind direction by watching the ripples on lakes and ponds, by the direction of smoke from chimneys, and so on. When the time comes for landing you will maneuver so that you land into the wind. If possible, you will pick an airport or smooth, level field, but you must remember that you can't "shoot" the field at low altitude as with a powerplane to locate surface obstructions before landing. Hence, you will drift in as gently as possible.

Suppose you have to land in a field of wheat or corn. Flying straight into the ground, as on an airport, might damage the ship. So you will come in and settle slowly, holding the ship barely above the wheat or cornstalks to the last possible second. Then you let it stall; the tail settles into the grain and drags you almost to a standstill by the time the wings come gently down, landing you lightly without so much as a scratch to the paint. A skilled pilot can land a glider or sailplane almost anywhere with little or no danger of personal injury, but a thinking pilot also will plan his landings so that he will not damage his ship.

We have barely scratched the surface in our knowledge of thermal soaring, although there are a few general observations that are quite reliable. We know, for example, that cities, steel mills, and other large sources of heat can usually be relied upon to provide the starting impetus required for thermal activity, but daytime soaring over cities is often difficult because of turbulence, except at high altitudes. Late in the day, when thermal activity in general declines, large heat-absorbing areas like lakes and forests frequently provide good soaring. We know that days with heavy overcast provide few, if any, thermals and that days with rapid formation of cumulus clouds are usually good for soaring.

We know that thermals occur practically everywhere, that good soaring can be found in almost any part of the country. For example: distance and altitude records have been established from such diverse soaring sites as Sun Valley, Idaho; Arvin, California; Wichita Falls, Texas; and Elmira, New York; and many flights which would have established records a few years ago are commonplace occurrences almost every week end at Detroit; Lockport, Illinois; St. Louis; San Bernardino, California; and Atlanta, Georgia. All it takes, anywhere it has been tried, is a good ship and a good pilot.

We know little about night soaring, although it seems to have possibilities, and not much more about winter thermal soaring, which may one day become a popular winter sport. After all, we do know that any bright day on which the surface temperature is raised by bright sunshine and the upper air has characteristics frequently found in winter as well as summer offers good possibilities for thermal activity; it is temperature difference, rather than high temperature as such, that makes convection currents.

Another type of soaring, riding the updrafts that occur in the clear weather preceding storm fronts, may turn out to be both safe and thrilling. A few pilots have tried it successfully and made startling distance and speed records, and several commercial power pilots have used their knowledge of front soaring to increase the safety and efficiency of their power flying.

The requisites for good soaring flight are a good sailplane, good judgment, a good understanding of soaring weather, and the faultless flying technic that comes with practice. Heretofore there have been few high-performance ships available, and distance soaring was largely limited to a few crack pilots. Now that federally certificated sailplanes are rolling out of factories and boys are getting instructions in good schools from skilled soaring pilots, we can expect to see our present records begin to topple in routine, sporting flights.

QUESTIONS AND TOPICS FOR DISCUSSION

1. What is the difference between gliding and soaring? Illustrate by showing how a toy airplane does both.

2. Do hawks, eagles, buzzards, or seagulls both glide and soar on a single flight of an hour? Explain.

3. If a man can glide and soar, why did Darius Green "crash"?

4. A flier can glide from a start on a steep hill or from a cliff. How does a glider or a soaring plane get started from a level field or road?

SUGGESTED FILMS

Two 16mm. films would be interesting to see in connection with the material in this section. *Birds on the Wing* is made up of slow motion scenes and shows how pigeons, gulls, hawks, and other creatures fly. This film can be rented from the Edited Pictures System, 330 West 42 Street, New York. *Sail Plane* is a beautiful film in natural color which shows sail planes in the air and explains how they are made and how they are flown. J. W. Love, Box 59, Chatsworth, Los Angeles, California, is the distributor for this film.

WE WIN WINGS[1]

By Lieut. Beirne Lay, Jr.

IN SEVERAL school anthologies two thrilling stories of flight written by Beirne Lay may be found. These are "Aerobatics, Thirty Minutes" and "Bomber 148." In 1937 Lieut. Lay wrote a book about his experiences in training for a commission in the Army Air Corps. In this volume he included those two narratives as chapters. Lieut. Lay's schooling was not at West Point, but at St. Paul's and Yale. His air training was at Randolph and Kelly Fields, San Antonio, Texas, and then at Langley Field, Virginia.

As you read notice the changes in size, design, speed, instruments, and tactics that have come in the six or seven years lying between the beginning of Lieut. Lay's training and the present.

*   *   *   *   *

I climbed into my bomber one morning with an hour's time to put in, but with no definite assignment. "Individual practice flight" the bulletin board said. I could do anything I wished. The sky above me was the same leaden sheet that had muffled Kelly Field with overcast gloom for the past nine days. It would be good, I thought, to see a clear blue sky and yellow sunshine again, if there was such a thing.

I took off, climbed, and nosed into the gray ceiling at eleven hundred. It became dark. Mist coated the windshield and the lenses of my goggles. I pushed them up and felt the sudden dampness cooling the skin under my eyes. I concentrated on my bank-and-turn indicator and air-speed indicator, to hold the Keystone in a steady climbing spiral. The needles stayed right where I wanted them, for in addition to the calm of the air the big ship was as stable as a Pullman running along a track.

---

[1] From *I Wanted Wings*, copyright 1937 by Harper and Brothers, New York.

The altimeter's hand crept doggedly around the dial, 4000 feet, 5000, 7000, 9000. I glanced briefly above the cockpit, but the damp, gray mass was as dark as ever. I commenced to feel as though I had sat in that gloomy cubbyhole for half an hour, and as though I would never reach the top of the stuff. 10,000 feet. I had expected to come out long before this. 11,000, 12,000.

My gray prison was chilly now. I could feel the mountain air of that altitude through my thin, cotton shirt, and I could see gooseflesh on my forearms, for I had rolled up my sleeves in the heat on the ground. The two Cyclone engines were losing power, gasping for air, so I leaned out the mixture a bit more, and saw their tachometers register an additional 100 R.P.M.

13,000 feet. How high up did this cloud layer extend, anyway? 20,000 feet, maybe. The ceiling of my bomber was only about 14,000. Perhaps I'd have to nose down in the long glide to earth without having reached the surface. I hoped not, for I had the feeling of a swimmer who has come up from a great depth to fill his lungs with oxygen.

13,400. A light gray bald spot showed suddenly above me— disappeared. The top. It must be close. The rate of climb indicator showed almost zero. I looked up again. The same old darkness. And then a blot of cold, white light fell on the cockpit, penetrating to me through a thin skylight of mist up above the nose.

As though a curtain had been whisked aside, I broke through into blinding light. I was at the bottom of an enormous crevasse, whose solid, snow walls towered up on each side of me, and across the dizzy top of the canyon was a roof of the deepest blue I had ever seen. The floor of that white canyon stretched gently uphill for miles ahead of me, almost parallel to my exhausted angle of climb.

With throttles wide open and the wheel back almost against my chest, I skimmed up that long slope, my wheels dragging through the snow, barely holding their own; I felt like a boy dragging his sled up a winter hill.

Eyes blinking, nose watering, hands shivering, I slowly gained the crest of the hill and rose above the dazzling winter wilderness until I could cruise at leisure around the loftiest peaks—a tiny, black speck between the burnished hemisphere of blue ice above me and the spotless white wastes below.

Toboganning down mountainsides, shooting out from steep cliffs, burrowing through mounds of fluffy snow, blood racing in my veins from the stimulation of the cold, I had exchanged a hot May morning in Texas for a February winter carnival in New Hampshire.

I looked at the clock, hesitated, then throttled back, nosed down and like a submarine, sank beneath the waves and settled once more through the gloom to my native habitat on the ocean floor at Kelly Field.

June was well under way, and the thought of graduation was overshadowing all others in our minds. It was there when we turned in at night, with the insects jittering in the grass outside, and there in the first moment of consciousness after the bell rang in the morning. Long a distant peak on the horizon, it had moved up suddenly into the near foreground.

Our flying training was in the wind-up process. We had completed our four-day "maintenance" cross-country, in which we swung around the State of Texas—Fort Worth to Midland to El Paso to Marfa, along the Rio Grande to Fort Clarke, and back to Kelly—staking down our bombers in the open and performing the daily inspections and maintenance ourselves; and we were devoting our time to polishing up our graduation-day formation maneuvers and getting our uniforms fitted.

The latter process was an absorbing one. It entailed endless trips to the San Antonio tailors and bootmakers for remeasurements and alterations. No debutante, at the dressmaker's before her coming-out party at Pierre's, could have been more finicky than we, as each of us supervised his trousseau of blouse, slacks, shirts, flight cap, garrison cap, "leather"—boots and Sam Browne belt—and "hardware"—spurs, saber chain, lieutenant's bars and Air Corps insignia. The outlay cost from $200 up, a sum which most of us had saved by having the paymaster take $20 from our monthly base pay of $75. For a year we had conferred on all officers unquestioning respect, and it was with the thrill of the imposter that we tried on the accouterments of the mighty.

While I'm on the subject of officers, it may be timely to get in a word on the nature of what our status was to be after graduation. We were to be commissioned second lieutenants in the Air Corps Reserve, with the pay ($207), rank and privileges while on active duty of a regular Air Corps officer. That active duty was to be a year or more, depending on Congressional appropriations.

A "regular" officer is a West Point graduate or an officer who has received his commission by surviving one of the periodic competitive examinations for the regular Army. In the picture of my class at Kelly there is only one regular, Captain R. P. Williams. The majority of the students were civilians like myself who went through the school as Flying Cadets. Perhaps half of the active pilots in the Army Air Corps at any one time are former Flying Cadets. The difference between the graduates of ROTC units in field artillery and infantry, when they are taken into the reserve, and members of the Air Corps Reserve is that the Air Corps Reserves are, as seen in the preceding chapters, fully trained, and, after their active duty training with tactical units, qualified for immediate war service. There can be no half-way measures about the training of even reserve military pilots, whereas other reserve branches of the Army receive, by comparison, only a smattering of training, and are not fully qualified for immediate war service although they have made a valuable start toward that end.

Recent legislation has provided that Flying Cadets, on graduation, be commissioned second lieutenants, Air Corps Reserve, and receive a total of five years' active duty, with a bonus of $500 at the end of that time. The officer can revert to inactive status at the end of three years, if he so desires, and if he elects to take the final two years he will then rank as a first lieutenant. All that compares pretty favorably with the one-year active duty allotted us back in 1933.

Another change that prospective Flying Cadet applicants will consider for the better is the toning down of the traditional Hell Month and hazing, of which my class received the last full measure. Unnecessary childishness and abuse of authority have fallen out of favor.

Toward the end of June we received an increasing number of talks and lectures on the social customs of Army life and how to conduct ourselves as officers. I recall particularly the sage words of a kindly major. Standing before us in the ground school lecture room, he uttered these words of caution:

"You gentlemen can congratulate yourselves on the completion of the most rigorous and the finest course of flying training to be found anywhere in the world. Each one of you has proved himself to be an outstanding pilot, or you wouldn't be here in front of me now. You are at the peak. You will probably never be as highly skilled again as you are at this moment. Now, out in the service you are going to come into contact with older pilots, like myself, who have settled down into being conservative old fogies, and whose technique isn't what it used to be. You can fly rings around them in individual combat, and put their aerobatics and formation flying to shame. You will find that they are not by any standard in the same class with yourselves. But gentlemen," his voice dropped to an eloquently pleading note, "I beg of you—break the news to them gently."

The Great Day came. I felt a gnawing pain of excitement in my stomach at breakfast, and in a sort of haze I found myself, with chute slung over shoulder, walking out from the Bombardment section hangar toward one of the fifteen bombers roaring at their chocks in the brilliant sunshine. Down the long hangar line I could see the Pursuit, Observation, and Attack ships drawn up in perfect alignment, whirling props glinting. Then we were rolling out onto the field, pausing for the leader's signal in a great left echelon of five three-ship elements, and, one element at a time, we were in the air at last and assembling ten miles back of the field in javelin—a tight column of three ship V's which looked from above like this: >>>>>.

Cadet Aigeltinger, our leader, led us about in wide circles, stalling for time until the precise second should arrive to start from our prearranged initial check point. It was a matter of pride, and of skillful timing, that the leader bring his formation past the reviewing stand at 9:00 o'clock on the dot, and we had practiced it for days.

Presently Aigeltinger nosed down over the initial checkpoint, followed closely by the elements behind him, and we worked lower till we were over the treetops, and invisible, until we flashed into view above the bombardment hangar roofs and thundered down the line. Out of the corner of my eye I could see the throng of mothers, best girls, Randolph cadets, and San Antonio spectators swarming the length of the hangars, and, as we pulled up at the end of the field in a climbing turn, the low skyline behind us teeming with the long parade of smaller ships.

We were on the ground again—lieutenants—stripping off our flying suits and crowding the running boards of cars on our way back to the cadet area to don those spick and span uniforms with new wings embroidered on the chests. We were sitting in a crowded hall, listening to an Air Corps colonel express appropriate sentiments. We were filing past him to receive our commissions, and then we found ourselves lying back in easy chairs in the quarters of our instructors, and sipping tall drinks.

It was all over. The long tension and suspense that had lived with us for a year, the doubts and discouragements, and the grand adventure. They were gone.

I shan't try to recount here in detail the days that preceded our assignments to active duty stations. Suffice it that we reported next day to Brooks Field, our temporary two-weeks' station in lieu of the permanent assignments on their way from Washington, and that we staged tremendous celebrations in the city of San Antonio, the extent of which was readily apparent to the flight surgeons at Brooks when they gave us the routine physical examination required of all officers reporting to a new station. In the Schneider test (pulse and blood pressure), whose index is zero to eighteen—eighteen being a perfect score—several of us registered zero, and in the eye test there were many who got no further than the foot-high "E" on the letter chart.

In due course, orders came through, sending some of us to March Field, California, some to Selfridge Field, Michigan, and others, including myself to Langley Field, Virginia.

I piled my bags into the '27 La Salle phaeton I had picked up second-hand, shook hands with the boys, paid fleeting calls on friends in town, said goodbye with a half-broken heart to a beautiful girl on East King's Highway, and with another Langley-bound classmate hummed out onto the road to Austin and, eventually, Virginia.

NIGHT FORMATION FLIGHT

I am sitting in the living room of my quarters at Langley watching the shaft of orange light that pours toward me from an early October sunset beyond the mile-wide landing area of the airdrome. The warm flood of color slowly dissolves into the smoky blue twilight. No sound comes from the long line of hangars, their windsocks barely discernible on the corrugated metal roofs.

I am thinking about the bad luck that has put me on night flying tonight, when I have a dinner date, instead of tomorrow night, when I'm free.

The order reads: "Nine plane formation Aberdeen and return. Take-off 6:30 P.M." Mentally I calculate the time it will take to fly from Langley to Aberdeen and back in a Keystone bomber. Aberdeen is a bit beyond Baltimore, and it's about 400 miles round trip. I couldn't take a shower, dress, and be in Newport News before eleven.

I walk over to the phone, call up, and tell her I can't make it. I sit down and stare again over the field through the smoke curling from my pipe. It is almost totally dark.

I rouse myself from the hypnotic doze, drive down to the post exchange restaurant and put a bacon and egg sandwich and a mug-full of black coffee where they belong, before I park my car near the 20th Squadron hangar. I can see that the mechanics have already arrived, for blocks of light illumine the glass panes set in the great sliding doors that close the end of the hangar. One of the seventy-five-foot wingspread monsters inside throws an eerie, distorted shadow across the lighted panes—an airplane designer's nightmare projected in black and white.

I step inside the hangar through a small door. I am standing in what would make a large auditorium, and yet the three huge Keystones squatting on the grease-marked concrete floor seem to fill every inch of the place.

I walk under the spreading wing of 146, my ship for tonight, and twang my finger against the taut, doped fabric of the wing's underside. There is a strong smell of gasoline and a faint scent of liquid soap in the close air.

A light is on in the operations office and in the locker room, its walls lined with green metal Flight lockers. No one has arrived yet but the squadron clerk, pecking away at his type-writer, his brass-buttoned olive-drab blouse draped around the back of his chair.

I am a bit early, so I step outside into the warm night. A soft breeze from the East cools the damp skin on the back of my neck. That means a crosswind when we head North, which has its good side, for a tailwind on the way up would cancel itself out on the return trip—make one half of the flight seem much longer in contrast with the other half.

I look along the flying line; the fifth hangar down, where the light spills out on the ramp from the operations office of the 37th Attack Squadron, catches my eye. There is an explosive commotion out in front, as six Attack pilots finish warming up their A-8 low-wing monoplanes.

Three long red bars and a green circle flash out on the roof of the post operations hangar. It is the signal for the Attack men to taxi from the line and take off into sector No. 3. The area around Langley is divided into four sectors, like Randolph and Kelly, for the control of night operations.

Promptly the six winged cigars roll from their parking places and string out behind the leader, as he trundles along out of the smear of light into the gloom over the field—six stealthy shadows, given away by their navigation lights bobbing up and down dimly through the cloud of dust stirred up by six props clawing at the air.

A minute passes, and my eyes stray to the bright stars that have already broken through the stifled glow from the banked fires on the western skyline, and then, half a mile out on the airdrome, the dust clears away. The A-8s have closed up into the symmetrical pattern of a right echelon. They are going to take off directly toward our hangar.

A muffled roar breaks from their direction and continues, but it looks as though the string of lights is still stationary. For several seconds more the string remains motionless, only the pin-points of light seem a bit larger, and nearer. And then, as suddenly as a tornado, the A-8s flashed out of the dark right on top of me, showering down a hailstorm of sound as they pass overhead. With rubber tires still slowly spinning, and with gleaming brown bellies exposed to the light for an instant, they pull into a turn, so as to avoid flying over the building area, and are gone as suddenly as they have come.

The Pursuiters are flying tonight, too. In sector No. 4, off to the east, 18 of their pea-shooters stamp red and green wingtip lights in the dark as they weave along in column, tacked on each other's tails—a phosphorescent snake that wriggles through the air as the leader climbs and turns. They close up into a column of three-ship V's and fly overhead at 2,000 feet—a flying Christmas tree. The thunder of their passing charges the night with a solid vibration of sound, like a thousand trucks rumbling across a steel bridge in the sky.

A moment later, the floodlights tear a sudden rent in the blackness on the far side of the field. The Christmas tree breaks up into six widely spaced three-ship elements, which circle the airdrome, drop out of the rat-race at even intervals, and glide into the glare of the floodlights, engines coughing. They squat on the ground and cast long shadows against the dusty glow as they taxi to the line. The pilots' helmeted heads stick up behind the windshields like tiny knobs, bobbing from one side of the cockpit to the other so that they can see where they are going.

I feel a sense of excitement in the air, almost like the days at Kelly, when it was all new. The illuminated windsock standing straight out in the steady breeze across the hangar behind me, the revolving beacon swinging its split beam majestically overhead, picking out the gray hulk of the balloon hangar for a brief instant as it goes by it, the shouting of mechanics, who are towing the nine Keystone bombers out and lining them up on the ramp in front of our squadron, the blinking of flashlights as the mechanics climb into the cockpits up on the nose to spin the Cyclone engines over with the squealing of inertia starters, the jagged explosions, and the streamers of smoky flame that spout from the exhaust stacks—all these things revive the sense of thrill that long familiarity has nearly succeeded in stifling. I walk back to the Flight locker room with a tingle of expectancy that seldom comes any more.

The other eight pilots have arrived, and are sitting or standing in various stages of aeronautical dress and undress, tugging into dove-colored summer flying suits with the painted squadron insignia sewn over the breast; twining white silk scarfs around their throats; adjusting the legstraps of their parachutes; stuffing wads of cotton into their ears; and fitting on helmet and goggles, leather chinstraps dangling. They are just an ordinary looking bunch, no different from any other eight men you might assemble at random in a room, except, perhaps, for two things—their eyes are all some shade of blue, and none of them wears glasses.

I hustle into my togs. Lieutenant Miller, who is leading the formation tonight, walks to the door and calls back over his shoulder, "Take-off and landing by flights." He pulls his sleeve back off his wrist-watch, and grins at a red-haired Irishman who is just thrusting his legs into his flying suit.

"Pull the cork, Murphy," he says, "we aren't going to wait for you." Murphy redoubles his efforts and brings up the rear, as the pilots file out, parachutes slung over shoulders, to the nine rumbling B-6s parked in three rows out in front, running lights twinkling, eighteen props turning over restlessly, kicking up a cool breeze, mixed with the warm smell of the exhaust.

I pause under 146's nose, which looms several feet above me, prop blades spinning on either side, and buckle on my parachute. I bend my head slightly and walk underneath the belly to the trailing edge of the right lower wing, swing up onto the black, corrugated metal walkway that protects the wing where it joins the fuselage, and step forward to the cockpit.

I test out each engine separately, running them up wide open, to see that they are turning out full power and that the oil pressure is okay. Meanwhile the crew chief, sitting on my left, assists by throwing the ignition switches from one mag to the other and by flipping the correct switches to give the ammeter and voltmeter readings. This is a check and double check, for he has already tested the Cyclones in the same way before I came out.

I ask a few routine questions: "How much gas have we?"

"A full service, sir."

"Have you a flashlight?" He points to the bulge in his knee pocket.

"How many men in back?"

"Two, sir."

"Okay." I hand him my map and cross-country envelope,

which he shoves under his parachute, and plug in my radio extension cord.

"142 to 146. 142 to 146. Come in, please." It is Lieutenant Murphy calling. He is leading my flight, B flight. I check back to Murphy. The rest of the pilots check with their leaders, to make certain that all radios are functioning before we leave the ground. Radio communication is important, especially at night. In the daytime, visual signals, motions of the hand or wig-wagging, can be relied on entirely, if necessary.

The mechanics on the ground pull the blocks from in front of the waist-high wheels. I release my hand-brake and hold the bomber in with the toe brakes, keeping an eye on Lieutenant Miller's ship. A green beam from the control tower stabs Miller. Immediately his lights move slowly forward, as he taxies off the concrete to the rough, grassy turf. Miller's Number 2 man swings his ship around with a burst of one engine and falls in close behind, followed in turn by the Number 3 man. In the same way our flight joins the column of bouncing lights in the darkness, and the third flight tacks on to our rear.

I keep about ten feet behind Murphy, holding my interval by guiding on the white tail-light set on the top of his rudder, right arm holding the wheel back against my chest, left hand on the two throttle levers between the seats, easing on first one throttle and then the other and pressing the toe brakes sepa-rately to hold the big heavy Keystone in a straight line as we jog along at a fairly fast clip.

Fast taxiing, in general, is a bad practice, but in military formation work we have to become accustomed to it in order to clear the airdrome for single ships or flights landing close behind. In war time there are many instances where it is neces-sary to take off or land a formation, either by flights of three or by single ships, and get them off the field in the shortest possible time.

I have my goggles pushed up on my forehead, to see better, but a blast of dust from Murphy's props catches me in the eyes, so I pull the goggles down and hold a careful, squinting eye on that tail-light ahead to keep from running it down. Our speed varies quite a bit, for Miller, up in front, has to turn to avoid rough places on the field. (Incidentally, the job of levelling off the gopher holes and mud flats that crop up on a field as large as Langley after heavy rains keeps plenty of soldiers on fatigue duty.)

"Right echelon," buzzes Miller's voice through our earphones. We have been taxiing straight out from the hangar line. Now Miller turns 90 degrees to the left and we line up diagonally back from his right, as in the right-hand side of an arrow head. We are pointing south, with the hangar line and building area sending up a glow on our left, for the wind has shifted since the Attack formation took off.

Miller has seen to it that the whole field is in front of us—a smart thing, day or night. If an engine takes a furlough on the take-off, you want a double helping of landing field—in front of you, not behind you.

The three ships of "A" flight slide forward into the black unknown. The three white tail-lights lift up level with the wing lights. The lights shrink, then rise from the ground. I see all this out of the corner of my eye, for I am watching Murphy's ship like a hawk, my motors halfway open, and I am tugging against the toe brakes. The pilot in the Number 3 position, back over my right shoulder, is on the *qui vive* * also, eyes fixed on me, as mine are fixed on Murphy.

Murphy motions his head forward, but the sudden blur of his props has already told me that his ship is about to move. I ease my toes off the brake pedals, and shove the throttles forward. Our three bombers roll ahead as one.

I keep my left hand on the throttles, and with the right hold the wheel well forward to get the heavy tail up into flying position. You have to learn to "drive with one hand" in formation take-offs and landings. I don't see the boundary lights rushing in toward me now, or the red lights along the hangar roofs at the left, or the full moon that is edging up into sight across the Back River. I only see one thing, the lights and the dim outline of Murphy's ship just beyond my left motor. I concentrate on those lights as if my life depends on it, which it does, so that I can hold my wing position as rigidly as possible. The sensation is like forcing your eyes to stay on some fixed point on the horizon while you shoot down the dizziest drop on the roller

* *qui vive* (kē vēv'): alert.

coaster at Coney Island, or like riding behind a blinded wind-shield through which the driver can see, but not you.

I am totally unconscious of what my hands or feet are doing as a light touch back on the throttles keeps me from creeping up on Murphy, and a light pressure forward on them checks me from lagging back into the Number 3 man, who is hanging on to my right rear. Any errors on my part will exaggerate the changes he must make.

We have been in the air for several seconds, but I don't know it. You scarcely notice just when you leave the ground in a night formation take-off; you aren't thinking about it, you are just watching a green and a white light in the dark and trying to keep them where they belong.

Murphy commences to pull away from me. I open my throttles wide and stay with him. And then I see the thin sliver of moon rise slowly up above the fuselage of Murphy's ship and climb until it is nearly overhead. We are in a steep left bank, left wingtips pointed down at the chain of automobile head-lights streaming over the Langley Field bridge on their way to Hampton. I am riding on my side, with Murphy below me, and below Murphy I glimpse the Number 3 man, who has closed in on Murphy's other wing after crossing over and down.

We come out of the turn, and start in pursuit of the cluster of light-specks up ahead that show us where "A" flight is cruis-ing along throttled back, waiting for us. We close in on them, our "V" fitting in behind their "V," slightly above it. I am looking down a staircase of lights. A quick glance back, under-neath my broad top wing, and I see the lights of "C" flight hovering on our tails.

We climb gradually, leaving Hampton and Newport News, two beds of live white coals, behind us, and Miller points the nose of the lead ship along the compass course that leads to Aberdeen. His voice comes through the earphones: "Route formation."

We all drop back until there is an interval of two or three hundred feet between ships. The pattern of the formation, and our relative positions in it, are still the same. Upon a call from Miller's radio or a wag of his wings, we can close up im-mediately.

A "route" formation enables the pilots to relax and look

around, watching the ship they are guiding on every few seconds instead of constantly. It would be a terrible eye-strain to fly a close formation for several continuous hours at night, or even in the day time.

We would take up this same formation as a defensive measure when under anti-aircraft fire, so that there could be only one casualty from any one shellburst. If attacked by enemy pursuit, we would close up tight to oppose the attackers with concentrated defensive machine gun fire and to give the leader control of the formation and to give the formation maneuverability. Should we stay strung out like this under hostile air attack, the enemy would pick us off one at a time like toy balloons. That's why we have to be able to fly close formations, normally close, because it is the only means by which a number of airplanes can be controlled by one man with safety.

I push my goggles up with one hand and rub my eyes. The air is cool and soothing against the hot skin where it was covered by the goggle pads. This is the first let-up in tension since we taxied out from the line, and it is a great relief.

The instrument board in front of me is a showcase of faintly illuminated dials. From long familiarity, half a glance is enough to tell me that the four needles which interest me, oil temperature and pressure on each Cyclone, point where they should, and that the altimeter shows 3000 feet. I look at the lights of the bombers up front, see that I have dropped back a bit, and touch the throttles.

We have crossed the York River. Off to the left, the glow of West Point, Virginia, reflects from the water. When I look to the right, the moon startles me. It is flush on Chesapeake Bay, a big, round end of a bottle, flooding milk toward us over the waves.

I shift into a more comfortable position on my parachute seat. This is going to be a long, tiresome stretch, sitting up here in this cramped, open berth, hung up in the star-roofed night, with the wind tearing past and the vapory earth below geared in slow motion—sitting between two roaring, unmuffled engines. They strike my eardrums with a hard, gritty drone, as though they were boring through solid granite.

I could almost reach out and touch the right engine, but I don't. At night you can see how hot those Cyclones really are when they're turning up horsepower. The exhaust collector ring is a rosy red, and out of the exhaust pipe that projects behind the trailing edge of the lower wing shoots an orange and purple flame, three feet long.

I am not thinking about anything in particular, except the next check point on our route or the location of the nearest landing field. There aren't many on this stretch, either.

I don't think, for instance, about Lieutenant McCune, who brought his bomber down at night in a forest with a dead engine, unable to jump because a man in back hadn't cleared the ship.

I don't look over the side and shudder at the thought of dropping off head-first into that inky void toward those dots of light several thousand feet down.

I am not sick with worry over the fact that the lives of three men and my own neck depend of what I do with my hands and feet, and my head, if an engine quits on me.

This is just a job. Routine. Nothing has ever happened to me at night. My imagination is dead as a roast duck, where danger is concerned, but it still reacts to the magic of the night.

The Rappahannock River edges by beneath us, and then the Potomac, a broad highway of shimmering light. The crew chief aims his flashlight on the gas gauge hanging underneath the upper wing tank, then nods off to sleep, helmeted head lolling on his chest.

Clouds obscure the moon now. The night becomes blacker. I creep up a little on the red and green lights ahead. I look at the clock, I yawn, I shift again in my seat, and then—

Murphy's voice roars into his microphone.

"ONE-FOUR-TWO AND FOUR-THREE! Stick with Miller. Ride down with him and pull a flare at 1500 feet. 'B' flight—DON'T—" The voice cuts off.

Coming to with an electric shock, I see Miller's ship cut sharply to the left, with a sudden loss of speed and dive out of the formation. His left engine has quit on him.

Murphy has cut his gun,* and I see that I am coasting up on him. I cut mine, too, and climb so as to ride over him. He is climbing too. My wing blankets him. I can't see him. Hanging

---

* *cut his gun:* slowed his engine.

over the side, my crew chief strains his eyes into the dark. Suddenly he grips my arm.

There is Murphy, right under my wheels. I could spit in his face.

He dives, at the same time I see him. I heave the wheel all the way back, bank clear out of the formation. My heart hangs fire, then pumps madly with temporary relief. That was a little too close.

All I can see is a tangle of moving lights in the blackness—no way to tell who is who—no horizon—no lights on the ground even, to tell which end is up. We are in a hell of a mess, and it has all happened in a fraction of the time it takes to relate it.

I have a panicky feeling that I will crash into someone or that someone will pull into me. I crane my neck in every direction, trying to figure out which triangle of skimming lights is Murphy. And then Murphy gives me a call.

"Murphy to Lay. Get back in where you belong."

"Lay to Murphy. Where in hell are you?"

"Murphy to Lay. Where in hell do you think I am? Wait. Watch for two blinks of a flashlight."

I peer a dozen ways at once, and then I see the double flash way up to the left. I kick the throttles wide open, close up the gap, and zoom up into my Number 2 position with a rush. Murphy directs the rest of the reassembly, and soon we are in a reorganized formation. I don't need to tell you that we are in there close, too.

Murphy has kept his head. As deputy flight leader, he automatically took Miller's place, and he gave orders fast, untangling a formation that was stacked up like a four-decker sandwich. When Miller's engine quit, his loss of speed without warning caused all behind him to ride ahead too far before they could close their throttles. You have no brakes in the air, and your reactions are a lot slower when you are strung out than when you are closed up.

I had almost forgotten about Miller, but now I see him and the two assisting ships a mile ahead below us. We are following them. Miller doesn't seem to be losing any more altitude, and I'm sure no flares have been dropped.

Presently he gives us a call: "Left engine has picked up again to about half power. I think I can limp over to Bolling Field. Follow me and circle over Bolling until I land."

Murphy acknowledges Miller's call, and then my earphones are silent while the minutes drag. Inside my leather gauntlet my fingers clench the wheel with a damp grip. Something has happened to me. Imagination has come alive again for the first time since months ago, when I wrote the article on aerobatics.

I am troubled once more as I was on that night in the P-6. I wonder if one of those sturdy engines is going to quit on me. If it does, I wonder if I can set these six tons of airplane down over obstructions into a small field by the oscillating light of a parachute flare. Suppose no field shows up? Can I get these men in back out in time to bail out myself? Will it be any fun to plunge over the side into the dark?

And I know that I'll be glad to be back on the ground again, with the next three hours over and done with. Imagination. Slowly I strangle it with mental fingers, and gradually my grip on the wheel relaxes.

The rotating beacon at Bolling flashes close ahead, with Washington glaring up in the background. We come over the field. The floods throw a white blot out on its brown turf. A tiny triangle of red, white and green dots swings in a wide semi-circle out over the Potomac River, and then Miller's yellow wings appear in the white blot. He is down safely.

The two bombers which went with Miller climb back up and form an abbreviated third flight behind us. A call comes from the ground: "Miller to Murphy. Proceed to Aberdeen." And the answer: "Murphy to Miller. Message received okay. Murphy off."

The eight of us growl along behind Murphy toward Aberdeen, to complete the night's chore. Yes, we get pay and a half for our chores in the Air Corps, flight pay, and sometimes we earn it, too.

TOPICS FOR DISCUSSION

1. Compare the Keystone Bomber Lay used in training with a Boeing Flying Fortress of 1942 or later. See *I Wanted Wings*, p. 151 and following.

2. "Night Formation Flight" gives you a picture of what a pilot's duties are on a routine flight. See how many of the details of the take-off you can recall without going back over the pages.

3. Compare with other readers impressions of details you do not fully understand. For example, what is an "echelon formation"?

4. Explain a V formation of three planes and an echelon formation for the same number. What is it called when a series of five or six planes fly in a straight line one behind another?

5. Explain how a rising full moon over a bay could remind the writer of a milk bottle pouring out milk over the water.

Suggested Film

Sky Defenders is a color film with a running time of forty-five minutes which shows how men win their wings at Randolph Field and Kelly Field. It can be rented from Bell and Howell, Inc., 1801 Larchmont Avenue, Chicago, Illinois.

MASS FLIGHT[1]

By Blaine and Dupont Miller

VERY few writers are better qualified to write authentic stories about naval aviation than the Millers. Blaine Miller is an officer in the flying service of the Navy and on active duty. From his accurate knowledge of planes and flying and his daily contact with other officers and men he draws the materials for his writing. The other member of this writing team, copilot of the typewriter, is Mrs. Miller. Sometimes they write articles and narratives of actual experiences, but more often they write fiction based upon accurate and technical knowledge of fact.

Mass Flight is a story of the latter kind. The interest in the story is in the fliers and their personal and family problems more than in the account of the flight of twenty-four bombers from San Diego to the Canal Zone thrilling as that may be. And then there is the problem of discipline and duty. The story is built around a situation in which two officers are both wrong, but come out both right.

*　　*　　*　　*　　*

To the Navy an officer is an officer. Furthermore, when there is work to be done, the Department can't worry about what combinations of men are thrown together by orders. Yet, all of naval aviation gasped when Cary Leighton was made flight commander over Nick Allan for the long hop to Panama. Everyone expected that before Squadrons 60 and 61 reached Coco Solo there would be fireworks.

All that the younger generation knew was that, before their time, Commander Leighton, the Navy's most famous flier, had made a fool of Nicholas Allan. The 5000-hour lads, however, could remember vividly that scene on the wind-swept flight deck of the old Langley. Nick's friends said indignantly that

---

[1] From *American Magazine*, July, 1940. Copyright by the authors.

there had been no call to dress him down before the entire squadron and the ship's company. Cary's followers claimed that Nick had been stupid. But everyone agreed that Cary and Nick as first and second in command were far from being an auspicious setup for a mass flight.

Not that the Navy used any such fancy term. It was the newspapers that referred to a "mass flight." The Navy Department merely issued a routine operations order: "Patrol Squadrons 60 and 61, upon completion of fitting out, will, on or about 1 November, transit by air from San Diego to Coco Solo, Canal Zone."

Very clear. Very concise. If you were one man flying 3000 miles over open ocean and jungle you had certain problems to solve. But you had only yourself to think about. When it was two squadrons you multiplied the problems, headaches, vexations, and apprehensions by 24 planes and nearly 200 men. Of course, everyone would get there. The orders were specific. The Navy expected it. But, during the week beforehand, an idiotic question came to all of them—the pilots, the mechanics, the radiomen. It came to Nick Allan, too, and lay in his mind, tugging, nagging: *Are we going to get away with this?*

Only Commander Leighton didn't seem to worry. He sat at his desk with the charts spread out before him, as jaunty, as unconcerned as ever. But then, thought Nick, bitterly, didn't Cary have a tradition to sustain? The legend of Cary Leighton, reckless, daring, and undaunted?

He'd had that reputation now through seventeen years of flying. Seventeen years that had touched him lightly, a dash of gray at the temples of his curly golden head, an emphasis of the weather lines about his intense blue eyes. He had a way of carrying his head, a way of wearing his uniforms—Cary Leighton, the Navy's speed flier! True, he had been sitting at a desk for the past few years, but his renown still held.

Now, his moving finger stopped at a tiny dot on the chart, and he spoke with crisp confidence: "We shall rendezvous ten miles off Bocas del Toro at sixteen-thirty."

Nick's lanky figure struggled out of coveralls. His lean, brown face was troubled. One of the plane captains had just reported finding metallic chips in the oil of an engine, and his own inspection confirmed it. His gray eyes followed Leighton's

Courtesy of Brown Brothers, New York

Crack student pilots of the U. S. Navy Air Training station at Miami, Florida, flying divebombers in formation

fingers as they traced an imaginary course across the high, rugged mountains of Nicaragua. Keeping his voice carefully toneless, he said, "If we're going to rendezvous, that is the best place."

It was going to be another one of their touch-and-go conferences. Like a dueling match. Like sparring. They should be talking everything over carefully, calmly, planning each detail thoroughly. But it was always like this. Cary was casual to the point of bravado, and his, Nick's, old resentment choked him so that he was curt and short.

Now Leighton's smooth voice rippled on: "I'd particularly like to fly a tight vee-of-vees for the last two hours."

"After twenty-eight hours in the air the outfit will be so tired that you won't care how you approach Coco Solo, just so we get there."

Cary leaned back in his chair and laughed pleasantly. "Look here; you truck drivers are going to have to come to precision flying. That's one reason I wanted to get into big boats. I think you're ready for it now."

Nick felt the blood beating at his temples. He'd had ten years of patrol boats; Cary had had none!

Leighton found the next item on his list: "Number One comes down first, of course. Let's have no slip-up there."

Nick nodded. He kept his voice deep in his throat because he wanted to shout, "Listen, darling; better you worry a little about getting fifteen tons of gasoline off San Diego Bay all in one piece Monday morning."

The older man leaned back and regarded him. "You still don't get much fun out of flying, do you, Nick? You never did."

Nick reached for his cap. "The fun," said he abruptly, "will come later."

Outside on the plane ramp he found that his knees were trambling. His hand shook as he lit a cigarette. He knew he should go back and talk to Cary about the plane stowage, discuss the metal shavings in the oil. Anger and remembrance held him silent. Remembrance of himself and Cary Leighton ten years before on the carrier's deck. Cary's mocking smile, his stinging taunt: "What's the matter, Nick? Can't you take it?"

It hurt still to remember that up until that moment Cary

had been just about tops in Nick's world. When he, Nick, had been just a green little ensign on a battleship, Cary was winning speed trophies at the air races. While Nick was learning to fly at Pensacola, Cary was the Navy's crack test pilot at Anacostia. His stunt section, called the Sea Eagles, with wings lashed together did such precision flying as had left the nation gaping, the press applauding. That was the day of the spectacular aviator.

By the time Nick came out of Pensacola, Cary had command of a fighting squadron—the Red Hats, so called because of the color of the helmets they affected. Even now, years later, Nick could feel again the surge of incredulous joy that had come to him with orders to that squadron. To work under the famous Leighton. To fly with him!

Only, as the months went by, something happened to Nick. A year made him older. New vistas opened up. The big, clumsy patrol boats began to fascinate him. Designers were talking of increased ranges, even transoceanic flying, and the Navy had to find an answer to patrolling thousands of miles of coastline. Nick was having fun. The fighters were a thrill. But he wanted to be in on the first flights when they started adding engines and wing span to the big boats.

It was unfortunate that he picked a time when they'd just come in from a long, hard problem, with an overcast so low they barely could see the wing tips of the section ahead. There had been no connection for Nick between the flight and the single-track purpose in his mind. Standing by Cary, he had blurted it out: "I'm asking for a change of duty, sir. I want to get into big boats. I think they have a future."

Surprise had held Cary silent. The other pilots had paused. Cary's face had flushed. People asked to get *into* his outfit, not to be detached from it. His eyes had narrowed. It was then he had asked as a prelude to more scathing remarks, "Can't you take it any longer?"

Now, ten years later, Allan knew that he had been right about big boats. He'd been in on the ground floor and it had been worth it, but here was Cary sitting on the top again.

He tossed his cigarette away and went on down the ramp. Boone, his own plane captain, came up to him, and the ex-

pression on his face meant bad news. Nick grinned at him, took
a long shot: "Now, don't tell me your wife is just about to have
a baby, Boone."

"That's it, sir! Doc thinks it will be pretty soon. I hate to ask
it, sir, but I'd like to have leave and permission to come down
on a transport."

Nick swore. It would have been a relief to utter the pungent
words aloud. Instead, he put his hand on the bluejacket's shoulder. "I'm sorry, but I can't release a single man from the outfit.
But go on home, now, and stay until Monday. I'll see that our
plane is ready to go."

A long-distance flight like this was a fabric, a tapestry of
preparation. New planes. New engines. On Saturday noon,
with less than forty-eight hours to go, the threads were pulling
tighter. The knots were showing up, and the frayed places.

Ned Billings was a weakness. He came into the office, his thin
shoulders more bowed than ever, his earnest face a map of
anxiety. "I've just had Five out for a two-hour check flight. I
don't like that port engine."

"What's the matter with it this time?"

Billings shook his head unhappily. "She just doesn't sound
right. I think maybe the carburetor ought to be changed."

"Nothing doing. We've only two spares left. Besides, you've
changed twice already. Quit fussing, Ned, before you drive
your plane crew nuts. The engineering officer says you are all
set."

Nick felt sorry for his outburst and more irritated than he
had been before. It was that voiceless appeal which lay in
Ned's eyes, in his eternal nervous fussing over his plane. Billings was a good naval officer. His trouble was something he
wouldn't put into words and nobody else could. He was afraid
of airplanes. The excitement and competition had carried him
through Pensacola, but now, out in the Fleet, the responsibility
of a pilot's job was getting him down. Nick wanted to run after
him and grab him by the lapels. He wanted to shout, "Stop being a fool. There's nothing heroic about sticking with flying
when you know you shouldn't."

But being executive officer didn't give him the right to be his
brother's keeper. Or, did it?

The phone rang. Already the weather hounds were on the

scent. There'd be the usual light fog Monday morning, burning off by ten o'clock. So far, so good. Only, the rest wasn't so good. They'd have head winds most of the way. There was also a tropical blow stirring up in the Caribbean. It might go north, or it might work west, catching them around Tehuantepec.

He was in the Navigation Office checking over the charts when Mike Reagan came in to announce that the chips in No. 10's engine came from a burned-out bearing. Well, he'd expected it. But by four o'clock the faulty engine was out, and by seven the replacement was ready for running in. That left Nick free to contemplate the problem of all the other bearings. Made of an experimental soft alloy, they supported the spinning crankshafts under tremendous loads. A shortage of lubricating oil, or an overload, and they would melt like so much butter.

Kline, the flight officer, stood over his desk. Nick didn't like the rueful twist of his smile. "I don't need even half a cent to tell you what your thoughts are," said Kline.

"All right, wise guy."

"You're thinking that if you can get the boys to hold down their revs and power on the take-off Monday, you'll be able to nurse those bearings along."

"Right."

"Then get a load of this." He laid a memorandum from Leighton on the desk:

"Squadrons will take off in sections of threes for transit to Panama."

Nick swore. Fancy-formation stuff when each pilot needed to be completely free to devote his attention to his own plane and engines!

Kline nodded. "The Old Man's nuts on formations. Are you going to give him his parade?"

Then for the first time in a long and obedient naval career, Nick knew that he was going to step aside. "No," said he, "we're not."

"Are you planning to faint at the controls?"

"Never mind what I'm planning. You watch me and do what I do. . . ."

Monday's fog had begun to thin, giving promise of the sun,

when No. 1 waddled down the ramp. She turned sluggishly downwind. At close intervals the remainder of the flight squashed into the water, hulls riding deep. Leighton, sitting beside Nick, regarded them intently, as they trailed aft. Nick hoped that with this physical demonstration of their over-loaded condition, Cary would countermand the order for a formation take-off. But, the word did not come. Nick was in for it.

Perspiration broke out on his palms. Here was the penult of all the weeks of sweat and worry and work. He glanced back quickly. The full length of the bay was clear. He blew the tail around with a violent blast from the starboard engine. As the plane swung onto the reverse course, he jammed both throttles forward, but still held the power down to a safe figure.

The engines began their throaty, muffled roar. But the plane might have been lashed to a buoy. At last the flailing propel-lers bit into the air. Loggy, slow, the big patrol boat began to move along, a tumbling white wave piling up ahead of the bow.

Nick thought he heard Leighton's shout above the fierce screaming of the struggling machine, but he gave all his atten-tion to the controls. The end of the bay was coming up fast, now. There was no time for anything except to get this baby on the step. The water clung tenaciously. He gave a final, de-cisive push forward on the wheel. The hull rode over the bow wave and onto the step, gathering speed as it skimmed along. His spine tingled. Now was the moment!

The air-speed indicator moved slowly around the dial. Then the hull broke suction. No. 1 took the air. The wing-tip floats streamlined themselves into the wings. Nick swung her nose and headed for Panama.

Out of the corner of his eye he stole a glance at the com-mander. Cary's face was flushed, his blue eyes snapping. He shouted, "You're not getting away with anything, Nick. I gave orders to take off in sections."

Allan increased the pitch of the props and synchronized them. The roar subsided. He set the throttles for cruising and began a slow climb up through the remnants of the overcast. All his muscles suddenly ached, and he realized how taut he had been. He said shortly, "The pilots would have dragged too much power out of their engines on a formation take-off and we might have had some more burned-out bearings."

"That was for me to decide. You're relieved of duty and under arrest for insubordination."

Cary's mouth chopped shut over the words, suddenly, as if they had surprised him, too. But he did not rescind. His lips remained locked and sullen. Now the voices of the other pilots began to come through the headphones, announcing that their planes were in the air. But still, through his fury and his chagrin, Nick was relieved at the sound of Billings's voice. No. 5 was safely in the air.

Nick sat until they were, at last, all off. Then, he relinquished his place to the third pilot. He fought down the sick bitterness inside him. Hell! They were all under arrest. They were all imprisoned in these metal cocoons, prisoners of the air, the winds, the storms, and their own ability to read the stars aright. . . .

At 10,000 feet, No. 1 leveled off, waiting for the other planes. The barren mountains of Lower California stretched as far as the eye could see, fat, cumulus clouds sitting on their crests. Nick heard Cary fretting, "They're straggling all over the sky. Can't they close in a little faster?"

Obediently, the order was given to close up more briskly. The engines jarred on Nick's nerves. His fingers itched to throttle them down, for they were wasting precious fuel. He could close his eyes and see the power-altitude-load curves. Their theme song from now on had better be, "How is the gasoline holding out?"

He sat at the navigator's desk and plotted their departure from Cape St. Lucas. He might be supercargo, now, but they'd have to tie his hands behind his back if they expected him to stop being interested. Once, he looked up to find Cary watching him.

The sun dropped behind the cloudy horizon, its rays blending into royal purples and rosy hues. When next they saw it the planes should be 1500 miles to the southeastward. The lovely, homely smell of broiling steak and bubbling coffee filled the plane. The off-duty mechanic, who was cooking, brought Nick a heaped-up plate. He finished his coffee and leaned back, thinking of the old patrol boats, with their crowded open cockpits, of squashed sandwiches, and the thermos bottle of coffee that was never, never enough. Well, it had been fun, all of it, even though now every mile was taking him closer to a court-martial.

Weariness, treacherous as a gray fog, seeped into the plane. The men felt it in their eyes, in the muscles of their backs. They knew they must not even admit its existence. For this was only the beginning of the onslaught.

Nick looked forward. Piling up ahead was a great, dark patch against the sky. Not earth mountains, for they were flying well at sea, but sky mountains. A vicious streak of lightning slashed across their face, revealing the solid mass of clouds. Cary decided to go around. The correct maneuver. But Nick bit his lip, drummed on the desk. Cary's detour was wide and graceful and sweeping. Instead of edging through just on the border, he swung miles wide of their course. Wasted fuel!

The stars were not so clear now. The air was rough, as though clouds were forming at their level. The first storm front had been just a vanguard. There was more to come. Nick had a hunch. Taking up the octant, he crossed Rigel's line of position with a Polaris latitude line, fixing their position. Now, even where he was, he could hear the headphones crackling as if they were tuned to the frequency of some infernal region. Ahead of them, great, looming cliffs of black against the darkness barred their way.

Flashes of lightning lit up the heavens on either bow as far as the eye could reach. Perspiration beaded Nick's forehead. He'd played around with the fuel chart, and he'd sneaked in a navigational fix, but now he was going to have to take it. He must stand by helpless. He watched Cary climb to 16,000 feet, and knew he was praying for an opening. But the storm's front towered above them still, like a nightmare.

There was no choice, really. But Nick could see that Cary was pondering possibilities. Should they go down and try to find a lane through? They had swung toward the coast, and the peaks hereabouts ran up to 14,000 feet. Should they mill around waiting for the storm to dissipate? If he did that, thought Nick grimly, then, later they'd probably go down one by one, out of fuel, scattered from Magdalena Bay to the Mosquito Gulf. Nick kept his eyes on Cary's back and prayed.

Prayed that he would get the same answer to the sum. They must go through.

Presently Leighton's shoulders stiffened, and the nose of No. 1 headed for the black wall of the storm. Nick sighed a sigh of relief, that died a-borning. What was Cary waiting for? Why didn't he give the command to deploy, to place the planes at a safer distance from each other? Had that little item escaped him, or, in sheer pigheaded stubbornness, was he expecting two squadrons to fly through such stuff in close formation?

Nick knew how it would be. As they went into it each pilot in the rear would watch the plane ahead swallowed up in the opaque mass. As clearly as if he could look into each ship, he saw the pilots and the crews. Men he'd flown and worked with for years. Men he loved. He strode forward between the pilots' seats and took the microphone from the startled cadet. "Planes take double distance," he ordered.

A pink flush crept up over the edge of Cary's collar. But there was no explosion. Cary's face had a quietness about it, there was a pucker at the corners of his mouth. Only now, it seemed, did he realize what they were really undertaking. "Sit down, Nick," he directed.

By the time Nick was seated they were in it. The terrific beat of the rain on their duralumin hull rattled like buckshot. Only dimly could they see the red and green reflections of their running lights at the ends of the wings. Beyond that was black chaos. Close astern were 23 other planes.

Nick knew that the pilots would have no difficulty for a while in holding their positions by instruments. But, as the minutes wore into hours, their strength and their nerves would fray. From the first, each flier would have to fight the desire to turn sharply around on a wing tip and get free. Each man would be struggling against the driven sense that if he slipped, if he changed course or altitude, the man behind might run him down. Each plane became a battleground between the pilot's instinct and his training. Oh, now what they needed, these twenty-four, was luck!

Cary was fighting the controls. It was taking all his strength and skill to hold the plane in level flight and on its course. The skin on his face was stretched taut, colored with a strange yellowish pallor, while perspiration beaded his mouth. Without taking his eyes from the instrument panel, he shouted, "All right, Nick. I can't go it alone. Get on the controls and stay with me. We need everything we've got."

They were in the thick of it, now. Between short periods of utter blackness, the entire cloud body would be illuminated as by a falling comet. Afterward, blinded, they flew by instinct. There was scarcely opportunity to regain an even keel before another terrifying flash would come. Rain covered their cockpit housing in solid sheets of water.

Every flash of lightning left a charge of static electricity in the hull. It rushed through to the whirling propeller tips, to appear as circles of flames on their peripheries. The projecting air-speed Pitot tube became a flaming torch. Great, fat sparks leaped from the radio set. Illuminated like medieval demons, their bows a vivid glow of St. Elmo's fire, they fled through the center of the storm.

A mocking flash lit up the blackness. Nick called, "My God!" and reached up to cut the throttles back, for he had caught a hazy glimpse of No. 5 close aboard on a collision course. Billings!

Nick dove the plane and prayed. He lived a lifetime in those seconds, and then, 500 feet below, feeling it safe to level off, resumed course and speed. Over the phones he called, "Number Five, you just crossed my bow. Return to base course and speed immediately."

He cursed himself roundly and soundly. Why hadn't he hearkened to his intuition in San Diego, and removed Billings from the flight?

The radio opened up suddenly. Kline's voice came ominously: "All planes from Ten. Number Five just crossed my course to starboard. Keep sharp lookout."

So now they had a plane wandering around blindly within the formation! Billings would be rattled, the chances would be very large that he would collide with some poor devil whose eyes were glued to his instruments. Without looking, Nick could tell that Cary was sitting in the same frozen agony, awaiting disaster. The minutes ticked off. So intent were they on No. 5 that the storm seemed to fade to impotence.

Eventually, Nick could stand it no longer. "One calling Five! One calling Five!"

Faint and distant came a garbled, unintelligible reply, miles distant.

Nick glanced at Cary, and their eyes met. Leighton said, "He must have reversed his course to have opened out that far. He's going to get himself lost."

Nick nodded. But better one stray plane than two in collision. He was so relieved that he felt ill. The jauntiness was gone out of Cary's shoulders. He said through dry lips, "So this is what you meant by fun?"

At three they were still in it. The planes made their hourly report. All but No. 5. Nick called Billings again and again. He had other planes try. No answer. Nothing but an ominous, foreboding silence. He turned to Cary: "Billings hasn't reported for this hour. What do you want to do about him?"

Leighton regarded his second with bloodshot eyes. "What do you suggest?"

It would have been a nice triumph to gloat over, except that Nick was too tired to enjoy triumph. And he was worried about Billings. "There's nothing we can do right now except get these other twenty-two planes out of this."

Suddenly, as quickly as they had run headlong into clouds, they emerged into a starlit sky. A few mountainous masses of flimsy stuff stood up from the lower overcast, but these were of no concern. Nick turned around and, like a shepherd counting his flock, was ready to cry with joy as the tiny spots of red and green running lights popped out of the murk.

If it hadn't been for the thought of No. 5, the world would be pretty good. Even being under arrest might be worse, now that they were out of the storm. He quickly worked out their position from sights of Deneb and Andromeda. Then he went back to relieve Cary, suggesting, "We'd better wait at Fonseca for word from Billings."

Cary nodded, stumbling aft to where the off-duty watch were sleeping like babies in their bunks.

This was the longest part of the night, when fatigue became as real as a broken bone, as consuming as a fever. Nick fought against the numbness that paralyzed his senses, his movements.

Faintly at first, then sharply, an aroma penetrated his dulled perception. Coffee! Cary had been busy, and now was standing beside him holding a cup in each hand.

He said, "You'd better sit down and talk to me. I'll go to sleep if you don't."

"I've been wanting to talk to you for a long time, Nick. A very long time."

The coffee was black and bitter. It scorched Nick into wakefulness, while Cary's words held him: "You must have known that this job required more rank than you had—even though you did have the experience."

"Sure."

"Then it's me you've resented?"

Allan flew on in silence.

"Nick, did you ever make a mistake?"

The darkness ahead was dissolving into gray dawn. Cary's voice was dead level, no jaunty overtones. He went on: "Well, I have—my worst mistake being what I did to you that day on the Langley. I was cocky as all hell then, and so narrow that I couldn't see anything beyond stunting in a single-seater."

Nick held his silence, wondering.

"I've learned differently since then. I was wrong and you were right, and the farther away I've come from that day, the more it has bothered me."

Thought Nick, "So, at the first crack, you place me under arrest!" But he listened.

Now, suddenly, Leighton was angry: "But you've been a bum these last few weeks!"

Nick stared at him, open-mouthed.

"You've been wrong ever since we started working for this flight. You've been silent as a clam and stubborn as a mule. The things about the men, about the planes, that I could have found out only from you, you've withheld. I don't blame you as far as I was concerned, but it hasn't been fair to the squadron."

Hot anger sprang into words on Allan's lips—and died. He could take this honest fury from Cary. He could take it because he realized that this time Leighton was right. The truth of it was reflected in his own heart. It had been a bad setup and he had made the worst of it.

"All right, Cary. You win on that score."

"Then let's start a new squadron log, fellow. You know big-boat flying. I know the other angles. Between us we can have the best outfit in the Fleet."

For a long moment Nick watched the unbelievable colors of sunrise as they reflected in the still waters of Lake Nicaragua far below. Then he turned and grinned. "Okay. We start right now!"

The radioman came forward. Perspiration glistened in the stubble on his face, but he was smiling. "Number Five just reported her position, sir. She's a hundred miles astern."

They roared across the Caribbean, flying low, in and out of heavy rain squalls. No. 5 returned to the formation with Colon just ahead. As they circled, Billings's voice came over the radio: "I'm almost out of gas."

Cary spoke up briskly: "Tell him to land first."

No. 5 was out of the water when Cary cut the switches of No. 1. They had lived to the beat of those engines for so long that now, when they were silenced, there was a queer, flat inertia about everything.

They looked at each other as they felt the tug of the tractor pulling them out of the water, realizing that it was all over. They'd done it.

One of the beaching crew called, "Boone!" and threw a message into the plane.

The mechanic's whoop filled the plane: "It's a boy! It's a boy!"

Everyone pounded Boone on the back very hard. It relieved their feelings about a number of things. They could see the commanding officer of the Air Base ready to welcome them. Nick felt happy and free. They were all here—and he was rid of an old hate.

As he climbed out of the plane, Billings was waiting for him. Something had happened to Ned during the long, black, lost hours. He looked ten years younger and inches taller. His shoulders were erect. "Nick," he said firmly, "I know now that I've had enough. Here's something for you."

Allan was still staring down at the wings Ned had thrust into his hand, when Cary came over. "We're going to find the two tallest beers in Panama."

"Right," agreed Nick amiably. "We've a lot to drink down."

Topics for Discussion

1. Do you need to clear up the pronunciations and meanings of any phrases or technical words, such as: 5000-hour lads; the old Langley; rendezvous, etc.?

2. Does the first paragraph give you a hint as to what to expect in the story? How?

3. What time of the day is sixteen-thirty?

4. What is a "tight vee-of-vees"? Make a diagram of it for twenty-four planes.

5. If Leighton and Allan were unfriendly, why did they go in the same plane?

6. In what way did Leighton deserve to be in command of the mass flight? Or should Allan have been commander?

7. How old were Leighton and Allan? How long had each been in the service? How far back was the beginning of their dislike for each other?

8. What reason had the authors to bring in the fact that Boone's wife was expecting a baby?

9. Since this is a story of the reconciliation of Leighton and Allan, why is so much made of the hot engine in Ned Billings' Number Five?

10. Is the end of the story, the reconciliation, convincing? Do you believe that the experiences of the flight would bring about the mutual respect of the two men that would lead to a friendly settlement?

TALLY-HO![1]

By Arthur G. Donahue

T*ALLY-HO!* from which the following selection was taken, is a thrilling story, but it is not a novel. It is a well-written narrative of the experiences of Arthur Donahue, a young American with the British Royal Air Force in 1940, after the heroic but terrible withdrawal of the British Army from France at Dunkirk. The months covered by *Tally-Ho!* are those in which the Germans, based on the French coast, were raiding England and bombing London and other cities. When a squadron of fighting planes arises to engage enemy fighters or attack bombers, it starts out in a close formation. But when the attack really begins the C.O. (commanding officer), using his radio telephone, calls out "Tally Ho-o-o!" It is the command to break formation, select your particular opponent, go "on your own," and get your man.

Arthur Donahue was a Minnesota farm boy who went into commercial flying at eighteen, but in times of unemployment worked as a garage mechanic or on the farm. At the outbreak of the war he was an instructor in a flying school at Laredo, Texas. After Dunkirk he decided to go to England and seek employment as a noncombatant in the air service. But once in England he soon qualified for a commission as a Pilot Officer in the R.A.F.

* * * * *

Our last instructions by our squadron leader before we left for our advance base next morning were in regard to staying in formation any time the squadron was looking for the enemy.

"It's essential that the squadron stick together as a compact unit as long as possible, until the enemy is actually being engaged. So whenever we're on patrol, and especially when the

---

[1] From *Tally-Ho!*, copyright 1941 by Arthur Gerald Donahue. Published by Macmillan Co., New York.

scent is good and warm, stay in formation. Fly wide enough apart from your leader so that you won't be in danger of colliding with him, but don't lag behind if you can help it. If you see a Hun don't go after him until I give you the O.K. And if we sight a bunch of them, stay in formation until I call out the 'Tally-Ho!' Then you can break formation and pick your targets. And then," he added, patting us both on the back, "Heaven help your targets!"

We got our airplanes ready and put on our flying equipment. As it was warm, we didn't wear any flying suits over our uniforms, but we put on pneumatic life jackets that were issued to us. These are called "Mae Wests"—quite appropriately, too, as you would agree if you could see what they do to a pilot's contour.

We took off in sections of three and assumed squadron formation over the airdrome. An R.A.F. fighter squadron consists of twelve planes normally, and we flew in sections of three, the leader in front with his section.

It was a tremendous thrill for me to be aloft with a fighter squadron for the first time. We circled the airdrome majestically and then swept out eastward toward our advance base on the seacoast. I was enjoying this, even though it was only supposed to be a little cross-country jaunt.

I heard the whine of a radio transmitter in my headphones, and then our squadron leader's voice.

"Hello, Control! Hello, Control! Tiger Leader calling. Are you receiving me? Are you receiving me? Over." ("Tiger" was the call name of our squadron.)

There was another transmitter whir, more distant, and a cheery voice sang out, "Hallo-o, Tiger Leader, Tiger Leader! Control answering you. Control answering. Receiving you loud and clear, loud and clear. Are you receiving me, please? Are you receiving me? Control over to Tiger Leader."

Another whir and our leader's voice answering again. "Hello, Control. Hello, Control. Tiger Leader answering. Yes, receiving you loud and clear also. Loud and clear. All Tiger aircraft are now air-borne. We are now air-borne. Tiger Leader over to control, listening out."

Control called once more to acknowledge this message, and then there was radio silence as we roared onward. We had to

The Curtiss P-40F, a pursuit ship

cover about seventy miles, which would take about fifteen minutes. It was a clear morning, and I idly wondered if we should be able to see the French coast that day. If so I should be seeing France for the first time. Also it would be my first view of enemy country, for that was German-occupied France.

Perhaps seven or eight minutes had elapsed when Control called us again. There was the transmitter's whine and a voice calling Tiger Leader and asking if he was receiving him. Then Tiger Leader's answer that he was "receiving you loud and clear."

Then the voice from Control again, this time slower, and with careful enunciation: "All Tiger aircraft, patrol Dover at ten thousand feet; patrol Dover at ten thousand feet."

Our leader immediately opened his throttle and put his plane in a steep climb, at the same time altering his course in the direction of Dover. We of course did likewise to stay in formation with him.

I wondered what it meant. Had something been seen there, or were they expecting an attack? It still didn't seem possible that I actually might see an enemy. Planes with black crosses and swastikas still didn't seem to exist in reality to me, in spite of the one I had seen that spun in at our training base. Somehow that one, a great broken thing lying on the hillside after it crashed, didn't seem real to me in memory. It still didn't seem posssible that I should actually see airplanes with black crosses in the air, whose pilots would be trying to kill me, and I them.

In less time that it takes to tell, our altimeters were registering ten thousand feet and we were racing level. The coast was visible now, not far ahead, with the waters of the English Channel beyond. I guessed that we were nearly over Dover.

Another command came through from Control. "Climb to fifteen thousand feet." And then the message that electrified me:

"There are bandits [enemies] approaching from the north!"

My pulses pounded, and my thoughts raced. This was it!

In quick response to this information, our leader sang out a command: "All Tiger aircraft, full throttle! Full throttle!"

That meant to use the emergency throttle that gave extra power to our engines.

I was flying in our leader's section, on his left. As he gave the command "Full throttle," his plane started to draw ahead, away from me. I pushed in my emergency throttle lever in response to the command, the first time I had ever used it, and my engine fairly screamed with new power. I felt my plane speeding up like a high-spirited horse that has been spurred.

Our leader now led us upward in a steeper climb than I had ever dreamed an airplane could perform. Trembling with excitement, trying to realize that this was actually happening and I wasn't dreaming, I pulled the guard off my firing button. For the first time in my life I was preparing to kill! The button was painted red, and it looked strangely grim now that it was uncovered. I turned its safety ring, which surrounded it, from the position which read "Safe" to the position which read "Fire."

Then I switched on the electric gunsight. This projects an orange light in the image of a machine-gun sight upon a glass in the middle of the windshield. It's more accurate than mechanical sights.

We were going forward and upward at terrific speed, and reached fifteen thousand feet shortly. A new command came over our radio receivers: "Steer one-three-zero and climb to twenty thousand feet."

We obeyed, every pilot now watching above and below and on all sides, the sections of the squadron closing in more tightly and the rear-guard pilots wheeling in swift vertical banks one way, then the other, to watch against any surprise.

Our course led us out over the middle of the Channel, and the coast of France was plainly visible—answering one of my hopes. I was getting my first view of France, and enemy France at that.

I was using oxygen now, controlled by a little valve on my instrument panel that released it into a hose connected with the mask that covered my nose and mouth. Oxygen is necessary at high altitude to keep your mind working keenly and to keep you from getting tired and weak. Pilots who don't use it at high altitude tire out quickly, and their minds become sluggish. Also they are apt to faint without warning.

More orders followed. New courses to steer. New altitudes at which to fly.

"Circle your present position."

"Watch to the left."

"Believe the enemy is now heading south and passing behind you."

Such orders as these interspersed the radio silences and kept us busy and on our toes while we hunted about for perhaps half an hour. I was in a sweat trying to look in every direction and still keep my place in formation. Our leader led us about like a group of charging cavalry.

As time went by, my hopes of seeing an enemy flagged.

We were at about twenty thousand feet altitude and a few miles north of Calais on the French coast, and doing a sweeping left turn. Looking in the rear vision mirror above my windshield I saw what looked like a little blazing torch falling in the sky behind me. For the instant I didn't realize that the first shots of battle had been fired, and I had to put my attention again on our leader's plane, to keep my place in formation with him.

I was flying on his left, and that meant I had to look to the right to see him; and out of the corner of my eye I noticed far below and beyond him the distant shape of another airplane heading for France. I hated to call out, in case it didn't mean anything, but it didn't seem reasonable that a British plane would be out here alone, heading in that direction. Also it seemed to be colored blue-gray on top, and I was quite sure no British planes were colored like that. It was too far away for me to make out its markings or even its design. Hesitating to call out, I looked at our squadron leader, to see if he had noticed it.

I saw that he hadn't, for he was looking the other way, to our left, where several distant black dots were visible in the air at about our level. And as I watched him I heard his transmitter whine and his voice sing out the Royal Air Force battle cry:

"Ta-al-ly-ho-o!"

As he sang it he swung his airplane over viciously into a wild vertical turn and laid out for the black dots on the left, which had now grown into airplanes; still little and distant but headed toward us. There weren't very many of them, and the entire squadron was breaking formation and wheeling toward them like a bunch of wild Indians.

I remembered the one I had seen heading the other way and our Squadron Leader's words that we might pick our own targets after the "Tally-ho" is given; and a second later I was peeling away from the squadron and down in pursuit of the lone machine which I had decided should be my target.

I went down in a screaming dive, pushing everything forward —throttle, emergency throttle, propeller control and all. The other had a good start, but I had the advantage of several thousand feet more altitude, and was gaining speed by diving. The wind shrieked against my windshield and the Rolls Royce engine bellowed, while the air-speed indicator needle moved steadily around its dial and on up past the four hundred miles an hour mark.

The Spitfire grew rigid in its course as if it were following a groove. The controls became terribly stiff, and I couldn't move the stick a quarter of an inch in any direction. It was hard to level out from the dive when I got down near the other's altitude. I had to pull out very gently to keep from blacking out too much. The misty curtain kept closing down in front of my eyes as I pulled the nose of my plane up, and I leaned forward and tensed my muscles to resist it. I was still a way behind the other when I got down to his level, but I was gaining on him fast, because of the extra speed I had from my dive.

I was holding my thumb over the firing button now and keeping my eyes glued to the little silhouette ahead, except for an occasional glance at the rear vision mirror to see that I wasn't being chased too. I imagine my heart was doing about fifteen hundred r.p.m., from the pounding I felt.

The other machine grew steadily larger in the circle of my gunsight as I drew closer. I could tell its distance by the amount of space it covered in the sight: six hundred yards, five hundred, four hundred—my speed was dying down a little, and I wasn't gaining quite as fast. He apparently was going wide open too.

Now I was only three hundred yards behind—close enough to open fire, but something made me hesitate. From directly behind, where I was now, it was hard to identify its type. Suppose it was a British machine after all?

To make sure I eased my machine upward just a little so I could look down on the other and see the upper side of it. The old feeling that airplanes with black crosses and swastikas on their wings and sides couldn't exist in reality still had hold of me; but it was banished forever by what I now saw.

For I could see that the other machine's wings were not curved, with nicely rounded tips, like a Spitfire's; and it was not camouflaged green and tan; and there were no red and blue circles near the tips. Instead, the wings were narrow, stiff-looking, with blunt, square-cut tips. They were pale blue-gray in color, and near each tip, very vivid, was painted a simple black "plus" sign!

I knew from pictures that it must be a Messerschmitt 109, and I dropped back into firing position behind it. My sights centered on it, and I squeezed the firing button with my thumb. B-r-r-rup-pup-u-pup! The sound came to me muffled by my heavy helmet; but it was a venomous sound, and I could feel the Spitfire shudder and slow from the recoil as the eight Browning guns snarled and barked their terrific fast staccato. I held the button in for about a full one-second burst—about one hundred and sixty bullets.

Then my plane bounced sideways as it encountered the turbulent slipstream of the other, and I lost sight of him for a second. He must have gone into a diving turn just then, for when I spotted him again a few seconds later he was far below. Mentally cursing my carelessness or dumbness, I rolled over and went down after him again; and while I was overtaking him I reflected that for the first time I had tried to take the life of another man. It didn't bother my conscience.

I caught up with him just over Cape Gris Nez * on the French coast, and that was how I entered France for the first time! As I drew close he abandoned flight and turned to face me like a cornered animal; but I was too close behind him now, and I simply followed him in the turn, cutting it shorter than he could and crowding in on him.

I knew I was outmaneuvering him, and felt I had him now. He was almost in the circle of my gunsights. This time I'd keep him there!

Powp!

It sounded exactly as if some one had blown up a big paper

---

* *Gris nez* (grē nā′).

sack and burst it behind my ears; and it shook the plane and was followed by a noise like hail on a tin roof.

I realized that I had been hit somewhere behind me in my machine by a second Hun, and guessed that it was an exploding cannon shell that made the noise. Most German fighters are equipped with cannon as well as machine guns.

I put all the strength I could muster on my controls to whip my machine into a turn in the opposite direction, then saw that I'd wasted the effort. My new attacker had already flashed by below and ahead, and I now saw him wheeling to come back, his black crosses vivid on top of his wings as he appeared spread-eagled in a vertical turn. The square-cut wingtips of his Messerschmitt looked crude but grim.

He must have dived on me and fired a shot as he went down past. I reflected a little grimly that a new "first" had occurred for me—for the first time another man had tried to take my life!

It's hard to recall details of the ensuing combat, but I know it was pretty wild. I made lots of blunders. It was terribly hard for me in my inexperience to try to get an advantage on one of my enemies, so I could open fire, without the other popping up immediately in firing position behind me. The three of us scrambled about in a terrible melee, climbing, diving, rolling, and pirouetting in screaming vertical turns to get at each other. A combat such as this is well called a "dog fight." One moment I would be maneuvering for my life to get away from one who was almost on my tail, and in the next moment I would have one of them in the same kind of spot and would be trying just as desperately to hold him long enough to get a shot.

And sometimes when I got separated from both of them a moment I would see bright flashes and puffs of white or black smoke in the air near me—shells from German anti-aircraft guns. The batteries on the coast below had joined the fight and were shooting at me whenever they got a chance to do so without hitting their own machines.

This went on for several minutes, before I finally managed to get one of them all by himself away from the other for a few seconds. I was in a beautiful firing position right on his tail.

Then I got a heart-breaking shock: my gunsight wasn't working! The precious image in orange light wasn't to be seen on the glass in front of me. Feverishly I fumbled and found the switch for it. Yes, it was on. I tried the rheostat which controls the intensity of the light for day or night use. It was on full bright.

It was hard to do this and keep behind the other's tail. He was dodging wildly, expecting my bullets every second, I suppose. I jiggled the rheostat and turned it back and forth, and hit the reflector sight base with my hand and shook it. Still no result. It took precious seconds to do this checking, and the loss of time was very nearly fatal.

A set of four long vibrating snaky white fingers reached across my right wing from behind and stretched far ahead. They were about an inch thick and made of white smoke and pulsated with bright molten-looking objects streaking through them. I knew they were tracers—the trails of smoke left by bullets to mark their course. Chemicals coated on the bullets do it. They show the pilot where his bullets are going. In this case they showed me too, and I knew I was being fired at by the other German pilot from behind. I panicked and rolled into a turn so violent that my machine shuddered terribly and slipped over into a tailspin—at more than two hundred miles an hour! It must have made me look like an amateur, but it shook off my attacker.

I felt that I was in a pretty bad spot without a gunsight, but decided to bluff them a little bit rather than to turn tail right away and let them know something was wrong.

The melee continued. I was terribly hot and tired and sweaty, and was conscious of that more than of being scared. I wished I could rest. The bright sun beat down hotly through the transparent hatch over my cockpit. My clothes were heavy and I was hampered by my parachute straps and seat harness straps as I twisted about in the cockpit trying to see above, below, behind, and to the sides to keep track of my playmates.

During those next few minutes I think I must have blacked out at least twenty times in turns. I remember starting to spin at least once from turning too violently. I wanted to flee but couldn't get my directions straight because I was maneuvering so fast. My compass couldn't help me unless I'd give it a chance to settle down. It was spinning like a top.

Finally I noticed across the water, in the distance, a ribbon of white lining the horizon, and I remembered reading years

ago in my geography book about the "white cliffs of Dover."
Just then that looked like the promised land.

One of my enemies was heading the other way. I made a
pass at the second and he headed in the opposite direction from
Dover, too, and I turned out across the sea and homeward. It
was an ignominious way to end a fight which had begun with
such promise, but I thought it was the wisest. My enemies took
after me, but when they drew close I turned around as if to
go after them and they turned back. They were apparently
willing to call it a draw, and I didn't feel quite so badly after
that.

When I went to land at our advance base I found that the
trimming controls for my tail were out of order. The wheels
actuating them spun loosely, so I knew the cables must be
broken.

On landing I taxied to one end of the field, where I saw
the rest of my squadron's planes, already down. I was flagged
into place, and mechanics and armorers swarmed over my
Spitfire. Some jerked off the removable metal covers above and
below the machine guns in the wings while others ran up
with belts of ammunition and began to refill the guns. A gasoline truck roared up and stopped in front of the plane, and they
began refilling the tanks. In a few minutes my machine would
be completely checked, refueled, and refilled with ammunition.

My squadron mates crowded around to hear my story. All but
one of them were down now, and they had already heard one
another's stories. I told them mine as well as I could remember,
and had to admit regretfully that I had come away without
bringing down either of my enemies.

We examined my plane, and it was easy to see that it had
been struck by an exploding cannon shell, as I had thought.
The shell had blown a fairly large hole in one side of the fuselage just behind the cockpit, in the lower part of the red, white,
and blue insignia. It would have been a bull's-eye if it had been
a foot higher.

The control cables, which ran close by where the shell had hit,
were in bad shape. In addition to the trimming control cables
being broken, the main elevator and rudder cables were also
nearly severed by the blast. A battery connection was broken
by the explosion, and that explained the failure of my electric

gunsight. The bottom of the plane was littered with bits of light shrapnel from the shell and there were a myriad small holes in the other side of the fuselage from the shell hole, where pieces of shrapnel had gone out. The shrapnel must have made the noise "like hail on a tin roof" that I had heard after the explosion. My machine truly carried an "after the battle" appearance. It would have to have a new fuselage installed.

I heard the story of the rest of the squadron. They had charged into the formation of Messerschmitts that they were heading for when I left them, and had shot down two for sure. There were also two other "probables" which they had seen going down but which they couldn't claim definitely because they weren't seen to hit the sea. One of the boys had damaged still another—had seen pieces fly off it when he fired.

In addition a Henschel 126 German reconnaissance machine had come steaming along right into the center of the melee, a terrible mistake for its pilot to make, for these machines only have two or three machine guns and can't travel much over two hundred miles an hour, so that they are cold meat for fighters. He must have been going on some business of his own and blundered into the middle of the show somehow, before he realized it. Two of our boys spotted this machine and went to work on it, but they were nearly out of ammunition by that time and they emptied all the bullets they had left into it without bringing it down. It just kept sailing right on, but they thought they killed the rear gunner at least, because he quit shooting back at them. It was credited to the squadron as being "Damaged."

This is one of three categories into which the R.A.F. successes are divided. The other two are "probably destroyed" and "confirmed victories" (definitely destroyed). Only the number of confirmed victories is given out in the report of enemy aircraft destroyed.

The score for the squadron that morning was two confirmed, two probables, and two damaged.

None of our planes that were back was even hit except mine; but one had not returned yet and the outlook grew bad. Two of the boys remembered seeing what looked like a Spitfire going down in flames in the distance behind the squadron at the start of the battle. This boy who was missing was one of the "rear guard" pilots, protecting the rear of the squadron. I also remembered the glimpse I had in my mirror at that time, of something that looked like a torch falling in the distance behind us. When no trace could be found of him and it was learned that no other British planes were missing, we knew he must have been the pilot. There were a lot of Messerschmitts about that morning, and it was pretty evident what had happened.

He must have seen some Messerschmitts coming up to attack the squadron from behind, had turned back and engaged them, and thus, fighting alone to protect his mates, he had gone out in a blaze of glory. Our squadron leader paid him a simple but meaningful tribute that we wished he could have heard.

"I noticed," he said, "that we weren't attacked from the rear."

I sought out Peter, and we lay on the grass near our machines and basked in the warm sunshine. There were a lot of scratches on my flying boots from shrapnel, and we found a little piece imbedded in one of them.

I felt strangely tired and lazy, not realizing that this was my initiation to a strange feeling of exhaustion with which I was to get better acquainted in the following days. I didn't want to sleep, but I didn't want to move, or talk, or fly, or anything else either, just relax. It's a feeling that's always pervaded me after a fight or a nerve-racking patrol. As nearly as I can describe it, it is a sensation of being drained completely, in every part of your body, though I don't know what of. But you seem to want to just surrender to relaxation, sitting or lying inert and absorbing whatever it is back into your system. I've heard many other pilots say they get the same feeling.

Peter asked, "Will you do me a favor, Chum?"

"Sure. What is it?"

"Let me have your notebook for a minute and I'll tell you."

I gave him the little memorandum book which I always carry, opening it to a blank page. He wrote a girl's name and telephone number in it.

"If anything happens to me," he said, "will you telephone this number and tell her the story? And then—" He paused, and indicated the silver identification wristlet which he wore on his left wrist. It had a little name plate, and also little charms of some sort strung on it. "If it's possible," he finished, "I'd like to have you see that she gets this."

"O.K.," I said lightly, "and let's hope that I never have to do that for you."

Looking at the notebook, I tried to realize that I had bought it only three months before, in a drugstore in Manitowoc, Wisconsin.

I still have that notebook, Peter, and the page you wrote on that day is still in it; though, of course, I don't need it any more because I've telephoned the number and told her the story, long since.

Topics for Discussion

1. Describe the means used by the Ground Control to direct the movements of planes in the air.

2. Describe the means by which the C.O. of a squadron can communicate with the pilots while they are all in the air. Can a pilot ask the C.O. for instructions—in other words, does the telephone work both ways?

3. Why are messages repeated, as in "Hello, Control! Hello Control! Tiger Leader calling. Are you receiving me? Are you receiving me? Over." What is the word "over" used for here?

4. Could enemy pilots also hear the orders of the ground Control and the Squadron Leader in the air? If not, how is "listening-in" guarded against?

5. Describe the differences between fighters and bombers: size of planes, number of crew members, number of engines, speed, duties, etc.

6. Lieut. Donahue thinks the English Spitfire a better plane than the German Messerschmitt 109. In what ways?

7. Are you surprised at anything in Donahue's account of a routine day? What? After a terrific fight 30,000 feet up at 350 miles an hour, breathing oxygen, rolling, pitching, tailspinning, could you consider having lunch and going into town for a movie?

8. List the duties on the ground of a pilot's day.

9. What do the mechanics and ground crew do in a similar day?

LEAVES FROM A PILOT'S LOG[1]

By Captain Burr T. Leyson

INSTEAD of fiction you will be reading here three separate experiences of a veteran pilot and writer. Captain Leyson knows how to write thrilling short stories presenting imagined happenings in which pilots and planes figure. When you finish reading these three narratives, point out the differences you notice between imagined and actual occurrences, and make up your mind as to which you prefer to hear.

* * * * *

I

The roaring of motors overhead subsided, a lone plane glided down, touched the earth lightly and then turned to taxi up the hangars as a hush fell over Roosevelt Field. The crowd tensed and the air became charged with expectancy. A moment later the harsh metallic voice of the loud speakers blared an announcement. A man would cast himself into space from a speeding plane three thousand feet above the field. He would let his body plummet earthward for two thousand feet and then he would pull the rip cord that opened his parachute. On and on went the voice of the announcer, soaring from one superlative to another as he described the coming "death defying spectacle, a leap for life!" To us pilots it was just another parachute drop, something to attract a crowd and help our business of taking people aloft for a short "joyride."

"Hey! Leyson! Take this guy up to three thousand and dump him, will you?" the Field Manager shouted.

With a glance I looked around, nodded my head and replied: "Okay. Let's go."

Swinging a leg over the edge of the cockpit, I slid into the

---

[1] From *Boys' Life,* March, 1941. Reprinted through the courtesy of the author and *Boys' Life,* published by the Boy Scouts of America. Copyright by the author.

seat. A mechanic swung the propeller. The warm motor caught, idled evenly and I turned to look for the 'chute jumper.

He was a youngster, clear eyed, clean looking but strangely pale. The muscles of his jaw were tightly set and his mouth was a firm thin line, his eyes hardened bright with the stress of excitement.

"Bit tense," I thought but that was nothing. 'Chute jumpers were a queer lot anyway. We could never understand why they should want to leave the comparative safety of a plane and thrust themselves out into the thin air.

"Snap it up. Let's go!"

I was tired, impatient. Five minutes later I idled the engine, went into a gentle glide over the center of the field three thousand feet below us. But the youth sat stiff and erect in his cockpit up front. I banged on the cowling with a fist and shouted:

"Bail out! I can't hold this crate here all day!"

He forced a grin, nodded and slowly clambered over the edge of the cockpit, holding to the cowling and resting his feet on the broad "walk" of the low-wing monoplane. His right hand left the cowling and grasped the rip cord ring of his 'chute. He was out on the left and I sat ready to thrust on quick left rudder to swing the tail surfaces away from his body as he jumped. But he did not jump. He clung to his perch, his eyes locked on the ground below.

"Get off of there! Jump! You're over the field!"

I might as well have saved my voice. Now we had glided past the field and I opened the engine, swung in a flat circle to bring him again into position to jump. All the while he clung there while I was forced to hold the controls hard over to the right to keep our plane on an even keel against his weight and the drag of the wind on his body. Again I idled the engine and glided across the field. And again he stood there unmoved by my shouts to get off the wing. For the third time we swung into position.

My arm was tired and my patience at an end. A 'chute jumper who wouldn't jump! I had been informed he'd made many jumps before so why not now? Then I saw something that set my ragged nerves on edge. The ring of his rip cord dangled free from the tight pocket that held it. And as it

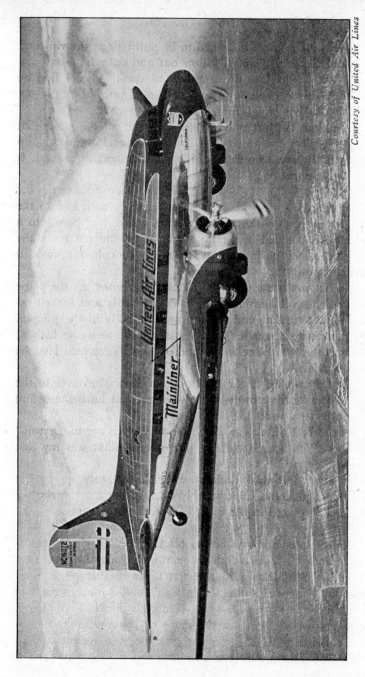

A modern airliner, "State of California," on its way across the continent

whipped in the wind it seemed to be pulling out the rip cord. If it did the 'chute would billow out and enfold the tail surfaces. We would lose the control and crash. Also, I had no 'chute. Why wear one for a routine five minutes hop?

"Get off that wing! Jump or I'll dump you!"

No action. He just stood there, rigid and all the while that dangling rip cord seemed to lengthen, reaching the point where the 'chute would open. My patience was at an end. It was time for action.

My left hand thrust the throttle full forward and as the motor roared I brought the controls sharply back and to the left. In an instant the little low-wing monoplane was into a "roll." She snapped over onto her back. As she did I saw the body of the 'chute jumper flash past my cockpit. He was still in a stiff position.

"I'll bet you'll use that 'chute now," I grinned. As the plane finished the roll I levelled off, banked sharply and looked below. Slowly turning end for end was the body of the jumper. He was near the earth. Then there was the welcome flash of white as the 'chute broke free and opened. A moment later he landed safely.

I had drawn up to the hangar when he walked over to the plane. Hot words crowded on my tongue but he spoke before I could utter a word.

"I'm sorry I didn't get off when you wanted me to, Leyson," he said. "You see, I was sort of nervous. That was my first jump."

My knees felt weak and my stomach curiously empty. My anger was gone and I felt humbly thankful for the courage the Maker had placed in the spirit behind those clear eyes.

II

Months later my own fingers reached for the rip cord of a 'chute and felt a great comfort in the cold metal of the ring. What had started as a routine test flight had developed into something far different. "Uncle Sam" and I were some two thousand feet above the same Roosevelt Field. Now, Uncle Sam in this case was not the more or less genial gentleman cartoonists depict but a great monoplane built for an attempt at the world's distance record. Uncle was a flying gas tank. I sat on gas tanks, had my head in a recess of a gas tank, had them behind me, ahead and over head. Uncle's engine was of five hundred and fifty horsepower and it was an inverted engine, the cylinders were on the lower side of the engine and the crankshaft on the top. Mayhap this accounted for its vile disposition. It seemed to hate to run evenly or for any length of time. Coupled with Uncle's innumerable queer traits of flying, the combination of engine and plane was a pilot's nightmare. Even Uncle's cost was fantastic. It had cost over two hundred thousand dollars before it ever flew.

We had settled down to a straight flight to test gas consumption. For the moment Uncle rode evenly and I relaxed. Then, as though he had behaved merely to lull me into a false sense of security, Uncle began to act up. For no reason at all he decided he wanted to fly in a sharp left circle.

Full and hard right rudder failed to correct the turning, although it did stop the all but spin. We still swept in a wide circle to the left. Then there was a shudder that shook the entire structure of the plane and Uncle turned more sharply to the left. I had to fight to keep the plane from going into a spin. Vibration in the rear of the ship told me the story. Something had failed on the tail surfaces. If it let go entirely—my hand sought the rip cord of my 'chute and I derived a great feeling of well being from it. Then I did not feel so well.

There was but one exit from Uncle, a narrow door on the left. The ship wanted to spin to the left. The moment I let go the rudder controls the ship would go into a spin to the left. And to jump I would have to release my feet from the rudder. I had visions of Uncle following me down, picking me up as I hung there on my 'chute. His disposition was perverse enough to do it, I was sure. Then I thought of the cost, of all the effort men had put into the building of the plane and most of all I thought of a pilot deserting his craft while there was still a vestige of hope of getting it down. I was alone but I still had the responsibility. I looked around.

There was small comfort below. We were wide of the field by miles. But our circle swung us near Mitchell Field, the Air Corps base. The wind was drifting us as we circled. In time we would be over Mitchell. Carefully I began to work Uncle down to a lower altitude.

A circle and Mitchell was close at hand but still too far

away. Another and we would be in position to land but cross-
wind. That was better than nothing. Down we came still lower.
Now we were too low to use our 'chute if we wanted to do so.
Roofs and trees tops were skimming feet below the under-
carriage as we swung through another circle and Mitchell came
ahead.

We roared across a long street of homes, a broken lot and
then came the low trees marking one side of Mitchell. One
seemed to stand out, bar the way. Contemptuously Uncle's
tons swept the top branches aside without a tremor. The green
grass of the field shot past in a blur of speed. It was now or
never. Would he swing and crash when the engine was idled
and the blast of air from the propeller no longer thrust hard
against the surface of the rudder? I cut the switch, snapped
it to "off" and braced myself. We hit, rumbled, left the ground
for an instant as the wind caught under a wing and then came
back. The great plane swerved, dust rolled up and then we
rolled to a stop—still intact.

I heaved a sigh of relief and thought of the times I had been
tempted to jump, leave the plane to its own devices. It had
seemed intent on destruction. A feeling of great satisfaction
swept over me. I had stuck by the ship! I grinned and reached
for the handle of the door, the only means of exit. Then my
grin faded and I recalled a scene just before I had taken off. A
mechanic had run to the plane, reached up and removed a key
from the door. He must have turned it as he pulled it out for
the door was tightly locked. I couldn't have jumped if I had
wanted to!

III

It had been a lovely day, clear sky and a gentle breeze, the
air smooth, the whole earth below smiling. Green fields were
scattered along our course, offering a safe haven if the engine
acted temperamental as engines had a habit of doing way back
in the 1920's.

The sun was low on the horizon as we swept across the Connecticut Hills and the air became rapidly cooler. At the time
I thought nothing about the cooling of the air for my mind
was on the gas supply. It was getting very low. Still, there was
sufficient to get into Hartford where we could refuel. It was

dusk when we saw the Connecticut Valley, rather, we saw where it was—we didn't see it. It lay beneath a fleecy blanket of white ground fog!

I had forgotten that the cool evening air blowing across the still warm waters of the great river made a heavy low fog in the mornings and at evening. A quick glance at the gas gauge showed the needle at the empty position. There would still be a small amount in the bottom of the tank, enough to get into Brainard Field at Hartford but—Brainard was also covered with fog! I idled the motor, went into a glide and shouted to the man in the open cockpit ahead.

He was a huge man, all of six feet and with a wrestler's build. In a way he was an oddity for he was a Chinese and we in America are not used to seeing six-foot men from China. We are accustomed to the smaller Cantonese, and this man was a giant Mongol.

"Sit tight," I warned him. "We're out of gas soon and the field's covered with fog. I don't know where we're going to sit down. Can't get back to where it's clear and there's no place on these hills we can land without a bad crash."

He grinned and nodded his head as though I had merely called his attention to the beautiful sunset that now colored the western horizon. Blandly he looked around, saw the fog covering all below us.

Now we were well over the valley and the field lay hidden two thousand feet below. Suburbs stretched all around and nowhere could I see a place to land without a bad crash. Then, in my mind's eye, I saw the entire land below us as though there was no fog enshrouding it. I had flown into and out of Brainard many times and was familiar with every bit of the field. My eyes sought the tops of the buildings protruding through the fog. There was a chance—a long one but it was a case of crash anyway. I thrust the throttle forward and headed directly for the Traveller's Tower in mid-Hartford.

Dropping lower, I swung around the Tower and took a bearing from its sides for Brainard Field. Idling the motor, I began a glide and shouted to the Chinese in front:

"Hang on! We're going down! Tighten your belt!"

Again he grinned and nodded his head as though to thank me for the information.

Now we were skimming the fog, and I strained my eyes trying to pierce the white haze below the wheels. We were nearly to the field or where it should be. Ahead I knew lurked buildings, a tall power house chimney and a high tension electric line. Beyond those hazards lay the field with its border surrounded at the north end by buildings. Somehow I hoped to dodge them and get onto the ground.

A blurred shape showed through the fog. It was the stack of the power house. Ahead lay the high tension line. I gassed up the plane, broke from the top of the haze and then, hoping we had passed the wires, boldly plunged into the fog. It was now or never.

Head out to one side, I stared ahead. Would those vague shadowy shapes never appear or would they rush out of the fog too fast for us to dodge? It seemed an eternity. A part of the fog thickened, grew rapidly darker. A building flashed past a wing tip, missed by feet! Another loomed ahead, directly in our path. I shot the throttle forward, prayed the engine would respond. It did and we hurdled the building by inches—too close for comfort! More buildings loomed ahead. They too passed inches below our wheels and a wind sock atop a tall pole seemed to pass directly between the wheels. We were over the hangars at the edge of the field. Down went the nose.

Gingerly I "felt" for the ground, easing the plane down a foot at a time. I cut the switch and the prop stopped. The earth was still hidden feet below us. My goggles were misted over and I flung them back. Then the ground popped out of the fog right under the wheels. We hit hard, bounced and returned to earth. We were down—safe.

I was still shaken, tense, thanking the blind luck that had guided us when the Chinese turned to face me.

"Velly floggy today, Capeetan!" he remarked with a grin, looking around as though to confirm his opinion. I was speechless. He never knew that the fingers of my right hand were fondling the cool bulk of a fire extinguisher and I was yearning to use it to wipe that calm grin from his face!

QUESTIONS AND TOPICS FOR DISCUSSION

1. Were you in sympathy with the boy when he would not jump—and fearful for him?

2. Why did Captain Leyson call this piece "Leaves from a Pilot's Log?" Is the title suitable?

3. In the third incident do you suppose the Chinese passenger was just naturally calm, or was he unaware of the danger?

4. These three are actual instances from the diary of Captain Leyson. Do you like them as well as you do fictional stories based upon probability and possibility but not actually true? Explain your preference.

5. What do we mean by the phrase: "Truth stranger than fiction"?

PARATROOPS [1]

By Captain Burr T. Leyson

ONE of the most spectacular developments of World War Two is the use of parachute troops, known in the American Army as paratroops. The theory that troops could be dropped far in an enemy's rear areas by means of parachutes was developed long before the break of this war. Even in World War One this technique was used to a limited extent in dropping spies and saboteurs behind the enemy's lines.

In the nineteen-hundred-and-twenties and the early part of the nineteen-thirties, the Russian Communist Army developed the parachuting of troops to a great extent. Mass demonstrations were staged and at one time over one thousand men were descending to earth by parachute. Training towers were built throughout the Soviet Union and both men and women participated in learning the art of parachute jumping. Military authorities in general were skeptical of the value of this method of attack and the Russian demonstrations were discounted as merely a part of the incessant publicity on the strength of the Russian Armies. The debacle * of Finland, where the Russians were soundly trounced until the Finns exhausted their supplies, gave added force to the argument that this method of attack was merely dressing for publicity.

One power considered such a method of attack seriously. That was Nazi Germany. It was generally known that the Nazis were experimenting with paratroops but it was not realized just how seriously they were training these men. Then came the attack on Norway.

Here the technique of paratroops was used and in addition airborne troops for invasion made their appearance. The short

---

[1] From *Wings of Defense,* by Captain Burr T. Leyson. Copyright 1942 by E. P. Dutton & Co.

* *debacle* (dĕ bä′k′l): disastrous failure.

distance across the narrow passage of the Skagerrak to the
Norwegian mainland offered an ideal place for a full-dress rehearsal of this new type of attack. Whole regiments were borne
from the German bases to Oslo in less than three hours. Regular commercial air transports were the carriers. Parachute
troops prepared the way, taking over the lightly held airports
almost before the Norwegians realized that war had descended
upon them.

The Low Countries * saw paratroops used far more exten-
sively. Rotterdam, Amsterdam, and other cities were attacked
by swarms of paratroop carriers. Here again effective defense
was not present. Airports and vital traffic arteries were captured and held. Communications were severed, chaos resulted
in the defensive efforts and the Nazi ground forces found the
roads open to them.

Although these examples of the use of paratroops gave the
world a preview of what was to come, their use as a military
weapon was still decried. It was not until the attack on Crete
and its fall that paratroops were given the serious consideration they deserve.

Crete, lying a short air distance from the Grecian mainland,
was an ideal base for the British fighter and bomber planes to
attack the Nazi forces in Greece. In a like manner Crete also
was a base from which the Dodecanese Islands and the sea
approaches to Greece could be commanded by air attack.

The British held several squadrons of fighters on the island
and based squadrons of bombers there as well. The island was
garrisoned by strong detachments of troops and defended by
heavy anti-aircraft installations. In addition the British fleet
had command of the seas surrounding the island. It did not
appear possible that a successful attack could be launched
against the island, as the Axis powers were without naval forces
which could be brought to bear on the British fleet. True, the
Italian fleet was still somewhat intact but experience with the
British had taught them the value of discretion, a trait they
have shown great aptitude in learning.

The Nazis had a considerable concentration of air power in
Bulgaria and northern Greece. This concentration had been

_____

* *Low Countries:* Holland and Belgium.

made in Bulgaria before the blitzkrieg in Greece. As Greece was naturally very hostile and swarmed with British agents, there was no possibility of concentrating air power there without its becoming known. The air forces were concentrated in Bulgaria for the most part. And here paratroops and all their necessary equipment were assembled. Then, for the first time in history, air power struck with an airborne troop attack. Due to British naval forces destroying a flotilla of small boats carrying some 5000 troops to attack Crete, the entire offensive was left to air power.

The British in Crete had been warned of an impending attack and measures were taken to repulse it. There was a feeling that paratroops would be shot out of the air faster than they could descend. Then the blow struck.

The British airports were heavily bombed at the first light of day. This bombing was peculiar in that it was confined to the hangars and the other buildings but the runways remained untouched. Unfortunately the British air forces were caught for the most part grounded. Previous bombing had driven the fighter squadrons to bases on the mainland in Egypt.

While this bombing was in progress, German heavy air transports flew onto the scene. Their arrival was timed exactly with the end of the bombing. Hordes of paratroopers plummeted down from the transports. Machine guns and ammunition, hand grenades, even light mortars followed them. Within minutes the airport was captured. It was Norway and the Low Countries repeated on a larger scale.

No sooner had the attackers taken over the airport than they set flares to signal the transports which circled overhead. In rapid succession, one on the other's tail, they landed and their fully armed troops poured out to add to the offense. Anti-tank guns rolled from the interior of the transports, heavy machine guns, quick firers, mortars, food, ammunition, medical supplies. A self-sustaining attacking force was well established and the British had lost the command of the air. Nor could their fighters, based on the distant mainland, relieve the situation. They lacked the range to fly to Crete, fight and then return. And Crete no longer offered them any haven. Now it was airborne troops against the garrison in a finish fight.

The British forces were hurriedly concentrated to eject the

invaders. But even as the orders were issued the full force of the air attack developed. Swarms of Nazi transports appeared and the sky was literally filled with descending parachutes. Thousands of troops dropped. Then transports appeared towing large gliders. The gliders cut loose from their tows and descended to the ground, guided by an experienced pilot. The moment they landed each glider poured out squads of men. The towing transport added to their numbers with paratroopers or dropped supplies to those on the ground. The results are history. Crete fell, fell to a strictly air assault.

There is little doubt but that the Nazi Luftwaffe tipped its hand in the attack on Crete and that this assault was a dress-rehearsal for the attack on England, if it is ever delivered. Our own paratroop training is based very largely on the events of Crete. Thus the technique used in Crete is worthy of attention.

The first consideration of a paratroop attack in force is to possess command of the air in that locality. If enemy fighters are present, the slow and cumbersome paratroop carriers and the glider trains are easy prey and they will be shot out of the sky.

This command of the air does not of necessity mean that the enemy air forces must be defeated generally. A strong concentration of fighters is sufficient if they are present in numbers such as to prevent enemy fighters breaking through their defensive blanket over the scene of operations. But, the operation must be completed before the enemy can bring to bear sufficiently strong fighter concentrations to retake command of the air.

This local command of the air was graphically shown in the disaster of Dunkerque. British fighters, based on the coast of Kent, were able to cover Dunkerque. Their range was sufficient to permit their flying over, remaining from thirty to forty-five minutes and then having to return for refueling. The Germans, having advanced at such speed as to outstrip their source of supply, were forced to base their aircraft far back, some even in Germany proper. As a result their bombers required a longer time to make the trips. A British fighter could make three trips covering Dunkerque while the Nazi bomber made one back to his base. As a result of the lack of bases and supplies, the Nazi fighters were not present in numbers. The British had temporary air command and used it to the fullest extent in defending the gallant remnants of their expeditionary force which huddled on the beach waiting to be taken off by vessels.

In Crete the situation was reversed. Bombing of the fighter bases was heavy before the attack had finally driven the fighters to the mainland. The Nazis had air command over the area. From German sources and from British accounts what followed as to the paratroop technique can be detailed.

As we have seen, first the bombers prepared the way with a crack-of-dawn attack concentrated on buildings and personnel shelter. Timed to the split second, a landing of troop carriers on the enemy field followed. Its capture resulted in a matter of minutes. Thus the Germans were possessed of a base, one which had good runways, for they carefully avoided bombing the field. They had no desire to spoil their landing place.

This establishment of the base was immediately followed by a concentrated paratroop attack. These paratroops were dropped from but a few hundred feet and their descent required few seconds. They were not suspended as targets long enough to suffer great losses.

In dropping from the planes the paratroopers lined up in the center aisle of the transport. At the command they stepped forward, snapped a catch onto a fastening in the frame of the door and then sprang into space. The snap they attached to the fastening was connected by a cable to the rip cord of their parachute. The moment that they were clear of the plane the cable came to its end, tautened and whipped the rip cord from its holdings. The parachute opened and down they floated.

The Nazis used special colors for certain of their parachutes. Those used by officers were of one color, the non-commissioned officers another. This permitted identification of these men by the troopers while still in the air and the instant they landed they unsnapped their own harness and darted to the point where the officers had landed. Here they assembled. Other colored parachutes carried down ammunition, machine guns, grenades, even light rapid-fire cannon in parts which could be quickly assembled. The paratroopers likewise were supplied with automatic weapons, such as sub-machine guns, by parachute. The speed of this attack is unbelievable. Within less than two to two and one-half minutes after leaving the plane these troops were in action, completely armed, machine guns, grenades and all.

Flying at low altitudes, paratroopers can be dropped with great accuracy. As a result full advantage can be taken of the terrain and it is often possible to drop them where they cannot be fired upon on the way down. Hills and valleys offer such cover for them. But it must not be thought that paratroops are defenseless while descending. They carry light submachine guns and are trained to fire with accuracy while coming down.

The United States Army is now training paratroopers and in the maneuvers held in the South during 1941 these men gave good evidence of their thorough training. It is a distinct tribute to the morale of the Army that this branch is composed entirely of volunteers and that there are a great many more volunteers than can be accepted.

The American paratrooper is first put through a thorough course of training in tumbling. This is essential. Often paratroops are required to drop in high winds. The parachute floats down through the air and is carried by the wind at approximately the same speed as the wind is blowing. If there is a twenty-miles-an-hour wind the paratrooper will strike the ground with a forward speed of about twenty miles an hour. Anyone who has ever dropped from a moving vehicle at ten or fifteen miles an hour can appreciate the difficulty of not taking a very heavy fall. In addition to this the paratrooper descends with the same speed that one acquires by jumping from a height of about ten feet. The force of the fall in calm weather is such that it is necessary to train the men to land with their knees bent and on the balls of their feet. Otherwise there is danger of sprained or broken ankles.

From this training in tumbling the men advance to making "captive" drops on a parachute tower. Here they are hoisted aloft on the tower suspended under an opened parachute which is guided down by a series of wires. As they reach the top of the tower the 'chute is automatically cut away from the hoisting cable.

From this the men are next introduced to actual drops.

During this training they are constantly studying the various weapons which they will use and the paratroop tactics.

The first "live jumps," that is, when they make their first jumps from a plane in flight, are from an altitude of some two to three thousand feet. Here they are equipped with two parachutes as a safety measure. One is the standard parachute pack they will use in service and another is attached to them so that in the event of failure of one they have a reserve.

In making these jumps the men do not pull the rip cord of the parachute themselves. The release ring of the parachute is attached to a cable which is sufficiently long to permit their falling clear of the plane before the parachute is opened.

It might be of interest to detail the working of the parachute. Modern "pack" types of parachutes are fitted into a canvas container about the size of the ordinary knapsack. Four flaps close the container or pack. These flaps have strong rubber cords attached to them and are held in place by a series of metal studs through which the prongs of the rip cord pass.

When the rip cord is pulled, the prongs are drawn from the holes in the metal studs and the flaps released. The rubber cords immediately pull them aside and the parachute pack is wide open. Folded in on the top of the carefully folded 'chute is a pilot 'chute. This is a small rectangular parachute which is forced open by steel springs somewhat in the same manner as an umbrella opens.

The pilot 'chute catches in the wind caused by the falling of the paratrooper and it immediately pulls the main parachute from the pack. The air rushes into the main parachute and it is forced open. The parachute does not open from the bottom as most people think. The air rushes in through the bottom opening and mushrooms the 'chute out at the top. The top fills and expands. This expansion rapidly flows downward until the entire 'chute is filled and it is extended wide open.

To ease the shock and the strain on the parachute as it fully opens and checks the fall of the paratrooper, an opening is placed in the top of the 'chute. This opening is pleated around its edges and has a strong rubber cord sewn into the perimeter. The pressure of the air when the 'chute first opens stretches the rubber cord and allows the opening to be enlarged. In this way more air is passed through the opening and the first strain of checking the fall is eased. As the speed of the fall decreases the rubber cord contracts with the lessened pressure and the hole closes still more, further checking the speed of descent. The hole is never fully closed as the flow of air through the parachute maintains it in its proper shape and prevents its folding on itself.

After training in jumping from two or three thousand feet the paratroops are brought lower and gradually they are flown down to an altitude of only a few hundred feet. This low altitude is necessary. It prevents the paratrooper's being in the air and under the fire of defenders for any period of time, and the men can be more accurately dropped on their objectives.

The American Army has adopted the colored parachute identification method for various weapons and supplies dropped. Service in the paratroop units is arduous. The training is intense and in addition to their parachute training the men must master every weapon used, the automatic weapons, antitank guns, grenades and so forth. They are also trained in taking cover, trained to act individually when necessary. Army authorities are enthusiastic about these new units. The initiative and resourcefulness that are a part of the American people make them ideally suited to this highly specialized form of warfare.

The paratroop carriers, large planes of the air-transport types, have an additional use which is highly important. After the Polish and Norwegian campaigns the Second World War settled down on the Western Front into a period of inaction which was jestingly referred to as the "sitzkrieg." The opposing armies sat in their positions facing one another and did little else. Then the blitzkrieg struck with stunning speed and force.

The French Ninth Army folded and the Allied line was ripped asunder like tissue. Through the gap poured the mechanized columns. They ran forward and spread out fanwise in every direction until the term "fluid" warfare was used to describe their movements. Confusion was everywhere behind the allied lines. Then the mechanized columns developed their real attack. They formed and turned on their objectives.

A column which had run through to the south suddenly turned abruptly to the west and darted for Abbéville and the coast of the English Channel. The Channel ports were endangered and the retreat of the British forces threatened. This mechanized column seemed headed for disaster, for it was operating at a fantastic distance from its base and any source of supply. How, asked the experts, could it support and sustain itself in enemy country?

The answer was by paratroop carriers. Using the identical technique which they used to drop weapons, ammunition and other supplies to paratroops, the Nazis dropped fuel and other supplies to their mechanized columns. These mechanized forces radioed their positions and informed their bases of their needs. Under a fighter escort carrier planes flew out, dived down over their positions and dropped the needed supplies.

For this type of service an extra-large and heavy parachute is used. The pack is opened in the same manner as is the pack of the paratrooper. The rip cord is attached to a cable and automatically pulled when the container of supplies is dropped. The supplies are packed in light metal containers, and the parachutes are designed so that these containers will not be descending at speeds which will damage their contents when they land. Where the need is great and the action too intense to risk the cumbersome carriers, this same container can be attached to a dive bomber and released.

In connection with the supplying of troops and mechanized columns from these carriers it is interesting to note that the Army Air Forces, working with the Civil Aeronautics Administration, are developing what are known as "landing strips" along our highways. Merely by widening the highway or by building a parallel strip to it, landing places can be established along all of our main arteries. In time of war this is an invaluable aid. It means that airborne supplies can be landed at points all over the country and at each of these points motor transportation can quickly distribute them to where they are needed. In this manner the carriers can be used to their full capacity for they do not need the added weight of the containers and the parachutes to deliver the supplies. The Germans, in their great system of super-highways, the "Autobahnen," * have constructed these strips. The roads, built as highways, are really military highways and designed for noth-

---

* *Autobahnen* (bähn′ĕn): auto roads.

ing else than the quick transportation of troops and supplies by auto transport.

The aerial carrier plane is a commercial type adapted for military use. Its chief value is its ability to carry heavy loads. Speed, although important, is secondary. These planes are not heavily armed and are not considered as combat types. They operate under the protection of fighter escorts where necessary.

We in the United States are particularly fortunate in having the world's best commercial air-line organization. It is provedly the most efficient and the largest. Our standard airliners can be transformed into carriers almost overnight. The paratroop carrier and supply carrier is merely a transport stripped of all its luxurious furnishings.

The seats are removed, the comforts and the fine furnishings disappear. They are replaced by light metal benches running the length of the cabin. Here sit the paratroops. If the carrier is not in service as a paratroop plane, the benches fold against the walls and make room for supplies.

Our civil pilots who fly the airliners are all thoroughly competent all-weather pilots. As a result we have ready a reserve of carrier pilots and planes that can operate in practically any type of weather, day or night. With but very little training or under the guidance of a trained paratroop officer these same pilots can maneuver their planes to drop our paratroopers wherever needed. Thus, in this newest and most spectacular method of warfare the United States is well prepared with pilots, planes and men.

TOPICS FOR DISCUSSION

1. Describe what happens from the time a man in a commercial plane with a parachute pack on his back jumps out of the door till he lands.

2. Do you think you would have the courage to step out into space 15,000 feet from the ground, count ten, and then pull the rip cord? Are many parachute jumpers killed because of failure to pull the cord?

3. Have you ever seen a pilot wearing a "caterpillar" badge? How does one gain membership in the Caterpillar Club? Do you have an ambition to join that club?

4. Which nations first made large military use of paratroops?

GRAB A PIECE OF THE SKY[1]

By Raoul Whitfield

THE lieutenant was mad—all six feet three of his lean body was filled with anger. It was a cold anger that showed in his dark eyes, and showed in his voice and in his choice of biting words.

"And so you didn't think it would hurt to cut across West Field? You were getting low on gas and your training crate was acting up and it was getting dark. And if you cut across the test field air you'd save time and get back here so that your nurse could give you a bottle and put you to bed—"

The lieutenant stopped, his dark eyes narrowed on the grey ones of Free Carson. He shrugged his shoulders. Eddie Blane, chief instructor at Blane Field, said nothing. Free forced a little smile.

"I didn't figure any test ships would be in the air," he said, his voice level. "I didn't think—"

"Right!" Lieutenant Ryder's voice was hard, sharp as the north wind hitting the field in the semi-darkness. "You *didn't* think. That's the trouble with a lot of kids. If you get up there by yourselves and something happens that isn't in the book—"

He broke off again, glaring at Free. Eddie Blane said quietly:

"Carson is one of our best young pilots, Lieutenant. He's getting a nice start. Soloed a month ago, and he's getting in a lot of time in the air."

The lieutenant smiled grimly. "Sure," he said slowly. "In the air over a government test field where he's not supposed to be. I come down out of thick stuff with a quarter million dollar job and there he is, in my way, wobbling along at about forty and cracking me five miles out of my way before I could back for a landing."

---

[1] From *Boys' Life*, July, 1941. Reprinted through the courtesy of the author and *Boys' Life*, published by the Boy Scouts of America. Copyright by the author.

Freeman Carson said quietly: "I'm sorry but I was getting a little worried about—"

"So am I," snapped the army lieutenant. "Worried about a private training school being so close to a test field that's important. And worried about wobbly crates getting in the sky close to bombers testing at better than three hundred an hour."

Eddie Blane kept his voice low. It was almost dark on the surface of the field now.

"It won't happen again, Lieutenant," he said. "I'll speak to all the students, make sure they give you plenty of room up above."

Lieutenant Ryder kicked at grass with his booted foot. Then he pointed a browned finger at Free.

"Me, I'm not so sure you'll *ever* be much of a flyer," he said slowly. "But one thing I'm telling you—I don't want to watch you learning. I don't want to see you wobble that crate near me in the air again. I've got enough grief, as it is. If I catch you over West Field—"

He stopped, let his hand drop. A spit of rain slapped against Free Carson's hot cheek. He fought for control, and kept it. And Eddie Blane's calm eyes were quieting him.

It *had* been a close thing. Lieutenant Ryder had dropped the big, two-prop bomber out of the clouds like a grey streak and Free had been high-tailing for home right in his path. The training crate had felt the prop wash of the big job; it had been that close.

"It was sort of an emergency," Blane was saying. "Carson felt he was in a spot and had to get in. The bad weather came on in a hurry. And maybe you're a bit air fagged, Lieutenant."

The tall lieutenant grunted, faced toward the roadster in which he had driven over from the government test field.

"I know—I know," he muttered. "He's had thirty hours in the air, he's still hanging on to the stick with both hands expecting the engine to drop out of the crate."

Free started to speak, but Eddie Blane shook his head quickly. Lieutenant Ryder faced him.

"I won't report you this time. But you'd better start using your head soon or you won't have any. Or any wings, either." His eyes were frowning; they looked tired.

Free Carson's grey eyes were narrow. "Tomorrow," he said

steadily, "I'll grab a piece of sky off to the south, away from West Field."

The lieutenant snorted. "Tomorrow," he replied, "I'm flying to Washington. You can grab a piece of sky anywhere else. But take a tip, pack some brains along with you. If you don't the time'll come when you'll be grabbing for that piece of sky and not hanging on!"

The lieutenant nodded to Eddie Blane, frowned at Free, and walked rapidly toward his car. Eddie watched a couple of the mechanics rolling the training ship toward a hangar. Then he turned toward Free.

"The Lieutenant's working pretty hard at testing," he said quietly. "He's had maybe a half million air hours and he's beginning to forget that he ever had to learn himself. Don't let that bawling-out get you down, Free. He needs a rest, an air rest, for a while. But you keep away from West Field."

Free Carson frowned up at the dark sky. "You can count on that, Chief," he said grimly. "I'll crack up before I wing over her air again. But he didn't have to give me the idea I might— never be a flyer—"

Eddie Blane grunted. "Forget it," he breathed. "You had a ship that was acting up, and some bad weather. You got in. You busted a rule and nearly had a mid-air smash. But the point is you didn't *have* it. You'll never tangle with Ryder again."

They walked toward the Administration Office in the light rain.

"Not if I see the lieutenant first," Free said very softly.

The trouble was that he did not see the lieutenant first. As a matter of fact he did not see Ryder at all until the racy little ship taxied alongside of his training crate on the Phoenix field. He was staring at her sweet stream-lining when the single prop stopped swinging and the tall army man slid back the fuselage cover and hopped to the ground. He started toward the training plane, then pulled up short as Free dropped from the cabin and faced him.

"You—again!" he said slowly and with plenty of disgust in his voice. "It's a wonder you didn't chase me to Washington and get in my way there."

Free moved close to the lieutenant. He was large for his

seventeen years; his shoulders were broader than Ryder's. But the army man towered over him. Free Carson had been doing cross country, a lot of hours in a slow plane over a lot of desert air miles. He was tired.

"What did I do *this* time, Lieutenant?" he asked as quietly as he could.

Ryder's eyes were colder and narrower than they had been almost a week ago. He looked wearily beyond Free at the trainer which was parked nearby.

"How many times did you circle this field before you came in?" he said slowly.

Free said: "Four. It's the first time I've ever seen the field. There was a T.W.A. plane coming in from the east I wanted to give her plenty of room."

The lieutenant groaned. "You held me off there—" he gestured to the west—"for a half hour while you practiced banks over the field."

Free said: "Wait a minute, Lieutenant. This Loring Trainer may be slow compared to the ships you test. But she isn't *that* slow. And I didn't see you."

A few of the ground crew men had drifted up and were standing around grinning. Lieutenant Ryder cut in sarcastically.

"That's twice you haven't seen me. And I'm beginning not to like it."

Free said: "You began not to like it last week. What you need is—"

He stopped. Ryder had straightened and his eyes were small, dark slits. There was a heavy silence, broken by the distant drone of a ship in the sky.

"What I need—" The lieutenant's voice was sharp, questioning. The ground crew men had stopped smiling.

Free Carson tried to keep his voice level. "What you need is a private piece of sky," he said, slowly. "A lot of it. Then you can—"

He broke off as the lieutenant started toward him. His lips set tightly and his hands were clenched at his sides. But Ryder halted a few feet from him, got control of himself. He smiled, and it wasn't a pleasant smile.

"Out of the mouths of babes!" he breathed and spread his

hands in a helpless gesture. "A half a dozen air hours and they start telling you all about—"

He broke off. "Okay, men, fill her up, will you? Never mind a check. I've got to get into West Field by dark."

Free stood motionless, weariness fighting his anger. It was Ryder's exaggeration that infuriated him. He said as quietly as he could:

"It's fifty air hours. And I didn't design the trainer and make her slow. And I didn't come out here to get in your way—"

The lieutenant faced him. "You'd get in *anybody's* way," he cut in. "You're the type."

He turned his back on Free and moved toward the racy little ship he was flying westward. One of the mechanics came up to Free, smiling a little.

"You were all right, Pilot," he said softly. "He was winging in low, right off the ground. And that little combat ship is fast and well camouflaged. You didn't hold him off long."

Free was frowning. "We nearly had an air crash a week ago," he explained. "And now, with all the sky in the country—"

The mechanic's smile widened. "He's sort of tough, anyway," he said. "But he's a sweet test pilot. He's been working pretty hard on all types. Maybe he needs a rest."

Free tried to smile. "I wish he'd take it," he said slowly. "The sky doesn't seem to be big enough for the two of us."

A helmeted motorcycle rider pulled close to the two of them. He spoke to Free.

"Administration Office wants to see the pilot of the Loring Trainer, Free Carson. There's a message from Blane Field. Came through an hour ago. Important."

Free nodded. The frown remained on his sun-burned face. The mechanic pointed out the Administration Building which stood apart from the hangars.

"Go ahead, Free," he said. "We'll roll your ship back near the hangar."

"Thanks."

As he started along the deadline Free heard Lieutenant Ryder's voice, heavy with sarcasm.

"Think you've got a powerful enough tractor to move that kite, Mister?"

Free Carson kept walking, didn't look back. He had spent six hours in the air since dawn and at his stage of the flying game that was a lot of hours. But he could lay over in Phoenix tonight, sleep at the field and hop westward for Los Angeles at the crack of dawn.

The field manager shook hands with him cordially. He was a middle-aged man named Keyes.

"Chief pilot at your field—Blane—called us over an hour ago. Wants you to call him back. Says its important."

He led Free to the phone in his office and a couple of minutes later Eddie Blane's voice came over the wire.

"Got through okay? Nice work, Free. Tell you why I called. Bender cracked up a trainer around noon, a bum landing. Didn't get hurt, just bruised. We've got two ships off the line for engine work. And I just had notice that a couple of Civil Authorities inspectors are coming out to look us over tomorrow morning. Think you'll have to wing in this afternoon, Free."

Free started to protest, but didn't. He'd bucked a head wind all the way to Phoenix, but that meant he would have it on his tail flying west. That is, he would if it did not change.

Blane said: "Can do? Nothing wrong, is there?"

Free said: "Can do, Chief. Nothing wrong; nothing except that I bumped into Lieutenant Ryder again. He's at this field now."

He heard Blane whistle. "Something else, Free. He reported you to Civil Authorities for winging over the test field. They want to talk to you tomorrow."

Free stiffened. He gripped the phone apparatus tightly.

"That was pretty rotten, Chief. He said he wouldn't report me."

Blane's voice was calm over the wire. "Well, he must have changed his mind. Anyway, load up with gas and drift back this way. You got good weather reports. Plenty of visibility. Check at your end. But you can make it by dark. Watch the mountains, and there's a field at Riverside—"

"I know." Free cut in impatiently. "Okay, Chief, I'll get them started on the gas."

Blane said: "Keep out of Ryder's way. He's a crack test pilot and against him your word isn't worth much. Keep clear."

Free said hotly: "I can't run all over the sky staying away from him—"

The chief pilot's voice was sharp. "You do as I tell you. You may be grounded, as it is. Keep away from him."

When Free hung up he saw that Keyes was watching him closely, a smile on his face.

"Trouble with the Army?" he asked cheerfully. "Don't let it get you down. They're a pretty busy outfit these days, and they don't like anything to get in their way."

Free forced a smile but he wasn't feeling that way. He checked on weather and headed back along the dead-line. When the ground gang started refueling the trainer he stood a short distance away, stretching his arms and legs. Lieutenant Ryder came out of a hangar and moved toward him and Free muttered to himself: "Steady, now, let *him* do the talking."

A heavy tractor came along the dead-line, towing a transport plane. Free backed out of its path.

"Want me to get out of your way, Carson?"

Free swung around and his anger got the best of him.

"Just as you like, Lieutenant," he snapped. "You might report me for walking into you on a dead-line. Only this isn't a government test field and I'm not in the army. And—"

"That's right." Ryder was smiling nastily. "You're not in the army and you're not likely to be. It seems to me that if you're in anything it's a daze."

Free's grey eyes were on the lieutenant's dark ones. His body was tense.

"I read that the army needed test pilots badly," he said as steadily as he could. "They must."

He watched the jaw muscles of Ryder tighten. The lieutenant half raised his right arm and for a split second Free thought the officer was going to swing. But the arm dropped to his side. And Free was calmer now.

"You've been riding me since we nearly tangled in the air," he said quietly. "Back at the school field and now here. You're going to keep it up, if you get the chance. And if you don't *get* the chance I suppose you'll *make* the chance. You said you wouldn't report me and you lied."

Ryder said: "Easy! I don't like that! I didn't report you."

Free stared at the lieutenant. And suddenly Ryder laughed. It was a low, unpleasant laugh. He looked straight at Free Carson, down at him, shook his head slowly.

"I wouldn't ground you, Carson," he said slowly, almost softly. "I don't *have* to. You'll never grab that hunk of sky, it isn't in you. You'll ground yourself!"

He turned abruptly away from Free, followed along behind the tractor and the big plane, toward his own ship. Free stood very still, watching his tall figure and hearing his words. "You'll never grab that hunk of sky—"

There was another gust of hot wind and it had force. It rocked Free a little. But he paid no attention to it. He was shaking and for the first time he really hated Ryder.

Keyes wandered over to the cabin training ship as Free was checking the last of the fuel. He held a small slip of paper in his left hand.

"Flight Eight out of Los Angeles reports a local storm over the Sierra Madre mountains," he said. "Local but seems to be picking up. You may have to wing clear of it, over west."

Free nodded. "Thanks," he replied.

"You can take off when you're ready. Use the north-south runway. The sky's clear."

Free glanced at Lieutenant Ryder's ultra stream-lined plane, down the dead-line fifty feet. The field manager followed his gaze.

"That combat ship of Ryder's won't take off for an hour or so. She does better than three hundred. Be home before you are, at that."

Free nodded, his grey eyes half closed. "That's all right with me," he said quietly. "I'm getting in air time. The more they write in the book for me the better."

Keyes smiled. "True enough, Pilot. She's a nice little crate, this trainer." He looked her over with his keen eyes. "And one thing nice—she doesn't need a mile runway to land on—not with her speed."

Free Carson shook hands with the field manager. "I'll set down a faster one, some day soon," he replied. "And that'll feel good, too."

Keyes grinned. "I'll be looking for you. And remember that Flight Eight report on the storm—"

Free climbed inside the tiny cabin, waved a hand. He warmed up the engine for a minute or so, taxied out to the north-south runway and took off to the south, into a gusty wind. There were only a few clouds in the sky. When he got altitude he circled to the west. The sky on the horizon was smudged with black. Looking down he got a final glimpse of the Phoenix field and Lieutenant Ryder's racy combat type on the dead-line.

He breathed: "I wish he'd swung at me—" Then his lips set in a tight line. Perhaps he would be grounded, but he didn't want Eddie Blane and the flying school to get in trouble. Not because of him. He frowned, shaking his head. He wondered why Ryder had denied reporting him. It wasn't going to be a pleasant session tomorrow, but at least he could tell the truth. But the Civil Authorities outfit could be tough. So many planes in the air these days—so many trying wings, learning—

He relaxed in the narrow seat, made his chute pack more comfortable. The exhaust beat was steady, monotonous. Through the head-set came the buzz of the beam, which he didn't need. He was winging home the shortest way, not as he had flown to the eastward. He was tired and there was dull anger inside of him. His altitude was three thousand, five hundred, and with the tail wind he was doing better than ninety. Everything in the sky was pretty good, except far ahead on the western horizon. There the smudge of black was growing. And the sun was beginning to swing low.

He muttered to himself: "I'll fool him—I'll grab such a *big* piece of sky for myself—"

He had stiffened in the seat back of the stick, tightened his hold on the rubber grip of the metal. Again he forced himself to relax. The little trainer banged along through the sky, toward the blackening, western horizon. Free watched it wearily, glancing at the desert below, from time to time. The air was getting cooler and he commenced to feel bumps. After a time the mountains became clearer and he banked a little to the north. There was no sun and the sky was getting steadily rougher.

He climbed at a mild angle and had seven thousand feet when he caught the first flash of lightning south-west of his course. It looked as though the storm was breaking up, but over the mountains a storm could be tricky. At eight thousand he leveled off and straightened in the cabin seat as his eyes picked up the other plane. She was streaking westward, to the north of him. It was almost as though the trainer was standing still in the sky. A stream-lined beauty, she was, with Lieutenant Ryder at the stick.

Free muttered: "If I piloted *that* baby I couldn't *help* but grab sky. She's a sweet job."

His grey eyes were narrowed on the streaking army plane and the next flash of lightning startled him by its nearness. Ryder was banking to the northward; it seemed as though the combat type ship whipped through the darkening sky. Free banked after her; there was a broken spot in the storm, to the north and the pass could be picked up in case of emergency. The wind was no longer on the trainer's tail and she was in rough going. Free pulled back on the stick and climbed another five hundred feet. Death Valley was to the east now and north of it would be Mount Whitney, some fourteen thousand feet above sea level. But he was topping the mountains in the vicinity, at eight thousand, five hundred.

The storm was closing in rapidly; the break toward which both Ryder and he were winging had faded into an ugly yellow color. Lightning was brilliant and constant and there was the first streaking of rain on the glass in front of him.

He breathed: "I can turn back—"

But that would mean that a storm had licked him. A local storm, about which he had been warned. And it might mean that he could not get to Blane Field before late morning if he was held up all night on some strange field or made a forced landing. Ryder was trying to slip through, to get over the mountains.

The Loring Trainer rocked in the grip of the storm and the lightning flare hurt Free's eyes. His vision was so bad he was almost flying blind. The throttle was wide open and the force of the storm seemed to be from the west. A particularly savage lift of storm wind tossed the trainer nastily and battered Free in the cabin seat. He snapped his safety belt tight, moved his head nearer the windshield glass. The altimeter showed less than eight thousand feet; she had dropped off too much.

There was a blinding flash of lightning and he heard the roar of thunder above the drone of the trainer's engine. The cabin plane was lifted and flung off on her right wing and Free lost more altitude getting her out of what might have become a spin. He muttered: "No go—got to run back out of it!"

He banked around; the rain ceased abruptly to beat against the cabin glass. Visibility wasn't much; he could pick up a darkening but still blue stretch of sky to the south-east. He had been a fool to try to follow Lieutenant Ryder, to try to slip through a tricky mountain storm. A slow training crate wasn't that sort of sailor.

There was a streak of lightning too close to the ship. Below he could see mountain slopes and the crest of one of the mountains was only a few thousand feet below. But the air action was calmer now, though he was being slammed about in the cabin. He held the metal stick with both hands; there was no beat of rain on glass but it was growing steadily darker.

And then a shape cut down ahead of him, not more than an eighth of a mile away. It was a plane shape, a ship going down in a wide, shallow bank. A ship whose propeller didn't have engine power behind it. Ryder's ship!

For a second Free Carson thought his eyes were playing tricks. But the wind-shield was clear of rain and even in the darkening sky he could recognize the super stream-lining of the lieutenant's plane.

Instinctively he nosed the trainer down; Ryder's dead-prop ship flashed past on his right. The slide cover of the combat type was back; Free could see Ryder's bare head. He had an arm out in the open; it made a sharp motion. The lieutenant was going down, but he was waving Free off, waving him on.

Free Carson was straight in the cabin seat now. His mind was working fast; already there were slopes of mountains on either side of Ryder's ship. She was no longer banking, there wasn't room. Ryder was taking her down in a shallow dive, down toward the floor of a narrow valley that cut east and west through the mountains.

Free cut throttle speed, followed Ryder down. He saw pine

tree shapes twist up past the trainer, saw once again Ryder's arm out in the open, pointing toward the sky, motioning him violently on.

And Free laughed grimly. It was as though Ryder was saying: "Grab yourself a piece of sky—get away from me—"

But Free was thinking fast. The floor of the valley was narrow; he could see a stream winding along it. Near the stream there was one fairly level stretch, but even that was dotted with small trees, baby pine and cedar. And that stretch was Ryder's only chance. And he had a ship that must land fast, much too fast for the surface below. When she tore through those trees, even though he could stall her some—

Free breathed: "Mister, if *you* can get down there *I* can. *I* can get down anyway, and if you crack up—"

That was the one big thought. There was not much about the lieutenant that he liked. But Ryder was in a tough spot and Free was going to be in it with him. There was no grabbing sky now. He was going to grab dirt, back of Ryder.

He groaned as he watched the speed with which the combat plane skimmed pine and leveled off for a landing. The valley was protected from the force of the storm; there was no rain. The winding stream was very narrow. Free throttled all the way down as he came in behind Ryder. He muttered:

"Why didn't he bail out and let her go down alone?"

He thought he knew the answer to that one, even as he breathed the question. A test job—months of work behind the plane. A defense program that needed the ship. Ryder was a fighter. And there was a chance, even for a pilot with overstrained nerves.

Free leveled the trainer off and picked a fairly clear spot on the right bank of the stream. He flashed a glance at the combat plane and saw that Ryder was trying to stall. Her nose was up, and then dropping. Free stalled the trainer; she had very little forward speed. He cut the engine switch as her wheels and tail skid hit. It was a sweet landing, but not sweet enough. There was a crunching sound as the landing gear tore loose. A wing ripped along the uneven ground, twisted up some low growth. Free's head swung against cabin glass.

He couldn't see very well as he shook off the stunning sensation of the crack. His hands fumbled at the cabin door, and when he got it open his safety belt held him. He tore at the buckle, got it loose. When he hit the ground he staggered and almost fell. There was blood on his left temple as he ran unsteadily ahead of the trainer.

He called out weakly as he got close to the army plane. She was a bad wreck, flung half across the mountain stream. There was a sharp explosion as Free got near her—she was burning!

He called as loudly as he could: "Ryder!"

The flames were roaring already and Free could feel the first heat as he moved unsteadily closer. And then he saw Ryder, on the far side of the ship. He was cut, too, and he was staggering into the stream, back toward the wreckage!

Free called: "No—Ryder—stay off!"

And then he was splashing across the shallow stream, hardly feeling the icy water. It was as though Ryder had not heard him. There was a second explosion. Free half fell in the water as bits of the burning ship dropped about him. But he moved on, reached the opposite bank. Ryder was staggering close to the flaming plane.

The heat was pretty bad as Free reached the lieutenant's side. The officer stared at him blankly and when Free swung him around he struck weakly with his right arm. Then Free was dragging him clear of the burning wreckage, staggering through the shallow water to the bank, moving slowly under Ryder's weight toward the protection of pine trees. Rain struck against Free's face but he hardly noticed it. He was dead tired, but for some reason he felt pretty swell inside. For once, where Ryder was concerned, he'd played the right hunch, done the *right* thing.

They were lying side by side beneath a shelter of pine boughs that Free had fixed up. They had blankets from the training ship and some chocolate to chew on. Lieutenant Ryder spoke in a low, tired voice.

"I didn't report you, Carson. That's one thing nasty I didn't do. Some one on the ground at the Field saw you that afternoon and made the report. But—" He managed a faint grin. "I can square you on that. I see how tired I was—must have been—these last few weeks. Too much air testing under too much pressure. And my nerves were breaking. I was taking it out on you, I guess." He turned his head toward Free, "you sensed I was cracking up. You came down after me and with that crack in the head that I got I'd have wandered right back into the burning plane. I've seen that happen."

Free chewed on a piece of chocolate. "I couldn't figure how you got that ship behind me. You were winging north—"

Ryder grunted. "Engine started missing, storm was tougher than I figured. I climbed and turned back. Then she just went dead. They haven't got 'em yet so they won't do that. Feed line break—clogged gas—don't suppose we'll ever know just what it was. But the Army's got the designs and they can crack out another. I figured maybe if I stuck with her I could save her. But she sets down too fast."

Free nodded. "I can get the trainer off from here, maybe. Or we can dismantle her and pack her out. They'll spot us from the air tomorrow, when it gets light. We got a break—just a couple of head bangs and some bruises—we'll both be reported missing and they'll be along." He stopped, frowned. "Eddie needed the ship."

Lieutenant Ryder said softly. "Sure he did, Carson. And the army needed mine. But it's easier to put a ship in the sky than a pilot." He was silent for a few seconds and there was only the sound of wind through the pine. "That's where I was so dead wrong, Carson—going after you the way I did."

Free said: "Skip it. I could have got back that day without winging across the test field."

Lieutenant Ryder chuckled. "Maybe," he said. "But I owe you a big one for *today,* Pilot. That was a sweet piece of flying, the way you walked her in here. You could have gone on, you know, grabbed yourself a piece of sky."

Free said: "It was one time I didn't want it."

Lieutenant Ryder nodded. "And am I glad," he said fervently.

Free Carson just lay quietly, his eyes closed. He felt very tired and very good inside.

DISCUSSION

1. Explain the situation as it is when the story opens with three men talking: Lieutenant Ryder, Free Carson, and Eddie Blane.

2. Were your sympathies with Lieut. Ryder or Carson up to and through the Phoenix incident?

3. Up to that time did you expect Carson to find a chance to clear himself and win Ryder's respect?

4. What do they mean when they say pilots are harder to replace than planes? How much does it cost to train an Army or Navy pilot? What do planes cost?

5. Is the story convincing or does it seem "made up" to come out right?

A MILLION MODELMAKERS[1]

By Ernest Gamache

(Executive Director, Air Youth of America [2])

WHEN Dick Everett of Hampton, West Virginia, became interested in building model airplanes he never suspected that his hobby would shape his career. He thought only of the pleasure he found in building and flying his own planes; today he is one of fifty model builders, all between the ages of 18 and 20, employed in the government research laboratory at Langley Field building and testing scale models of actual planes.

For years Dick has been active in the association of model builders in his home state and he has built and flown all types of model planes. Last summer he competed in the contest held at the National Aviation Forum at Bolling Field, Washington. He flew a stick model, a cabin rubber-powered model, and a Class "A" gas job. Piling up the highest number of points as the best all-around-performer in the contest, Dick won an airline trip to the nationals held in Chicago in July, where he turned in some excellent performances. He has held the national record for a R.O.W. stick model (that's a rise-off-water model, in case you don't know) and he builds from original designs, having worked out a Wakefield type model of his own this summer.

A short time ago the United States government through its official aviation research bureau, the NACA (National Advisory Committee on Aviation), announced that jobs were open for expert model builders. Dick took the examinations,

---

[1] From *Boys' Life,* copyright by the publishers. Reprinted through the courtesy of the author and *Boys' Life,* published by the Boy Scouts of America.

[2] Air Youth of America, with headquarters at 17 Jackson Place, Washington, D. C., is an organization to promote interest in aviation among young people.

and passed with flying colors thus securing a job in which he is making a real contribution to the basic aviation research that has made and is keeping the United States the pioneer in aviation.

Dick's boss, Dr. George W. Lewis, Director of Research of NACA, has written the foreword to a new book, "Building and Flying Model Airplanes," published for Air Youth of America. About the work of Dick and the boys associated with him at Langley Field he says "many of them have had no training other than that afforded by their experience as model builders and a high school education. They had been selected not only for their manual skill and versatility but for their initiative, originality and resourcefulness in developing new ideas."

With the world becoming air conscious and dramatic developments in the sky stirring the imagination and interest of boys everywhere model building and flying has become the hobby of more than a million American boys according to a recent survey. Nor is the interest in model building and flying confined to boys, for adults share in it too; men already a part of the great aviation industry. Transport pilots, plane designers and engineers the country over—not to mention the builders of scale models and wind tunnel models who are now at work in many of the big aircraft plants in the country, find pleasure and profit in model building.

To work with and help these model enthusiasts in every way possible the organization known as Air Youth of America has been founded by Winthrop Rockefeller who long ago realized the value, both to the nation and to the boys themselves, of the tremendous enthusiasm of these million modelmakers. Air Youth of America is a central organization developed to inspire and to help model enthusiasts in America. The objective is three-fold: recreation, education and vocational guidance. In recreation—To encourage model plane building and flying as a wholesome hobby and sport, particularly among boys of limited opportunity. In education—To provide junior aviation materials for use in public and private schools and through the training of teachers and youth leaders. In vocational guidance—To serve, to a limited extent, as a source of information for young people who wish to plan careers in aviation.

The sponsors and National Council of Air Youth of Amer-

Courtesy of Brown Brothers, New York

A seminar at Randolph Field, Texas, with an army instructor using a model airplane to illustrate his point

ica include such well-known figures as James E. West, Chief Executive of the Boy Scouts of America; Captain E. V. Rickenbacker, the noted flyer; Lowell Thomas, Dr. John W. Studebaker, and other men of national importance.

At a recent meeting of the National Council of Air Youth, Mr. Paul McNutt, Administrator of the Federal Security Agency, the bureau that coordinates the government's youth work, gave voice to the value which he, as a member of our national government, places on the activities of the million modelmakers in America.

"The drive that finally put the Wright brothers into the air is not dead," Mr. McNutt said. "Today model aeroplane building ranks first among the hobbies of the 30,000,000 American boys and girls of school age. Many a school has a workshop better equipped for experiment than the bicycle shop laboratory of the Wrights. There is scarcely an ingenious boy in America who cannot duplicate, in model, their feats, or who cannot, through such an organization as Air Youth of America, demonstrate far more advanced principles of flight for every type of plane. The American boy who goes down into his basement workshop to build a model—let us say one of the five models that Air Youth of America has designed—may not realize that he is demonstrating for his own amusement things which learned scientists declared were quite impossible.

"Among these boys who go in for model building we find the likeliest prospects for apprentice training. The magic of the air is by no means making them all ambitious to be pilots. Many are taking the courses in our high schools and vocational schools. Many are building models and organizing clubs who have no special desire to fly themselves. From the boys and girls of America now engaged in model building will come our mechanics and designers, dopers, skin fitters, angle benders, bumper hands, anodic operators, pattern makers, parachute packers, and airline hostesses of the future."

An Exhibit of Model Planes

So many students have already had experience in modelbuilding that two or three class periods might well be spent in arranging an exhibit of model planes. Some have perhaps gone into the miniature-engine type of plane. Bring in all kinds. Bring all the books of instruction you have. Let the students tell of the problems they have met and of their disappointments and successes. If there are enough planes to exhibit, they might be displayed for the public to see them either at school or in a display window in a business building. Have charts, drawings, photographs, books, and planes arranged in an attractive display, with students in charge to explain the exhibit. And, best of all, a contest of the planes in flight may be arranged.

SUGGESTED FILM

Youth Trains for Aviation is a one-reel sound film which shows how air-minded youth are learning the fundamental principles of flight through building and flying model airplanes. Bray Pictures Corporation, 729 Seventh Avenue, New York, rents and sells this film.

ARMAGEDDON [1]

By Robert Nathan

YOU multitudinous Angels, great Cherubs, broadwinged
    Seraphs,
  Raphael, dark Azrael, Michael of the sword, Gabriel,
Speak with the hollow trumpet, cry from the storm clouds,
    tell us
How goes the battle now?
               It is an old war,
Gods against giants, Gog and Magog, the Titans,
Lucifer, falling, falling, burning across the heavens,
Searching the dark with doubt. The angels hunted him down.
Now evil itself is ranged and marshaled against us.
How quickly mortals forget.
             In their peaceful valleys,
In the fresh spring of the year, with the air like honey around
    them,
See how slowly they move, drowsy, clinging to summer,
Under the orchard spell. Or huddled to fires in winter,
Fearful, with backward glances, questioning and uncertain,
Heaven is peace, they say.
          But this is the war against evil,
Man's enemy too and God's, the soul's implacable foe.
Not for oceans alone, not for harbors and rivers,
Not for the use of mines, not for valleys of wheat.
What will the valleys be like if the light goes down on the
    hills?
If the cold comes down forever? If the spirit of man is slain?
But men are quick to forget.
           They forget the fury,
The son set against father, the children killed at their prayers,
The used and stolen women, the poison set in the heart,
The ramparts stormed with lies.

---

[1] From *Harpers Magazine*, May, 1942. Copyright by the author.

They cry for peace in the night, for truce in the midst of
battle.
There is no peace in heaven, the Seraphim make no truce.
This is the Armageddon, there is a sword in the sky.
Oh take it and hold it.
Harden the heart against evil forever and ever. Harden the
mind
Against the corruptible soft. Never say peace.
Never forget the fury, the dark, incredible malice.
Never forgive the evil. Never forget and forgive it.

WINGS OF GOLD[1]

By Boone T. Guyton

THE following selection is a narrative account of the training course for a naval pilot.

*   *   *   *   *

I heard you—you wanted to fly a fighter. You want to sport a pair of wings, roar through the sky at 200 knots, dive, roll, loop, and listen to the cheering crowds as they acclaim you a second Lindbergh. You want to be a Navy Pilot.

Well, so did I. I had visions of hurtling out of a blue sky, riding serenely behind a roaring power plant, to land my snarling little fighter in front of a crowd of gaping, staring laymen. Maybe you can get a similar picture. Maybe you think you are a rare physical specimen. All right, I'll try to give you an idea of what you need to fly for the Navy, and what you go through at a training school before you can expose to the world a pair of gold wings, why some get through and why more don't.

Take it from me, these birds you see caressing a pair of Navy wings earned and deserve them. Their ability does not stop with mere manipulation of the controls. They know all the essentials of flight, the art of applying sense and precise judgment, the timely grasp of an uncanny situation. That much I know now, after three years of flying over the blue waters of the Pacific, over the Rocky Mountains, and cross-country to the East Coast, down the Midwestern plains and rolling hills to the Gulf of Mexico, and over the sand dunes of Florida. There is more to flying for Uncle Sam than kicking a rudder or jamming a throttle. . . .

We were still in college when the letter came out—one year of training, three years with the fleet as a flying cadet and a $1500 bonus. It sounded mighty good. I signed the necessary

[1] From *American Magazine*, October, 1939. Copyright by the author.

Courtesy of Consolidated Aircraft Corporation

Bombers in high-flight formation

papers, and just three weeks later with a college song still fresh in my memory, I marched up the tiled steps of the Naval Reserve Air Base in St. Louis, confident that I could make history —well, at least a good loop.

At the desk a man took the papers and pointed to a door marked "Medical Doctor." "In there," he said, "and they will take care of you."

They did. Five other applicants, stripped to the waist, were lined up against the wall. All six of us had gone in that little white room with all of the dapper conceit accrued to football stars. Only one of us came out with just a breath of egotism left. That was I. Why, I do not know for sure. The other five would be any coach's dream for meat and muscle, but just one little thing wasn't there.

The average eligibles from this test are about three out of twenty, and you can forget the four letters you made on the varsity at old Pottsville, because they don't mean a thing. Whether you start flying for Uncle Sam or not depends on the ocular refractive errors, balance of ocular muscles, mental stability, sense of depth perception, and a score of other technical physical necessities.

I was spun around in a chair until my hair was curly. Then someone yelled, "Sit up straight!" Whereupon I promptly fell against the wall. We read figures, pulled parallel sticks together, said "Ah." They call it the "medical knockout," which is why three all-conference giants and a rugged-looking boxer were rejected.

After the tests the commanding officer took me in hand. "Your elimination starts Monday," he said. "We send two of you first four cadets to Pensacola after one month here. There is where your real work begins."

I signed some more papers and went out. Amidst the brilliance of the field floodlights a big Douglas transport was settling down gently on the paved runway. That was nearly three years ago, but I still stop to watch these big planes come in with the grace of a dove alighting on a green lawn. After more than a thousand hours of flying numerous planes in numerous places it is still thrilling.

So we started out. There were to be thirty days of indoctrination, in which we were to learn the rudiments of Navy life, etiquette in the service, a touch of radio practice, and enough flying to prove our ability to solo a plane safely. My instructor was a young lieutenant who had been through the mill, and he could handle a plane with cool precision. He was standing by the training plane, a Curtiss Fledgling, when I walked up.

"Ever been up?" he queried, flipping his cigarette away and sizing me up with an easy glance.

"No, sir."

Ten minutes of discussion about controls and instruments, and we were ready to take off. Flinging the parachute over his shoulder, he continued talking as he buckled it:

"All you have to do this hour is follow me through on the controls. If I want you to take it I'll tell you through the gosport." (A gosport is a helmet with earphones attached, through which the instructor makes you blush, quiver, or swear, at will. You can't talk back.) "Relax, and don't get nervous."

I climbed in somehow and fastened the safety belt. The green light flashed, and a shuddering throb gripped the old plane as the throttle went home. The runway dropped away, and the nose looked for a cloud. Up we went smoothly and easily until the altimeter read 3000 feet. I hung on all the way, holding the stick like a vise when the word came, marveling at the man who sat before me, while watching and wondering how he landed so easily when we came down.

There are ten more hops like this first one, each one a little more exacting, until the student is ready either to wash out or to solo. You start with the flippers and master them to some extent. Then comes the rudder, the throttle—and your head. It's really wonderful how much you can do without using your head. How the instructor stood for all the mistakes I made over and over is beyond me. My head seemed to be just another piece of bone. Sometimes we would get back on the ground after a hop and he would merely wrinkle up his stubby nose, shake his head, and stroll off muttering.

I was shaking all over as the skipper of the squadron climbed into the little yellow crate for my final check and signaled that he was ready for me to demonstrate my ability to keep him out of the hospital. We went caroming down the runway. It was do or die now—Pensacola or home. It seemed as if a whole lifetime of precious dreams would slip right through my fingers if something went wrong. The windshield turned into a moving picture of a boy with a suitcase walking down a lonely street—going home a failure. If I could just stop shaking!

A check consists roughly of a complete examination in the air. I say "rough" because it adds up to that. The check pilot says, "Do this," and you do it—roughly. Emergencies, landings, slips, fishtails, and all the rest come up in a single hour. If you pass, the check is called an "up." If you bust, it's a "down."

At 4000 feet the throttle was jerked closed. I stuck the nose down and headed for what appeared to be a nice, smooth wheat field covered with waving grain. At 1000 feet some smoke from a chimney gave the wind direction, and I slipped down to the edge of the field, kicked her into an easy skid, and leveled off to land. The head up in the front cockpit nodded; the gun went back on with a quivering blast; and we shot upward again. Back at the airport I made a bouncing good landing, taxied cautiously up to the chocks, and cut the switch. Then I crossed two hands full of fingers and waited.

The skipper hopped down and dropped his chute. "Okay, Guyton!"

Forty-eight hours later two happy young men boarded a Dixie-bound train. My roommate from college was one, I was the other. Sinking into the green cushions, we decided we were about the luckiest two people in the world. As I look back now, I laugh to think how little we knew what was in store for us.

As the train pulled into the little depot we jumped off into a blaze of Florida sunshine. All around us stretched flat, white sandy country topped with small dunes and covered with scrubby blackjack or scrub oak.

"Where to, gents?" asked a taxi driver.

We tried to assume a natural nonchalance. "Naval Air Station."

"This is my fourth trip out there today," he said. "I take 'em out as they come and bring 'em back if they don't make the grade."

He couldn't discourage us with that line. We were interested in a formation that just hummed over the cab as we passed the last bayou and entered the Air Station property through the gates guarded by sentries.

Since ours was the first class of cadets under a new bill of

Congress, and we were obviously to be an example of the entire
five-year program, it was up to our class to make a go for the
ensuing classes. All 74 of us were safely lodged in a wing of a
big building, and after another physical we were ready to start
to work. When we graduated there were just 43 of our class left.
Many of the fellows "busted" out for lack of flying ability; several for other reasons. Waste no tears on those who didn't make
it. They are alive today; they might have been sod pushers.

To earn a pair of Navy wings you spend approximately 13
months of intensive training, including your indocrinatorial
month at the nearest reserve base. If and when you reach Pensacola, the Navy's Annapolis of the Air, you go through five
squadrons for flight instruction in 12 months. Simultaneously
you complete 38 weeks of ground-school work.

"Loosen up, dodo, and stop thinking of that girl back home."

"Stop kicking that rudder like a football, Mr. Cadet, and
get the nose down."

"Sure, stall it in. We're only thirty feet up."

This sarcastic lingo greeted me in a steady stream during
the first few weeks as I groped steadily in the darkness while
trying to "feel my wings." From the beginning, I had an instructor in each squadron who tried to understand me and my
peculiarities.

My first was Lieutenant Meadson, tall, dark, blessed with
the patience of a man born to teach and the knack of making
you want to learn. After showing me how to get aboard the
plane without tumbling into the water, we shoved off and
taxied out to take off. At 4000 feet my instructor raised the
gosport mouthpiece and said, "Take it over and feel it out."

I patted my head, the signal of acknowledgment, and took
the stick, sliding my feet up on the rudder pedals. For the better
part of an hour I did the things we were taught at St. Louis that
first month, at the same time getting a bird's-eye view of the
surrounding country, the different courses, and the landplane
squadrons.

Each day the routine continued until we covered the funda-
mentals—gentle turns, glides, landings, spins, and a few emergencies. After ten hours came the first check, a solo check.

Fortunately, I managed the first squadron without a "down"
check. There are no instruments in the planes for the students

in the squadron, so you learned to fly by feel or you didn't learn. The wind whistling through taut wires and over airfoil sections hum a weird tune in a glide, and as I came down over the blue water of the bay for the practice landings, the tune indicated the right speed. That sensation of "mushy" controls, a dropping feeling when nearing the stalling point, is soon evident after several attempts, and you soon learn to keep flying speed. "Keep Flying Speed!" Those are the three little words in aviation that mean the difference between live and dead aviators. Mr. Meadson drilled them into me, and I'm grateful. They were his last words of advice as I left for Squadron 2.

There, I soloed, passed my eleven-hour check, "shot the circle" (plunking in five landings out of six with a cut gun in a circle not 200 feet in diameter). We ate airplanes for breakfast and dreamed airplanes all night. We studied and built fuselages, tore engines down and rebuilt them, read theories, drilled, and studied the Navy.

Two weeks before my final check, came a crash which cost a life. A student from Squadron 5 (the final stage) was over the bombing target in his fighter. He had just completed three dives and was preparing for the last one. It's always a thrill to watch those hornetlike Boeings dive down 3000 feet at about 300 miles an hour, then drop an "egg," and pull out in a screaming zoom. It takes a cool head, an easy touch on the stick.

I was pointing my plane for home after an hour of stunts, and as usual watched the dive-bombing off to the left as much as I could. The little fighter rolled over and started down to deliver a last bomb at the target. With his eye glued to the telescope the pilot still had her pointing straight down at 2500 feet, when I saw a wisp of black smoke streak back along the fuselage. My throat clogged.

Suddenly a blaze swept the entire fuselage, and I could just see a puff of black smoke as the roaring plane buried itself in the sand and exploded. The student had bailed out at 1500 feet, but his chute was burned full of holes before he got clear. If he had only waited one more second. . . .

Two months later two observation planes doing gunnery maneuvers crashed in mid-air. Check off two more student pilots. Unfortunate? It's hell, but it can't be helped. As long as

there is motion on this earth there are bound to be accidents.
Winter days, cold, blustery, drizzly. All flights canceled, no
hops out, radio drill. Then we played cards, looked glum, or
just looked. Maybe a lecture on safety rules or discipline broke
the monotony. We spent hours in ground school learning about
the sky, the clouds, the winds, sea navigation, engines, or rig-
ging planes after a major overhaul so they would fly nose first.
We did paper work—quick decision tests designed to fit us for
emergencies. It took ten weeks to finish up Squadron 2, the
"high hurdle" in the course.

You get, in Squadron 3, your first feel of a military plane, a
Vought Corsair, powered with a 450-horsepower Wasp and
built for observation with a gunner's cockpit in the rear. We
were divided into groups of 18 for formation purposes, and we
went through a routine of gunnery, navigation hops, radio drill,
and nine-plane formation flights. You are now supposed to be
able to know the flippers from the rudder, but you still get
those dreaded checks. Roaring engines, whistling wires, the
sky full of planes. Nights spent writing letters home—"Dear
Mom, passed another check today." But more often the regular
"bull" sessions which sound like this:

"Old weasel puss cut my gun over the Bayou Grande today
on my eight-hour check, and we just about went in the drink."

"Yeah? Well, I slipped down to the edge of Veterans Field
just before our third-hour hop was up, and got a down check
just because it was a little slow."

"How many hits did you get, Bill?"

"Plenty, but some dodo shot the sleeve away."

We finished up ground school just as the word came to report
to Squadron 4. Were we proud little fledglings! The big Douglas flying boats were swell. I liked to bring these big six-pas-
senger winged hulls in, and to feel the throb of the two Wasps
as you push on the throttles. The pilot and co-pilot sat in the
bow with a clear view of the sky ahead, and it makes you feel
pretty important to maneuver the "flying barn" around. The
new cadets looked on us with awe and respect, and we strutted
at every opportunity. We were flying blind, we were flying big
boats, we were being shot off a catapult. Just 12 more hours in
the air and we would be flying fighters!

Three hours! Two hours! We took off on that last bombing hop in Squadron 4. One bomb, two bombs, three bombs. That last jerk on the release lever, that last bomb punched my ticket to Squadron 5. I was there. Today I still prize that first hour in a single-seater fighter. Twelve months we had been pulling, pulling. Now, it was "anchors aweigh" and a clear sky above. You wanted to be a flier. You worked, worried, wished your way through small field work, circle shooting, down checks, and navigation problems. You spent some enjoyable week ends on wonderful beaches and participated in a few first-class parties. Now you crawl in the cockpit for a ride in a Boeing fighter!

It's snug and comfortable to sit there waiting for the word, "All clear," but as I looked out on the 12-foot wing I wondered how such a tiny thing could support a man in flight. I pushed home the throttle and held my breath. With a roar and a bounce we were off the ground, and my head seemed glued to the headrest as we cleared the trees past the south runway and vaulted to 1000 feet. Was that a take-off! I threw my head back and laughed. The slightest movement on the stick made the little plane jump. A touch on the throttle was like applying a stinging blow to 450 wild horses in tandem. I was in a flying bullet.

At 4000 feet I leveled her off, slowed down to 90 knots, and jerked the stick back for a snap roll. Then I put the nose down, waited until the air speed showed 160, and pulled back on the stick. Up, up, up, over in the loop I'd dreamed about. Below the bay glimmered in the morning sunshine and the sandy bit of strand running through the blue-green water looked for all the world like a white piece of string instead of Santa Rosa Island. Corry Field, the Navy's main flying field at Pensacola, was stretched out flat and regular, blackjacks on two sides and pine trees on the others. I could feel the rugged beauty of it now.

Rolling the little plane over on its back, I hung there against the belt wondering what the belly of a fighter looked like sticking up in the air. When the engine coughed and quit, I eased back on the flippers, pointed the nose at Corry Field, and, rolling out of the inverted position, glided down to the 1000-foot traffic level, dodging Squadron 2 planes all the way. After joining the inner stream of traffic around the field I came in with a bounce, tapping lightly on the brakes, and rolled to a stop on the far runway.

We spent a month in Squadron 5 altogether, learning advanced stunts, practicing carrier work, dive bombing, and trying to hit a sleeve towed at 90 knots. You use telescope sights to aim, and soon discover that it takes plenty of practice to blast a few holes in a target by pointing a fighter and squeezing a Bowden. There were hours of "dogfighting" and navigation hops cross-country, several close calls in which the students had to bail out and float home. One poor chap was doing some fancy stunts at 5000 feet when his plane fell into an inverted or outside spin which he couldn't cope with. At 2500 feet he pulled on the safety belt, and the centrifugal force of the whirling plane threw him several hundred feet before he managed to yank the ripcord. He got down minus a shoe and goggles.

We ended up our careers as students in a furious dogfight which six of us had arranged the night before at the Officers' Club. Setting a rendezvous, we slipped away from the field individually and joined up as two three-plane sections a few moments later. We attacked each other with the frenzy of fighting cocks, and finally came back to the field with oil-drenched, gasless planes. The skipper eyed the planes and then us, but we caught no more than that knowing look and a slight "uhm" or so as we evaded his glances.

Our orders came the day we got our wings. Mine read:

"When directed by the Commandant Naval Air Station Pensacola, upon completion of active duty undergoing training, you will regard yourself detached from your present station and will report to the Commanding Officer, VB Squadron 5B USS Lexington for active duty involving flying in that squadron."

I was more than satisfied to be sent to a dive-bombing outfit. Our pay was boosted nearly $100, and there remained but three more years before our $1500 bonus.

I had hardly been in my new squadron a week before we received orders to dive-bomb the radio-controlled Utah,* a stately old battleship of yesteryear. I was still munching a sandwich of course rules, Air Battle Force Instructions, and other informa-

---

* The old Utah was sunk at Pearl Harbor in 1941.

tion for green pilots when someone yelled, "Conference in the ready room!"

"We climb to 12,000, ahead and south of the horizontal bombers. When we pick up the ship, which is to be heading north just above the Coronados Islands, I'll put you in eche-lon." (That means formation.)

"Where do we rendezvous after the attack, Captain?" I looked down the table at him past the 17 old-timers as I spoke, self-conscious, like a rookie shortstop in his first big-league game.

"Inboard toward the coast, at 2000. You are flying 18, Guyton. . . . All right; let's go—and remember we want some hits."

Out on the line 18 Boeing fighters were warming up, bombs hung in place, and mechs giving a last swipe at telescope sights. Twenty minutes later we were to be in position to attack—nose to tail!

At 12,000 we leveled off, swung out in an echelon, and closed up. 'Way back from the tail I could see the skipper's plane start an easy turn toward the islands, and halfway across the solid blue stretch of sea I picked up a white spreading wake. We were going in with the afternoon sun at our backs. The radio cracked.

"Bombing Five, attack, attack."

I picked up some white spurts of spray around the battle-wagon far below, and knew that we were going in under the last section of horizontal bombers. Those were bomb splashes.

I checked instruments and ran over the dive check-off list. Cowl flaps, landing flaps, arming wire, sight open, seat down, high pitch. All set. It was follow the leader now. No. 1 peeled off and started down, followed in a pouring movement by 2, 3, and 4. In the rippling wingover I caught the flash of silver wings as the planes ahead rolled. Through the telescope sight I watched the tail and stubby back of 17 as I hung on in his slip stream wondering if everything was okay. There he went, up and over. I hauled back and rolled right behind him, my prop as close to his tail as I dared put it. The nose dropped down, down, straight at the tiny white target. Through the sight I counted six planes diving straight at the water, and far below three or four pulling out in a rounded arc. The air speed jumped to 200, 240, 280, and the altimeter started to unwind.

That tiny speck on the water, superstructure, stacks and guns, grew fast as more and more white splashes encircled it. Seven thousand, six, four. My hand slid up to the bomb release. The wind got that moaning yet whistling shriek, and I crouched as low as I could into the cockpit behind the windshield. Three thousand—time to get out! I jerked the handle, and pulled back on the stick, still tailing the plane ahead.

Ship, water, plane, and horizon started to merge into gray, gray into black. I had pulled out too fast. The weight I felt was not three trucks on top of me, but gravity getting in her lick. I swore—not in pain, but in anger. Then the strain eased off, and as the horizon came into the ring cowl I saw several of our planes rendezvoused off toward the shore line. The water, a thousand feet below, was going by in a blur. The squadron was well joined up, circling lazily, waiting on little me to catch up with them. Even the wings of my fighter seemed to be turning bright green.

On the way back the section leader turned around and grinned. I wiped the oil smudges off my goggles and stored up for future reference the uncomfortable experience of pulling out too fast. That is the way you learn this bombing business. With a little practice your wings change back from green to the customary silver.

When you go aboard a carrier, your routine is something like this: Up at 3 A.M. sitting around a smoke-filled ready room, waiting for a mock war to start. . . . Four-thirty. You have your navigation worked, courses plotted, and have manned the upper ready room on the flight deck. . . . Four-forty-five. You crawl under what seems like 1000 planes in the damp, murky dawn to your own cockpit, with even the eyes in the back of your head watching for propellers. . . . Seven o'clock; and you have been flying a grueling formation for several hours searching for the enemy. . . . Twelve noon; and you are back aboard grabbing coffee and sandwiches, and standing by to get off again when the word comes. . . Three o'clock. You nose over to bomb the three light cruisers which have been hiding in rain squalls all morning. . . . By six o'clock the last plane has crossed the ramp, and after a game of cribbage and a lot of shop talk, you drag your weary frame up the ladder and stow it in a gently rolling bunk.

Naturally, if it happens to be the "Big Cruise" and the car-

rier is close to Honolulu, Panama, or San Francisco, there is
plenty of gossip flying about as to when you get in, what to see
at Waikiki, or how much shore leave you are going to get. By
the time you are ready to check out with the Navy, you will
know a hawser from a windlass, how to tell a light from a heavy
cruiser, why not to miss the last shore boat, and how to be a
champion ace deuce player in 6000 easy lessons. Most of that is
free of charge.

You entered this business in dead earnest, with your eyes
wide open. When the captain pins on your gold wings, shakes
your hand, and wishes you good luck, he is putting you in commission, like a new battleship. You are going out to the fleet to
work for Uncle Sam. You are going to fly numerous planes in
numerous and peculiar places. You are going to carry out assignments toward objectives to the best of your ability. You'll
meet a lot of nice people, have a good time wherever you go,
attending parties with the Navy, that small world in itself. It's
not all work—but it's not all play, either.

"The Navy is no place for a sissy nor for a quitter. We want
men who will take a job and carry it through."

Those were the words of the captain of the Air Station at
Pensacola to his departing flock as he presented us with our
wings. Truer words were never spoken.

Student Activity

After reading this narrative of the training a naval pilot un-
dergoes, make an outline of the training course in the order the
items come. Compare your list with those of other students and
supply at the proper places the activities you have overlooked.

TORPEDO TERROR[1]

By Blaine and Dupont Miller

HERE is a new kind of pioneering. Bob Wakefield as a young naval air pilot was having his first experiences in the varied kinds of flying that have to be done in the Navy. Immediately before the adventure called "Torpedo Terror" he had had some experience with dirigibles at Lakehurst, New Jersey. Now he had been transferred as air pilot to a warship. He had already served on planes belonging to a carrier ship. These planes were launched from the deck of the carrier and alighted on the deck after flight. Cruisers and battleships were just beginning to carry two or more planes each. The planes had to be amphibians (flying boats). They were shot out by catapult from the ship's deck, and were hoisted up when they returned. Some commanders of ships were doubtful of their usefulness and thought them impractical. Bob was assigned to the U.S.S. *Denver,* a cruiser whose captain was opposed to airplanes on a fighting ship. Bob's duty as a pioneer was to prove to Captain Rumble that a seaplane was needed on a cruiser.

Bob Wakefield, as we know from previous selections, is an imaginary character.

*   *   *   *   *

The majestic length of Chesapeake Bay unrolled beneath the wings of Ensign Bob Wakefield's trim new Albatross seaplane. The engine, fresh from the test line at Anacostia, beat an unbroken rhythm. It was grand to have a stick in his hand again, and the feel of the rudder bar at his feet! For the moment, he forgot, in the joy of flying, that he was on his way to the strangest assignment he had ever had.

Presently he picked up Cape Charles far below and over the

---

[1] From *Bob Wakefield, Naval Aviator,* by Blaine and Dupont Miller, Dodd, Mead & Co., New York. Copyright 1936 by the authors.

port bow. Stretching in a glittering, formidable line from the Cape, lay the Fleet. Somewhere in that grim procession was the U.S.S. *Denver,* the cruiser for which he was bound. He looked around, waving his hand toward the ships, and yelled "There they are!" to Ajax in the rear cockpit.

The mechanic nodded and grinned from ear to ear. Turning back to his controls, Bob reflected that Commander Deering's kindness in letting him bring Ajax with him was the one ray of sunshine in an otherwise gloomy detail. His mechanic had become a sort of good luck charm in his life. Well, he was going to need plenty of luck on the *Denver!*

The ships were below them now, and without much difficulty he spotted his cruiser. He had about three thousand feet, and it was time to start down preparatory to landing. Instead, he circled slowly around, fighting down a strange reluctance. Normally, Bob would have had a far different approach to a new job on a new ship. Joy at belonging to such a fine, seagoing craft would have prompted him to zoom the deck a couple of times. In his enthusiasm he would have blimped his gun so that there could have been no doubt in anyone's mind that a happy aviator was coming aboard. But, in the case of the *Denver,* Bob had no such impulses. To begin with he wasn't happy to be going aboard—and, to end with, nobody cut any aerial capers around a ship commanded by Captain Josiah B. Rumble, known throughout the Navy as "Ramrod Rumble."

When Bob's friends had heard that he was being ordered to the command of that hard-shelled mariner, they had commiserated with him.

"Old Ramrod has an aviator served up to him every morning for breakfast," they had assured Bob.

Seriously, Bob knew Captain Rumble's reputation as a naval officer of the old school who had never bowed to the modernity of airplanes. He stuck fast to his opinion that aircraft merely cluttered up the deck of a man-of-war and nothing he had seen to date had given him any reason to change his mind.

To be sure, Bob had expected orders back to the Fleet following the loss of the airship, U.S.S. *Miami,* and he was fully prepared to find himself on duty which would not be as exciting as he had just experienced aboard the Navy's giant lighter-than-aircraft. He had come to love his little fighting plane, the

Sparrowhawk, and the hook-on work he had been doing had
proved fascinating. But, he had to admit that he never expected such an assignment as that upon which he was now going to embark.

In desperation, Bob had gone to Commander Deering, the
Detail Officer, hoping to have his orders changed. Now, as he
circled over the *Denver,* losing altitude slowly, the strange tenor
of that interview came back to his mind.

Most respectfully, Bob had pointed out that such an ardent
advocate of aviation as himself would undoubtedly irritate
Captain Rumble. He called Commander Deering's attention to
the Captain's opinions on aviation.

"I know all that," the older officer had assured him equably.
"I've sent three Senior Aviators to that ship in eighteen
months."

"But—I—well—I'm afraid I don't understand, sir."

"Bob, Captain Rumble is one of the most valuable men we
have in the Navy. You know, of course, that he is a famous old
submarine commander?"

"Yes," Bob had assented, puzzled as to what all this had to do
with aviation.

"Well, he was just as conservative about submarines at one
time as he is now about aircraft on ships. Why, he simply
howled in outrage when they ordered him to submarines. Yet
before he ended up he had not only been decorated for gal-
antry in action in the old L-29, but he was largely responsible
for the present development of the pig-boats."

A light had begun to dawn on Bob.

"You mean—?"

"Exactly. Old Ramrod is a man who likes as thoroughly as he
dislikes. You're really on missionary duty. I believe that you
can convert him to aviation at sea."

Bob had shaken his head helplessly. He loved to maneuver an
airplane, nobody more so! But when it came to maneuvering a
stubborn man—and that man his Skipper!

"I wouldn't know where to start," he protested.

"I should say that the best start would be to take him up in
a plane," suggested the Commander. "I happen to know that
he's never been in one. Get him up. Make him like it!"

Now, with this strange assignment literally staring him in

the face, Bob had a fine case of cold feet. But there was nothing
for it but to come down and report aboard the *Denver*. He went
into a long glide, calculated to get him into the water close
aboard * the ship.

In order to give himself the widest path into the wind it was
necessary to pass over the ship and come down on the port side.
Afterward, Bob was never able to tell quite how it all happened.
Certainly, with old Ramrod Rumble in the back of his mind,
he had never been so anxious to make a safe and unobtrusive
landing. Perhaps, the ship's super-structure set up turbulent
air currents. Gliding over the *Denver* with engine throttled
down, a down current dropped the plane with sickening
rapidity.

There was a sharp impact and Bob could feel the metallic
shudder that went through the fuselage. The controls were
steady, however, and Bob completed the landing. By the time
he'd coasted down a swell and turned back to the ship, he began
to think he'd imagined it all.

But after they had been hoisted aboard and he had stepped
on deck, looking up to the scene of some commotion, he realized
that the pontoon of his plane had carried away the ship's radio
antenna. Bluejackets were swarming over the superstructure to
repair the damage. Bob's face was a deep crimson as he stepped
forward to speak to the Officer of the Deck.

"Ensign Wakefield and mechanic, reporting aboard. I'm
also delivering the ship's new scouting plane."

"Glad to see you, Wakefield. I'll get an orderly to show you
your cabin and—"

Before he could finish his sentence, a marine came up to
them, and saluting smartly announced to the O.D.†:

"The Captain wants you to send the aviator who just landed
to him at once, sir."

The ship's officer regarded Bob sympathetically.

"I'm afraid that means you."

Bob followed the orderly down the companionway to the
cabin. He had not felt such a fine mixture of chagrin and trepi-
dation since his plebe year at the Naval Academy. And under-

---

* *close aboard:* alongside.
† *O.D.:* Officer on Deck (in charge).

neath his confusion was a feeling of discouragement. What a swell beginning this was!

Through the curtained door, Bob could hear himself being announced to the Commanding Officer. There came a sonorous clearing of a throat followed by a gruff, "Come in."

Seated at his desk was an old salt of the sea. Bushy mustache. Eyes which gleamed blue and sharp from overhanging gray eyebrows. A face on which wind wrinkles had carved, in amazing design, the record of his years at sea. In short, Ramrod Rumble.

"So you're the 'flying sailor' who just attempted to wreck this ship?"

There was obviously no answer to that one, so Bob said nothing.

"Since Washington sends me aviators, I have to accept them, but you may as well know my feeling in the matter right now," announced Bob's new skipper in ringing tones. "The Navy should be made up of seaworthy ships—not screaming mechanical toys."

"But, Captain—" began Bob, only to be warned by an ominous rumble of a cough.

"So far, in my opinion, aircraft aboard a ship are just a noisy nuisance."

Anger surged through Bob. What hope was there with a skipper like this!

"On this vessel we have comparative quiet because our planes don't fly except when absolutely necessary, and, I might add, it is seldom necessary. I shall expect you, furthermore, to see that no grease or oil gets on the decks from those rattletraps."

The interview obviously was at an end, for the Captain turned back to the papers on his desk.

Bob answered all there was to answer, "Aye, aye, sir."

With a sinking heart he went forward to find his assigned quarters and get squared away. Never had he felt so blue. He knew that aviation was not the backbone of the country's defenses, but he did feel that it had a mighty important part to play. He had met older naval officers before who were skeptics, but none of them had given him the feeling of being up against a blank wall as old Ramrod did. And that was the man he was supposed to take up in a plane!

As he went topside and forward past the planes he heard a

troubled voice call, "Look here a minute, Mr. Wakefield."

Good old Ajax! Already in his dungarees, he had been turn-ing to on one of the planes. In his hand he held out a plane's log book.

"This isn't going to be like the old Sparrowhawk, sir," he complained. "Look there, sir. I don't think these crates ever fly!"

Bob took a glance at the meager figures recorded on one page of the book. They confirmed his worst fears. However, he hid his gloom from Ajax as best he could. "Don't worry. We'll prob-ably have to take food and water up to the plane crews!"

In the days that followed, there were no signs that this happy prophecy was going to come true. The *Denver* was a trim, sea-going ship. Life aboard her was pleasant for everyone but the aviators. They did everything but fly. They maintained their planes ready to go at all times, but the word seldom came.

Time and again, Bob's flight schedule would be returned with the simple phrase, "Not approved," scribbled on it, fol-lowed by a bold flowing "R," as definite and unmistakable as the Old Man himself.

Occasionally, to break the monotony of discouragement, there would come a curt little note from the bridge: "Oil spots on deck under port catapult. Remove immediately."

Bob had never felt so disheartened in his life. He was sunk. Only pride kept him from appealing to Commander Deering for a change of duty.

Meanwhile, Fleet exercises went ahead apace, and gunnery competition, always keenly fought out between ships, narrowed down to the final contest. The *Denver* and the *Salem* were to fight it out for the trophy.

On the morning of the Official Practice, reveille roused out the crew at four o'clock, an hour earlier than usual. There was an air of expectancy in the preparation that went on all over the ship. All hands were clothed in fresh underwear to remove the possibility of infection should anything go wrong which might result in injuries.

Recoil cylinders were filled with liquid which would absorb the powerful kickback of the guns. Breechblocks were carefully checked. Sights were handled with the same care an anxious mother might give to a small infant. Electrical firing circuits were checked over for shorts. The decks around the anti-aircraft guns were swabbed down with a thick lye solution which would absorb oil and grease, in order that the wooden planks might be easier to clean.

There was excitement in the very air, and the crew of the *Denver* was strung taut as a brace wire. Tension underlay all the quiet commands of the officers and the ready replies of the men. Who should win the Gunnery Trophy depended upon this day's work, and the crews of the *Salem* and the *Denver* were keyed up to the occasion. Bob shared the general enthusiasm. Indeed, the desire to win permeated the atmosphere.

The sirens of the two cruisers gave long wails, and the whistles were tested half an hour before getting under way. The crew went to breakfast and the mess tables were cleaned up and stowed away with alacrity—no one intended to miss seeing this practice!

A short blast on the whistle and the ships were under way, standing out to the firing range. A month's hard work had been spent by each crew, every minute pointing to the hour which was about to begin.

Final checks were made and at last the Gunnery Officer reported to the Captain, "The ship is ready to fire!"

Bob, set to watch the firing from the port catapult, followed the preparations with eager eyes. He was envious of his fellow officers who had things to do, for in this way they were able to work off the tenseness which enveloped the ship. Aloft, he could see the twin-engined flying boat which was to tow the sleeves high in the air for the practice. If he could do nothing on the *Denver,* he would have liked to be at the controls of the patrol plane. It seemed so long since he'd used his wings.

The *Salem* began her firing runs first and, from the appearance of the brown puffs which surrounded the sleeve, her gunners had done reasonably well. However, many of the shells trailed well aft of the target, and the *Denver's* gunners, standing by their pieces, talking among themselves, were optimistic that they would have little trouble improving upon the firing they had just witnessed. At the conclusion of the firing, the towing plane swept low and dropped the sleeve neatly upon the quarterdeck of the *Salem.*

Now, it was the *Denver's* turn. The enunciators on the bridge signaled the engine room for more speed, and the cruiser, trembling as though she were afflicted with the general excitement, began to surge ahead in response to the increased steam acting upon her turbine blades. Plowing through the heavy seas, the sleek hull left a boiling wake which served all the more to emphasize her flowing lines and high speed.

A red flag was run up at the yardarm, and the *Denver* was officially ready.

The towing plane started its run. Trailing far behind, one could faintly make out the fabric sleeve, scarcely visible at that high altitude against the light blue sky.

Except for the wind rushing by, all was quiet. Crews stood by their guns, tense and eager to pump out their shells. The First Loader of each gun held a shell in his arms. Gun pointers sat on their saddles with hands on the controls while the Second Loaders, whose job it was to feed the shells into the ammunition line, fingered the projectiles with nervous hands.

Above, the towing plane droned monotonously as it dragged the sleeve at high speed. The target was nearly in position. Time was brief.

A short blast on the whistle.

"Commence firing!"

"Commence firing!" repeated the Gun Captains.

Now, the tenseness was transposed into action. The gun crews worked with the methodical exactness of a great machine. With a heave the Loaders sent the shells home with a crash. Breechblocks closed with a mighty clatter. Pointers and Trainers, eyes glued to the sights, moved their cross wires upon the swiftly moving targets. Guns responded to the rapidly moving controls.

Buzzers! Down came eager fingers to close the electrical contacts which launched the shells on their flight. The decks shook. The sharp, acrid odor of burning powder filled the air. As the breeches swung open, the hot, empty cases flew clear, only to be replaced by new charges.

Buzzers! Salvos. No excitement now—only action, with not a false move by any of the gun crews.

The sky around the target became dimpled with brown and white puff balls. They might have been cotton bolls, as the shells burst to spray the target with shrapnel. In spite of the rolling of the ship in the swells, it was evident there would be plenty of hits in the *Denver's* target.

The Black Gang, up from the hot engine rooms to see the practice, shouted words of encouragement to their gunnery shipmates. But, the smiles were shortly wiped off their faces, and a loud murmur of dismay arose. Something happened against the pale blue horizon on which they were so intently gazing. Something not in the books!

As they watched, the sleeve fluttered casually about for a moment, then with open end pointed downward, it began a long plunge to the made whitecaps far below. The towline had been shot in two!

Bob, watching its careening plunge, was sick with disappointment. No matter what his personal feelings might be, the *Denver* was his ship, and he wanted her to win. With the sleeve lost, she would have no score and the *Salem* would win by default.

Then, suddenly, came a surge of his old confidence. Jumping down, he dashed past his mechanics grouped by the planes.

"Ajax!" he shouted as he ran, "warm up Number One as quickly as you can. Stand by the catapult!"

Mounting the ladder on the double he found the Skipper on the bridge his face filled with gloom and disappointment.

"Captain," Bob said, "this sea is too rough for the towing plane to take off even if the pilot would take a chance on landing. I can fly out there and get the sleeve while you steam over and pick me up."

"Humph," grunted old Ramrod, "and lose your plane, too!"

"I'm sure I can do it, sir!" pleaded Bob.

"It's worth trying, Captain," urged the Gunnery Officer. "We've lost the trophy unless we recover the target."

"Very well," assented old Ramrod. "I don't suppose it could make matters any worse."

Even this grudging acknowledgment that planes might do some good, filled Bob's heart with joy as he rushed back to the catapult. Pulling his flight gear from the locker, he hastily issued instructions.

"Get in the rear cockpit, Ajax."

Pulling on their parachutes took a moment. Bob tested his engine on both switches. He turned up full gun. Oil pressure was normal and the temperature was satisfactory. An instant later, they were gliding down the catapult track and into the air.

Banking sharply, Bob sped over to the area where the sleeve had gone down. As he thought, the pilot of the patrol plane had deemed it impossible to land in such a seaway. Yet, the target would not float long enough for the cruiser to recover it.

On he went, until he located the sleeve, half of it well under water now. He would have to hurry. Swinging around in a steep flipper turn he headed into the wind. Gliding down toward the swirling whitecaps, he cut the gun, holding the craft off until the crest of a huge swell came along. Then he let her settle, slide down the swell, and come to a bouncing stop.

"Off with your chute, Ajax," he shouted.

He unbuckled his own straps and taxied toward the small piece of fabric visible in the water. Coming alongside, Bob ran out to one wing tip. Ajax knew his part, and he dashed madly out on the other wing. Leaning far downward, Bob barely managed to grasp the very tip of the sleeve as it was going down.

Pulling it aboard, Bob taxied toward the oncoming cruiser. Alongside, Ajax hooked the bridle to the extended crane and soon the plane was cradled on the catapult.

The eager group that had crowded about Bob opened up as the Captain came down from the bridge.

"R-um-ph! Well, well!" said he as he inspected the riddled sleeve. "Guess we have the Gunnery Trophy cinched!"

Turning to Bob, he hesitated for just a second, then exclaimed gruffly, but so loudly that all hands could hear: "Nice work, Wakefield. Nice work!"

"Thank you, sir," replied Bob happily.

After that, things changed slightly for the better. The word "approved" now began to appear on Bob's flight schedules followed by the same flowing "R." Bob actually began to hope he might get the Skipper into the air. The target episode might have made a good impression on Captain Rumble, but it had not, Bob knew, by any means made him air-minded.

He began to watch for an opportunity to take the Captain up. Then, one day it came, most amazingly, from the Captain himself. Bob had been summoned to the cabin.

"Wakefield," said the Skipper, "we've been assigned the job

of testing a newly designed torpedo. Not only has it a new steer-ing mechanism, but it is built for long range work."

Bob's pulse quickened. This sounded good!

"In the tests, we are going to use a real warhead in order to try out the new explosive it contains. Can a plane be of value to observe it from the air?"

Something told Bob, "This is your moment!"

He replied, "Under one condition, our plane would be the finest place in the world, sir, to see what a torpedo is up to."

"And what is the condition, pray tell?"

"That you are in the rear cockpit, Captain," Bob replied, putting all the earnestness he could muster into his voice. "You are an old submarine man and you know torpedoes as few officers in the fleet do. Might I suggest, sir, that you go up with me as observer?"

For a long moment, Ramrod Rumble's piercing blue eyes re-garded Bob from under bushy brows.

"You've rather got me on the hip, haven't you, young man?"

"Yes, sir," agreed Bob, praying under his breath.

"Well, by gad, I will go up with you. If nothing else it'll silence those old women in Washington who say I'm behind the times! But remember, I haven't committed myself about aviation on ships!"

It was an elated pilot who supervised the adjustment of the safety belt in the rear cockpit of Number One plane the following morning. His instructions were concise as he pointed out the various controls and warned the Skipper to keep clear of them while the plane was flying.

After he was settled in his own cockpit, he looked around to say, "All set, Captain?"

The Captain nodded his head vigorously. His moustaches fairly bristled with determination, and beneath the aviation helmet his eyebrows were more formidable than usual. He was going to see this thing through!

With throttle open, Bob grasped the control stick firmly. As the ship rolled to the swells, the outboard end of the catapult track started upward. Then came a slow movement of the plane. With his chin well tucked in, and his entire body tensed from the shock which was to follow, Bob still had a thought to spare for the Captain. How was he making out?

Bob remembered his own first catapult shot very well. He knew that within a second the Captain, held down in his seat by inertia, would find the breath leaving his body. His feet would fly up. He wouldn't be able to catch his breath, and for a split second everything would become dark. Then the acceleration would ease up and he would find the world returning to normal.

Once in the air, Bob circled about waiting for the torpedo run. Far on the distant horizon was the towing vessel, the cruiser *Helena,* while scarcely visible was the target.

Up went the red flag on the foremast of the *Denver,* and as the whistle blew, a long, slender object could be seen to jump from nowhere and splash into the water, disappearing immediately below the surface. It broached with a leap into the air, then settled down to a submerged run. Bob could see its yellow nose ten feet below the surface.

On and on went this new weapon without a waver in its course. Swift as an arrow, powerful beyond belief.

Suddenly, when well beyond the halfway mark, it broached again. All was not right, and the two observers sensed it. Again it surfaced, but this time instead of resuming its original course, it pulled slightly to port. The steering gyro obviously had failed.

For a few minutes, now, it seemed to have settled down, even though it was on the wrong course. Holding his breath as he flew over it, Bob decided it would pass some distance astern of the *Helena* which still steamed along on her course, totally unaware of the mad cylinder of destruction plunging toward her.

Then, again, the torpedo leaped to the surface and, striking the water at an angle, began a fast turn. It was close enough, now, to the towing vessel to be seen. The Captain of the *Helena,* recognizing his danger, slipped his tow. He began a turn which would head his vessel toward the on-coming torpedo—the best maneuvering position.

Bob glanced back at old Ramrod. The Skipper's face was grim, filled with hopelessness of the situation. Zigzagging back and forth over the wild missile, Bob endeavored to keep the *Helena* informed of the torpedo's position.

The cruiser was now steaming on all boilers. The mad torpedo crossed the stern of the *Helena,* and for a second the men in the plane breathed a sigh of relief. But it was short-lived. Again the missile was seized with frenzy. Leaping wildly to the surface, it began another circle toward the now desperate cruiser.

Another miss would be a miracle. The time had come, Bob realized, to put forth a desperate scheme, born of the last few minutes of harrowing uncertainty.

"Captain," he screamed, through the interphones, "I think I can explode the torpedo with our machine guns."

"Go to it, boy!" the Old Man yelled back.

"It may crash us!" warned Bob in shrill tones.

"All right! All right! Just don't let it blow up the ship," shouted back the excited Skipper.

"Good Old Ramrod," breathed Bob, as he pulled the charging handles back on both guns, and raised the triggers into firing position.

Pulling up into a steep wingover, Bob's eye went to the telescopic sight. Down came the nose of the howling craft, and it steadied as it worked into a power dive. Ailerons put the plane into a slight spiral as Bob found the yellow-nosed torpedo in his telescope.

He squeezed the triggers and his two guns spurted out two streams of steel. Rat-tat-tat-tat. The cockpit echoed to the burst of shells. From the spray it was clear that the bullets had trailed aft of the warhead. It was difficult to shoot at an object under water.

Glancing up for an instant, Bob saw the torpedo on a collision course with the *Helena.* It would hit her fairly amidships! He had one more chance.

Pulling over the charging missile, he reared back on the stick and stalled the plane. As the nose fell sharply down, his telescopic sight bore full on the yellow submerged spot. He aileroned the plane slightly and moved his point of aim forward.

Again, his fingers pressed down on the triggers, and once more the rat-tat-tat sounded in his ears.

Two hundred more feet and the torpedo would find its mark! And he himself had only four hundred feet of altitude. The water was raising up to meet him. His heart was in his mouth as he realized that he had barely recovered flying speed. Now, now, was the time! His fingers moved on the triggers. The spray of steel gushed forth.

Then the seas opened! From a small spot in the green water a geyser started. Up, up came the white spray. It rose to the height of the *Helena's* masts. Solid green water, Bob knew, formed the core of that eruption.

He reared brutally back on the controls. The plane wobbled and staggered out of the dive. But her speed had not been great enough to give good control. The lowest point of the aircraft's arc was just at the geyser's peak.

The plane shook as though it had struck a solid wall. Spray flew. Somewhere in the midst of it, Bob could hear the life being crushed from the plane. With throttle wide open he felt her losing speed. Nosing down, he looked back to see that his flippers had been practically torn away. There was scarcely anything left of the rudder.

Bob held the craft as best he could while they wobbled slowly to the water. As it slumped into the sea, the pontoon crumbled and folded up. With a sort of fatal determination, she started going over on her nose.

Bob looked back to see Captain Rumble, with his safety belt already unsnapped, climbing calmly out of the parachute straps.

He had just time to warn, "Jump clear," before the plane went over.

Even as he floundered upward through the water, burdened as he was with his flying jacket, the thought went through Bob's head, "Well, this settles it! A crash on the Skipper's first flight." Promotion was further away than ever!

When he had shaken the water out of his eyes, and caught his breath, Bob discovered old Ramrod Rumble up before him, and calmly treading water. Beyond the Captain's head he could see the *Helena's* motor launch coming toward them.

"Hurt sir?" he inquired solicitously.

The water dropping off his moustaches made the Captain less formidable, somehow. He looked for all the world like a benevolent old walrus. Bob discovered that his eyes were twinkling in positive delight.

"You know, Wakefield!" he cried delightedly, "this is like the

Old Navy! Something to keep one's blood stirring. How soon do you think it'll take 'em to replace our plane?"

Questions for Discussion

1. If you do not already know, find out what these words and phrases mean and how to pronounce them: (Most of the words will be known by some member of the class. Let everybody help.) cruiser; stick; port bow; cockpit; reluctance; zoom the deck; blimped his gun; commiserated; modernity; "hook-on work"; tenor; equably; pig-boats; maneuver; port side; unobtrusive; superstructure; turbulent; fuselage; pontoon; plebe; skeptics; topside; dungarees; turning to; crate; "old man"; monotony; catapult; reveille; taut; permeated; sirens; alacrity; aft; enunciators; turbine blades; boiling wake; projectiles; cross wires; aerial; salvos; cotton bolls; shrapnel; turned up full gun; taxied; warhead; "got me on the hip"; inertia; acceleration; broached; "submerged run"; steering gyro; "slipped his tow"; interphones; wing-over; telescopic sight; ailerons; missile; "stalled the plane"; flying speed; flippers; treading water.

2. Show from the time this story was written to the present how the use of planes in the Navy has grown.

3. Describe how an airplane towed a target for firing practice by the ships.

4. Describe how a ship's guns are loaded.

5. Describe how a plane is launched from a ship's deck by a catapult.

6. Do you understand that the plane was a total loss?

BOMBER TO BRITAIN[1]

By James L. H. Peck

THIS is an account of a real flight across the Atlantic, but the flight was not made by Lieutenant Peck. The narrative was made up from the story told by the pilot, who is not himself a writer. Lieutenant Peck is a veteran aviator, only twenty-eight when this was written. He flew with the American defenders of Spain in the recent Spanish revolution. Since then he has been a test pilot and a writer for magazine and book publication. His two books are: *Armies with Wings* and *So You're Going to Fly*.

* * * * *

I climb into the left cabin seat and set about preparing the nine-and-one-half-ton reconnaissance bomber for the take-off. The real job of readying the ship for flight has been attended to by the men of the Ground Section—inspection, checking of those hundred and one details, and fueling. Reaching up and flipping the switches for the ship's electrical equipment, I watch dead dials spring suddenly to life, shocked into instantaneous movement by the current from the batteries. Mute faces and pointers that reveal the pulses of the big Cyclone engines; others, the flight instruments, that will guide us across the dark expanse of sea to an aerodrome somewhere in Britain. A few strokes of the wobble pumps build fuel pressure in the carburetors, and the tiny red warning lights glow as the poundage becomes adequate. Carburetor and oil temperature controls are set, respectively, on HOT and COLD and will remain so until the engines are started and warmed up. Mixture controls are adjusted for RICH so that the hungry cylinders may be fed a greater proportion of fuel. I move the port engine's throttle forward and backward, then leave it cracked slightly open. This action "primes" the motor by in-

---

[1] From *So You're Going to Fly*, copyright 1941 by Dodd, Mead & Co.

jecting raw gasoline into the cylinders and supercharger. After setting the starter selector on LEFT, I push a button which sets the electric starter into motion. The three-bladed, 10½-foot propeller kicks over; the Cyclone coughs, clears its throat, and commences an uneven metallic growl. The spinning, black-painted propeller dissolves into the drifting lake fog. I set the starter selector on RIGHT, then the starting procedure is duplicated. The bomber bird is flexing its wings for flight.

Sergeant Bennett of the Royal Canadian Air Force joins me in the dimly lighted cabin (it is night outside) and slides gingerly into the righthand seat. While the motors warm up we check the lights, engine, and electrical instruments, hydraulic pressure for the ship's retractable landing gear and wing flaps, and the vacuum pressure for the gyroscopic flight instruments and "George" the gyro pilot. Then I check each of the propellers to make certain that the hub mechanism is functioning properly. Bennett switches on the radio-compass, the only communications equipment we are carrying, for a ground check. It will probably come in handy over the Isles, but hardly before then. There are no "beams" to guide us across the ocean.

I go aft once again to see that things are shipshape, nothing loose to jostle around during flight. A few last-minute words with the Commander, then the cabin door thuds. That is the most "final" sound I have ever heard. With the closing of that curved metal door contact with the dark outer world seems lost. For about ten hours Ben and I shall be imprisoned in a peculiar sky world of which the ship is only an infinitesimal, isolated part. True, we have tremendous speed and freedom of movement at our command, but speed must be limited in order to conserve fuel, and there is an invisible wall on either side of the course plotted on the chart. To stray from the path, to fly over either of the walls—intentionally or unintentionally—is to court disaster.

I settle into the seat and eye the glowing instrument panel for a moment, then I glance at Ben. I think he feels it too.

"All set?" he asks. "Yep." Neither of us is in a talkative mood; too busy, too much to do. Crews in five other Hudsons are also busy. These men have been going through much the same routine. I wonder how they feel. It is their first crossing, just as it is Ben's and mine. We were chosen to lead the others because Sergeant Bennett is the best observer-navigator of his Group and because I have a bit more instrument-flying experience than have the other pilots. Only one thing worries me. We are carrying no armament except side arms, which will do us little good if anyone gets in our way as we let down over the Isles. Maybe it's for the best however. I'm in mufti,* have credentials of a sort but no combatant status—this is a civilian job. If I shot down a Jerry, were crippled in the fight and forced to land in France, it would mean the firing squad. . . . Ben is a little better off, he's wearing the RCAF uniform. Funny thing, this international law.

I raise my left arm out of the cabin window and the signal is passed on down the line while the mechanics pull chocks from under the ships' wheels. The lights cast queer shadows as the men move about the planes or duck beneath the wings, and the red and green running lights on the wing tips tint the men's faces with evil colors. The Commander and a group of officers stand off to the side. I wave to them and to the crew of Ground Section, men upon whose skill our mission and lives largely depend, then I ease open the throttles. Above the Cyclones I hear Ben holler something about "See you in England —not enough Jerry—!" The six Lockheeds rumble down the edge of the great Newfoundland Airport as we taxi slowly to the take-off position. By the time I return—and there is no doubt that I shall—the airport will be more than just a huge, partly completed base; it will be one of the greatest airdromes in the world. Indeed, strange things are going on in all parts of this forbidden, barren island—things that will amaze any unwelcome "visitors."

I swing the ship into the breath of wind that there is, and Ben and I become very busy with the check-off routine. Tail wheel locked. Parking brake on. Fuel selector on proper tank. Fuel valve on both engines. Mixture control still on RICH. Fuel-analyzer switch on. Flaps up. Tabs in neutral position. Propeller governors' controls set for low pitch. I ease the left throttle open until the manifold-pressure gage—revealing the density, or "boost," of fuel-air mixture in the engine's intake manifold—reads 30 inches, note the motor speed (r.p.m.'s) and

---

* *mŭf'tĭ:* citizen's clothes, "civies," not uniforms.

.the fuel and oil pressure and temperature gages. I switch on the left, then right magnetos to make certain that the engine runs regularly on either. Then the starboard motor is checked in the same manner. If anything is wrong now is the time to find out. But all is well.

Again my arm goes out the window. The others are ready. Sergeant Bennett releases the parking brake. As I open the throttles I glance over at him. His young face is alight. I guess mine is too. There's always a thrill in taking off in a big ship, but I have never felt like this. As the ship moves forward the feeling becomes more intense. It is a take-off into a strange land of uncertainty. We know what the ships will do, we have a pretty fair idea of what the pilots will do. The unknown factors are the behavior of the weather and what is in store for us when we reach the Isles.

The Cyclones growl mightily, live up to their name, as I run them wide open. Visibility is none too good, and my attention is divided between what is outside and the instruments inside. For all the overload, the Lockheed buoys up easily; it seems anxious to get into its element. The controls feel more firm, the wheels stop rumbling, then the dark, speeding ground sinks away. We're up.

I ease the throttles until the manifold pressure comes down to 35 inches and adjust the prop controls until the engines are turning over at 2050 r.p.m.'s. The highly supercharged motors may be run wide open for only a few minutes at sea level because they are designed to operate at peak efficiency in the rarer air of higher altitudes. Ben looks back as I swing into a shallow climbing turn to the right.

"They're all off okay."

II

I am wishing that at least one of the ships carried two-way radio equipment; it would certainly simplify matters. In a couple of hours matters are going to need simplifying, but of course we do not know that now.

Only a few dim lights are to be seen in Hattie's Camp and Whitmans. Cobb's Camp, farther west, seems to be blacked out completely. I adjust the knobs on "George's" face so that the ship will climb on the desired course, then I switch on the hydraulic valve; he's the pilot now. He takes us seaward in an easy climb. The other Hudsons are strung out behind in a loose formation which we shall maintain unless thick weather closes in. The ground fog is far below and visibility is good. I throttle back to 28 inches of boost, and adjust the propellers so that the engines are turning up 1900 r.p.m.'s cruising speed.

According to our weather data, there is a nice westerly tail-wind of 26 m.p.h. at about 5800 feet which will help us along our way. Visibility becomes better as we mount into the early morning air. The rough Gander Lake country far below is shrouded in mist and stratus, which is just as well. This terrain gives me the jitters every time I fly. I'd prefer the ocean —not too far out though—if forced down; the country is that bad.

Moonglow glints on the plastic-glass nose of the Hudson climbing just behind ours, and the light sparkles on the transparent "egg"—the streamlined housing of the radio direction-finder's loop antenna—on top of the plane's cabin. The craft resembles a huge, twin-tailed, deep-sea monster as it heaves gently on the air currents. In the moonlight the brown and green camouflage on the fishlike fuselage suggests great patches of scales, and the illusion is intensified by the ship's silvery underside. There is little shimmer from the whirling propeller blades; they are painted for that reason.

Ben calls my attention to the coastline. Windmill Head passes beneath the port-engine nacelle. This rocky promontory is 53 miles northeast of the airport, and now it's good-by to Newfoundland. It is the jumping-off point. From here on our progress must be plotted by nautical miles, and the airspeed readings will be converted from land miles per hour into knots. Wind velocity will also be expressed in knots. We are aerial mariners.

I level off at precisely 5800 feet, the level at which the first part of the voyage is to be flown. Ben switches the fuel selector to the lowest tank and turns off the cross-feed fuel valve while I adjust the mixture controls and check the instrument readings. The propellers are a trifle out of step. I can tell by the behavior of the little pointers on the synchronoscope dial and also by the blades' crackling song. I "tune" the props so that each is whirling at the same speed.

The horsepower percentage, manifold pressure, fuel anal-
ysis, r.p.m.'s, barometric pressure (altitude), and air temperature bear a certain relation to one another in so far as performance is concerned, and their proper combination is essential to
top performance. This is not always wide-open speed. In this
case, cruising speed with only 60 per cent of the Cyclones'
power is most desirable because of the necessity for saving fuel.
We have enough for the trip—and a certain "margin of safety"
—but one can never tell about the weather.

Right now the weather is pushing for us. Ben makes a quick
calculation, then says, "Not bad, we're making 232 knots
ground speed."

"Wait till we hit the edge of the Current.* We'll go upstairs
a bit and get some real wind. Just hope it won't veer more
than a few points northwest. Oh—you'd better contact the
others."

Ben takes the Adlis gun—a thick-barreled signalling light
fitted with a pistol-like grip and trigger, whose powerful beam
can be seen only by someone directly in the beam's path—aims
it at the cockpit of the leader of the other three-plane flight,
and begins signalling. The guns are our only means of inter-
plane communication. He then checks with each of the other
ships.

"All of 'em are okay but Number Five and there's just the
matter of his starboard engine running slightly hot. He set the
mixture up a bit and now it's better."

"I don't like that word 'better,' Ben. Set your mirror and
tell him to give his thermocouple and fuel-analyzer readings
every three minutes until you tell him different. Check on his
r.p.m.'s and boost too—both engines."

After four reports I begin to feel easier. Blythe's figures are
the same each time, and that indicates constant motor behavior.

"Okay, Ben, tell him to signal the minute those readings
change." "Right."

I make a couple of adjustments on the gyro pilot, then
study the flight plan and weather data, while he completes the
message to Number Five. The plan of course was prepared

---

* *Current:* the Labrador current.

some time before the take-off. Our avigation across entails several "sights" and drift observations if the weather behaves according to the forecast and pilot chart. If it misbehaves, a not-too-easy job will be made tougher. We shall have to fly fairly close formation in order to maintain contact with one another. I'm in command of the expedition, but I am not "leading" the others across. They are all competent pilots and navigators, and are carrying the same charts, weather data, and avigation tools with which we are equipped. We fly this loose formation now because this is the best way to fly a group of planes to a destination under the command of one individual. These craft are badly needed by the RAF, and our job is to get them to the Isles intact and in good condition.

It is owing to this urgent need and to the great amount of time saved by so doing that the flying deliveries are being made. The flight takes slightly more than ten hours elapsed time; the convoy requires from two weeks up, depending upon the weather, commerce raiders, U-boats, mine hazards, and bombers. And this time in transit is only one factor. When shipped by sea, Hudsons must of course be partially dismantled: propellers are removed and packed into specially designed boxes, as are wing panels, tail surfaces, cowlings, and other small parts. These parts and the engines are sprayed with a wax compound to combat the corrosive effect of salt water and spray, then wrapped in oilcloth or waterproof paper and taped up. The fuselages and boxes have to be taken to the pier and loaded aboard ship. On the other side, two or three weeks later, they must be unloaded and carted to an aerodrome where Lockheed mechanics and maintenance men —who, incidentally, assemble most of the other makes of American planes that are shipped to Britain—can set about making the craft flyable again. Furthermore, the safety percentage for aerial deliveries is actually higher than that of the convoyed freighters.

Ben has just completed his first series of star "fixes," or observations, through the turrethole in the after part of the cabin. Our position is 50 degrees, 45 minutes N (north latitude) by 47 degrees, 25 minutes, 10 seconds W (west longitude); all of which puts us well into the Labrador Current, or rather, over it. We could have guessed as much though by

the sharp drop in the air-temperature reading. That is not all
that's dropping. A high veil of stratus draws across the moon,
and ragged companion clouds are gathering, appearing from
out of nowhere, round and beneath our formation. Ragged
cumulus usually means wind, with trouble closely following.

"Signal them to hold formation and switch on their running lights. We'll drop down enough to make a drift check
before this stuff gets any worse. Check on Blythe's engines too."

"Right," says Ben, then he goes to work with the signal gun.
A couple of minutes later he says, "He's doing rather well now.
Readings constant, propellers synchronizing nicely."

"Fine. Here we go." Then I disengage the gyro pilot, ease
the throttles, and nose down into a steep power glide, careful
meanwhile not to swing off course. It certainly won't help matters to have to hunt for the other ships in a growing storm.

Ben lets himself down into the glass-enclosed nose to use the
drift indicator. About 500 feet down a nice clear stretch appears, and I level off and put on power.

"Ready!" I steady the Hudson and hold her so. It seems a
long time later that there is a flash as the phosphorus bomb
meets the water, then it slides from view. It will not be too
long before other kinds of bombs will be aimed and sent on
their way from that floor window in the nose.

Ben climbs out of the hole. "It's veered all right. Drift angle's
eleven degrees left. Just lined the sight in time, a bit of scud
blotted out the light." We start climbing wide open. It's getting thicker by the minute. I pick up Number Six's tail light,
and in another few minutes we have caught up and settled
into place. Ben immediately signals the other pilots to let
them know the amount of drift. We allow a couple of points
for the 500-foot change in altitude, and even more correction
will have to be made as the ships climb.

During October the prevailing wind in these latitudes—48
to 52 degrees, north—blows from westerly directions, anywhere
from southwest to northwest. Occasionally, and for short periods, it comes out of the north, northeast, and southeast at
high velocity. We hope that there will be no such periods during this or any other subsequent trip. Storm tracks, for the
most part, run from southwest and follow the Gulf Stream.
And they really run.

This blow apparently is no exception. Nor is there any particular mystery as to its origin. Examination of the Weather Station charts reveals the fact that a previously slow-moving air mass—which was a good 80 miles to the south of our course—has taken a not-so-slow tack to the northward. It is just our luck to be intercepted by a "cold front"—the boundary, or leading edge, of a cold air mass which is invading territory formerly held by a warm mass. We are about to become refugees from an aerological blitz. Only there is no outrunning this offensive. There is a slim chance, however, that we may be able to climb above it.

Ben keeps the Adlis gun going. The other ships snuggle up closer. We head upstairs in a hurry: the Hudson climbs pretty fast for a big ship, 2215 feet per minute. The altimeter hand creeps round the dial, but the air temperature is easing the other way—down. We are being buffeted about by the turbulent air and Ben and I keep a firm hand on the control wheels. A sudden gust of a windshift smacks us like an invisible hand. The ship creaks a bit, but that is only natural. We know that the Hudson is just about the sturdiest plane a-wing in anybody's air force to-day. Only two have been shot down in the whole war: others have limped home bent and battered; but they did reach home, even on one engine.

The outside air temperature keeps dropping. I begin to wonder whether or not I have used judgment. A "cold front" pushes beneath the warm air mass, forcing the warm air upward; that is why we are climbing. There's ice in these clouds, that is, potential ice. The temperature is 36 degrees. Although this is four degrees above freezing, ice can and will form under the present conditions.

To make bad matters worse it begins to rain. If there was any hope of escaping ice it is indeed a slim one now. The rain drops are approximately the same temperature as the air at this altitude, but they are chilled by the evaporation resulting from the plane's speed. Only a portion of each droplet freezes, but when they come thick and fast, as is now the case, the freezing drops build up on one another. That is what causes the trouble.

As if by magic, the black surface of the de-icer "overshoe" on the port wing gets ashy, then a fine white ridge appears out on the edge. The outlandish streak of white disappears as the "overshoe" swells and deflates. Then it comes again. Ice is coming faster than the de-icer can crack it and the icy area is spreading back on the wing, behind the "overshoe." It is pretty hard to see now. Rain sloshes against the window and steam is forming inside. There's little need to see. A peculiar message comes to me through the control column, a subtle vibration. I know that the ice outside is changing form, changing for the worse. "Rime" ice rarely gets thick enough to cause vibration; therefore it must be changing into hard, "clear" ice. Bad news.

III

"What's that?" Ben asks. He has never experienced this sensation. It is truly a sensation. The ship seems vibrant and hollow, the controls feel peculiar, and the engines sound queer. Airspeed and rate of climb have both fallen off. Not only is the ice heavy, but its formation changes the contour of the wing and thereby decreases the wing's lifting power. Not even the rapidly turning props escape its frosty clutches if unprotected; but ours are equipped with rubber spinners—a large cap fitting over the hub—and "slinger rings" which throw oil over the blades and keep ice off.

I can barely make out the green running light of the ship on our left through the sleet curtain. "Can you see Number Two?" I holler to Ben.

"Yeah. Only faintly though." The red light—on the ship's port-wing tip—carries through rain or fog better than green. I'm anxious about the others. Any number of things can happen to five planes in a mess like this. If we only had two-way radio. Bound to be ice static, but we could at least get word to one another.

"The temperature," Ben hollers, "it's down!"

We are at 11,000 feet now. Must be getting into the warmer air. The ship is still vibrating, but there seems to be less sleet. Now it's rain again and somewhat finer. It stops as suddenly as it had started. We are plunged into a queer murky darkness. Can just make out our own wing light. I know Number Two and Three pilots are in a similar fix. We are in the middle literally and figuratively with a couple of 9½-ton ships somewhere close by, no telling how close. The thought of a

marcelled wing tip this far at sea is not too comforting. Nor
is this sonorous vibration.

Then, ever so gradually, it begins to change tone. So do the
motors. The ice must be melting, thank goodness. Yes, the
controls feel different now.

"Coming off, isn't it?" Ben asks anxiously.

"Yeah. I'm sure it is. Can you see anything now?" He
reaches out and wipes off a small space.

"Nope. Still closed in over here."

The words are hardly spoken when we break through on top
of the cloud layer. Then he shouts, "Here's Number Two!"

I peer out my window, and hardly a moment too soon. A
green light appears out of the ghostly mist, and I instinctively
push the wheel forward. Only one way to go, down. And on
a perfectly straight heading too. I don't know how close Number Two is on the starboard side. I do know that Three's wing
tip was not more than two or three feet from ours—that's
darned close in the air! Another couple of minutes more in that
cloud mist and heaven knows what would have happened.

I lift the Hudson back into formation again. There's a
clammy moisture between my helmet and forehead, cold sweat.
Ben just looks, doesn't say a word. Funny, when things happen
—or almost happen—in the air one is too busy to think about
it until later. Then one imagines what might have happened.

Lights flash against the windshield and Ben's mirror. I turn
to catch the message from Number Three, then Ben cries from
the other side, "There's Four—Five—Six! We're all here anyhow."

I motion out of the window for Number Three to keep climbing. We must surmount this higher cloud layer in order to get
a "fix." The planes could have drifted far and fast in that hec-
tic hour's time.

"Tell them to keep on up till we get above the 'secondary.'
Everyone okay over there?"

"Yeah," says Ben presently, "but from what Crowder reports,
Number Six was iced up heavier than any of us. It's almost all
gone now though. He had a lot of vibration in the tail."

"Hmmm, it was close going all the way round, eh?"

"Yeah, sort o'." He gives me another of those vague looks
that speak more adequately than the uttered remark. He picks

up the log and starts writing. Each crew is responsible for a complete record of the flight, with particular emphasis on plane performance and the weather. The data will be of great value to pilots making subsequent flights, just as that of some of those who have gone before us are coming in handy this trip.

There is just a hint of the moon through the striated layer of altocumulus just above; a small blot of light appearing as if through a pane of yellow frosted glass. The plane is enveloped in a weird pall of cloud for just a moment, then it emerges into a strange new world. There is a floor of bumpy pearl, and here and there billowy bits of cumulus tumble along the floor like pieces of cotton blown by a draught. The ceiling is bluer than the ocean 14,000 feet below, almost navy blue, and thousands of glittering stars and planets wink back and forth at one another. This is the sky that the landlubber never sees. This is that vastness of which I thought when the cabin door banged shut more than three hours ago back there in Newfoundland.

IV

Just how far back that was I shall soon know. Ben takes his sextant and chronometer and goes aft. I turn the ship over to the gyro pilot again. The robot is indeed a gadget of aliases. In the States he's popularly known as "Iron Mike." The Pan American Airways boys call him "Filbert." Those of us in the service of Canada or the R.A.F. refer to him as "George." The sergeant comes forward presently and sits down to his little table and begins figuring.

Our position is "fixed" at 52 degrees, 20 minutes, 30 seconds North, by 41 degrees, five minutes West. The blow downstairs carried us a little over three miles north of the course, but, at the same time it pushed the ship along at a nice clip. We have averaged 242 knots (283 miles) per hour for the past two hours, and are approaching the "equitime point." In fact, it is a matter of 13 minutes.

I wish I had looked at the clock a little later, or earlier; for this is the critical point beyond which there is no turning back in the event of trouble. From here on it's keep on. The position is considerably short of the half-way mark because of the westerly winds. Should we attempt to return from beyond this spot the planes would be bucking strong headwinds all the way.

Gas would run out before we reached land, much less the air-port.

The air temperature is way down again, but we've no fear of ice up here because the clouds and precipitation are far below. Wonder what it's doing down there beneath the shimmering floor? The airspace is truly a thought-inspiring vista, and there is plenty of time for thinking. An occasional message to the other ships, an adjustment now and then to keep "George" in line with the compass, or to trim ship, is all that is required. Ben took another "sight" shortly after we returned to the original course, and all is well.

The moonlight, coming down from more of an angle now, makes the red-white-and-blue cocarde on the wing stand out in contrast to the patchy camouflage. Makes one think about what lies in store ahead. This ship will soon be in service with the R.A.F.'s coastal command, dumping great yellow "eggs" upon Nazi shipping and invasion springboards from France's Biscay ports to Norway. In the States we hear mostly of the fighter and bomber commands, but there are seven of these commands in existence and another is being planned. There is the training command, which is concerned with the procurement of pilots, observer-gunners, navigators, bombardiers, radiomen, armorers, mechanics, and various miscellaneous personnel. The balloon command includes most of the Auxiliary Air Force groups—composed of men who followed civilian pursuits and studied aviation subjects during the evenings and week-ends—and these men man the barrage of "old floppies." Then there are maintenance and reserve commands: the former comprises all the R.A.F. utility squadrons—troop transports, cargo and ambulance planes—and the latter includes all types of craft for replacement or supplementary purposes. The several American pilots who are ferrying ships from factory to aerodrome are civilian members of the reserve command. The new unit, according to rumor in the Dominion, will soon go into service and will be known as the army co-operation command.

These units form the keystone of R.A.F. organization, and they are divided into junior echelons known as "groups," each of which has its own headquarters and controls a number of "stations." These, in turn, comprise a number of twelve-plane squadrons.

At the moment it is smooth sailing with our half-squadron. The pretty pearl floor is cracking up. Fissures and great gaping chasms appear here and there like those caused by some aerial earthquake. The ragged edges of the separating clouds indicate wind and lots of it.

Ben breaks the long silence, "It's kind of lonesome, isn't it?"

"Yeah. Wouldn't mind seeing a ship or two for a change. This overcast is breaking up fast now."

In an hour only scattered clouds round the horizon are to be seen. These are the formations never seen over land. The fluffy, shadowed domes of the clouds remind me of pictures of the balloon barrage. They are fairly equally spaced and the rounded tops all lean in the same direction. "Old floppies" guarding the edge of the world. It is easy to appreciate the feelings and beliefs of the pre-Columbus mariners. In flying over land the scenery slides out of the horizon's edge like a painted panorama on rollers. At sea there is only the water, a vast wavy reach that finally meets the sky far away. Only a landfall breaks the monotony; ships just seem to be little chips wandering around in the watery expanse, a part of the seascape.

The moon is way down and the stars grow dim. One spot on the edge of the world is silvery gray, then the grayness spreads slowly over the sky to blot out all but the morning star. Ben has just finished taking a "sight"; the next one he shoots will be Old Sol, for the sun is already on the way up. Gray dawn gives way to a pink glow.

I turn and watch Number Three riding the morning currents; then, to break the monotony, I take the Adlis gun and shoot off, "won't be long now." It is 05:03 Greenwich time, which, incidentally, we have been using throughout the flight. The sun has been up for an hour in London, but it will not rise for another three hours back at Newfoundland; that will only be 06:03 local time.

"We shouldn't even see it yet if we were down close to the water, should we?" asked Ben.

"Nope, just a glow." We are still maintaining the 14,000-foot level, and from up here one gets a "preview" of a sort. But maybe it's too pretty. There is that old saying, "Red in the morning sailors take warning." I have seen it happen more than once.

"Gosh, that's beautiful," remarks Ben, turning from the out-spread charts on the little table. The imagination goes to work. We seem to be looking at a mill furnace from behind an opaque-glass screen. A steel ball is being heated by raging, red-orange fires; the ball is a different shade of red. As the heat mounts the glass screen becomes more and more transparent and the ball assumes a pinkish hue. It keeps fading in color but gets lighter and hotter. Then the ball comes to white heat and the fires beneath fade out as if their job were finished. The now molten white ball is the sun; the fading fires are the reflections; the opaque screen in the haze over the seascape, but now it is almost gone. This is the airman's sunrise.

There's another flash on Ben's mirror. He turns and takes down the message. "Number Five's heating up again!"

"Oh—ooh!" It might run better at a lower lever where the air is not so rare. He can lean out the mixture more too. "We're going to have to go down. Won't get as much tailwind, and we'll have to slow up a bit for Blythe, but it might help."

After an exchange of signals I ease down into a steep glide. When we level out again the altimeters read an even 1000 feet. Number Five's engine cooled off somewhat during the long descent, but whether or not the cylinder-head temperatures will stay within safe limits remains to be seen. Leaning the mixture helps if the engine is run at reduced speed—which is why we have to slow up—but this procedure can make the engine run even hotter if r.p.m.'s are kept high. A lean mixture, because of the bigger percentage of air to gasoline, burns somewhat more slowly than the comparatively rich mixture we use to get maximum power output.

More trouble appears in the distance; maybe that sunrise was too red. I point over the nose, "Look what's coming."

Out of the southeast comes a crazy line of low clouds whose topmost masses shimmer white in the climbing sun's rays. But there is nothing pretty about their ominous gray undersides, from which slanting, blurred curtains of squall rain streak. Again we close up the formation, but not too tightly this time.

The squall blots out the sun and races toward us at what appears, from the distance, to be great speed. The big bomber sloughs in the rough air immediately preceding the squall line, but she rights instantly. "George's" mechanical mitt is steadier on the controls than any human hand could possibly be. We must keep low. In order to climb through the oncoming blow we should have to use almost full power—too much work for a sick motor. Number Five's misbehaving Cyclone will have to be nursed until we make a landfall.

First there is fine mist, then churning gray rain sloshes against the cabin windshield, topside, and side windows. We're now "on instruments" and "George" will keep us so. Suppose for some unlikely reason our Cyclones or those of one of the other ships should falter. I know that the ocean is seething just like the sky, and I realize too that if we should plow into a 15-foot wave at 235 knots this aluminum bird would be smashed into twisted ruins, much the same as if it had hit a mountain peak.

"Wonder how Blythe is making out?" shouts Ben above the shriek of wind and spraying rain.

"Just keep your fingers crossed, fellow!"

It lets up a bit outside, and just when I begin to hope, it pours harder than ever. I keep a wary eye on the air temperature. Ice at this low level would be pretty bad medicine. But the outside air-water combination seems relatively warm.

Ben looks up from his charts. "If we haven't been pushed very far north we should be just a few miles south of the Porcupine Bank!"

Now the blow seems to be subsiding. The rain is streaked and no longer appears as a liquid wall. Then it assumes a bluish cast. This means we are coming out of it. The Hudson is enveloped in a golden explosion of dazzling sunlight. It is slick and wet and the now bright light glistens on the wing. Number Three rides along almost in the same position as when we entered the pall.

"See the others, Ben?"

"Here's Two. Four and Six are back farther, and Five is just breaking out. Wonder how her engine's going?" Then he puts the signal gun to work.

"Sun's up good now, I'll take a 'sight' and compare notes with Gregg." Then he goes aft. I check our fuel consumption meanwhile. This is done on a plotted chart determining the gas used against the miles flown. When Ben returns and reports our position as 52 degrees, 50 minutes North by 12 degrees, 50 minutes West, we can compute almost the exact mileage. We are 10 miles north of the course and just an hour and 50 minutes from our destination.

V

Shortly after we return to the course I sight three fishing smacks, the first craft seen throughout the whole trip. The sun is again blotted out by some higher clouds which do not look too forbidding. They look friendly in fact compared with what I think I see in the southeast—something I have been uneasy about for the past couple of hours.

I give Ben rapid instructions and he starts sending with the signal gun. Still I am hoping against hope that what I see isn't what I am so certain it is. Here we are so near and yet so far from "home." I grab the glasses to make certain.

Ben says, "Blythe's engine is still too hot, but a burned-out engine's better than being done in. . . ." Which is right enough. *Nine Nazi Heinkel bombers are coming our way!*

I disengage "George," take over the controls, and boost the Hudson up in the steepest S-climb she will take. If we can get into the cloud bank before the Nazis cross us we can outrun them by a good bit. The other ships draw in closer. But Heinkels also are drawing closer. They change course suddenly; their leader must have guessed our purpose. If we only had some armament I should welcome the scramble although I'm supposed to be a non-combatant.

Ben switches on the radio compass and turns the little crank that swings the tuning pointer; the idea being that we are near enough to tune-in *** station once we get into the clouds, flying on instruments until we shake the Heinkels. If we can't shake them—and it is going to be a close race for the protecting clouds—our only hope is that one of the trawlers is an "official boat," sees what is happening and radios *** for help.

We're going to need it. Jerry has the advantage of altitude, and the three, three-plane V's slant down at our practically helpless ships. It's no secret that the trans-Atlantic bombers fly unarmed; the Germans know this, which is why they're so anxious for "combat."

I signal for the Hudsons to break formation. The pilots

know what else to do. A formation of unarmed planes is too good a target.

We scatter but of course continue to climb for the ceiling. Here they come. Gray threading tracers stream out from the noses of the leading V. Then there's a staccato drumming of bullets through the starboard wing. I can feel it in the controls, and something about my stomach feels vague and empty. Bullets *pang* through the plastic glass in the nose, and the emptiness in my stomach crowds into my dry throat where there doesn't seem to be room for it! I kick rudder and slip out of the fire. The Nazis scream by, hardly 20 feet overhead.

There are more bullets—probably from their floor guns— then the prayed-for clouds loom up ahead. I look back at Number Three; she is apparently okay, but we are too far away to tell.

"See the others, Ben?"

"Only a couple. Everything's all mixed up. Here they come again, same three I think!" His voice is unsteady, even as I know mine is. It's one hell of a feeling.

Tracers thread across the port wing from behind just as our ship is swallowed by the murky, semi-darkness of the cloud. It's like seeking refuge in a cave of some sort.

"We're all right now, boy!" I cry almost convincingly. Ben is pale. I don't think it was so convincing as it sounded to me.

He fiddles with the radio compass' course-indicator sensitivity knob and I turn the ship slowly until the compass pointer is perfectly vertical. Jerry may be looking for us to come through on top of the clouds, or maybe they expect us to drop down again. We, however, are staying right in here. The blacker it gets the better I'll feel. I shall never again cuss clouds—even stormy ones—so long as I fly.

The compass pointer waves slightly to the left, toward the little "L" on the dial, and I know by this that the ship is to the left of the heading toward the radio station to which we are tuned. A bit of rudder swings the Hudson back in line. I throttle back the engines to cruising speed once more, and now we are making 212 knots.

"Wonder how the others are getting on?" Ben asks.

"We can only hope, Ben. I think we'll all make it okay, unless both of the crew should happen to be badly hit. The ships can take it. Glad those Heinkels weren't pursuits. Wonder what they were doing so far out anyhow?" I'm feeling very voluble now.

We come out into sunshine again—a hole in the clouds—then back into the murk. A strange fascination—like that which prompts a criminal to return to the scene of a crime—or, more properly, just plain curiosity—makes me want to sneak down to see what has become of Jerry. Also to see if I can spot any of the other planes. I play safe for about fifteen minutes more, however, before I ease down into the clear.

"There's Ireland, boy!" I shout.

Ben just says, "Ummmm!" An expression of combined gladness and relief.

VI

Looking up from his map, Ben says, "We can start letting down"—altitude is now 6300 feet—"in just 50 minutes if we speed up a bit."

"Right, fellow. We've plenty of gas, even for another blow over the edge of the Irish Sea. Let's get this over with."

I open up to 80 per cent cruising speed for the sprint down the home stretch. Once more land gives way to water, but only for a few minutes. As I nose down into the long power glide and England's shore looms on the far horizon, I feel like a long-lost little boy coming home. This is a home that is strange to me, though.

Ben and I both spot the aerodrome at the same moment. Our descent has been nicely timed, and we arrive over the field with 450 feet altitude. As we circle Ben points and hollers, "Here come three of 'em!" I glance up only for a second, my attention being on landing.

Ben sets the hydraulic valve for the landing gear, and the Hudson slows as the wheels gain their downward-hanging position. When the wing flaps drop she hesitates still more. I adjust the elevator-tab control, then bring her in. The wheels touch, the Hudson bounces ever so slightly, then sits down heavily as though tired from the long flight.

Ben says, "Exactly eight hours and fifty-six minutes! Not bad, eh?"

"Not at all." Owing to the fact that we flew at times faster than usual, we lopped almost an hour off the usual flight time. I suddenly feel very tired as I taxi the plane to the edge of the aerodrome. With the exception of a few bullet holes, the ship has been delivered in good condition, and the others—crippled Number Five bringing up the rear—are coming in for the landings.

The place doesn't look like an aerodrome at all. There are just a few camouflaged sheds or "huts" and a lot of sandbags. Men of the Ground Section taxi the recently landed bombers out across the meadow in different directions, and presently they just seem to disappear. Each ship is rolled into a "bay," or pit bordered with sandbags. These are scattered over the field so that no more than one or two ships would be destroyed by a single bomb if raiders came.

Now I have a contract which says something to the effect that I am to make 23 more trips, two each month. The worst part of it all will be going back to Newfoundland on a freighter. Shipping is dangerous business these days.

Topics for Discussion

1. How does a "propeller dissolve into the drifting lake fog"?

2. What is "retractable landing gear"? How is it drawn up?

3. Someone find out about "George," the gyropilot, and report.

4. Do the same for radio-compass.

5. Explain the international law about armed civilians.

6. What are "Lockheeds"?

7. Why is the flight made from Newfoundland, and not from Detroit, Los Angeles, Quebec, or New York?

8. What does a "fuel selector" do?

9. What are "wing flops?" Are they the same as ailerons?

10. What is r.p.m.? m.p.h.?

11. What is: a prop; a stick; a "fix"; stratus; cumulus; terrain; drift check; fuselage; nacelle; nautical mile; synchronoscope; thermocouple; avigation; glass enclosed nose; drift indicator (how is it used?) aerological; striated; alto-cumulus; ceiling; sextant; chronometer; robot; "aliases upstairs"; "downstairs"; "equitime point"; airscape; armorer; "old floppy"; echelon; seascape; Greenwich time; sloughs; tracer bullets.

12. Learn to pronounce: camouflage; fuselage; nacelle; synchronoscope; barometric; avigation; aerological; striated; chronometer; robot; aliases; cocarde; echelon; Greenwich; opaque; sloughs; Heinkel; pursuit planes; voluble.

13. How does the pilot spell out or signal or question with the Adlis gun?

14. Describe the duties of the co-pilot (who is also the navigator on this trip).

15. Were you anxious about the outcome of the flight or did you have confidence in the ships getting through? Why?

TO POETS AND AIRMEN

By Stephen Spender

THINKERS and airmen—all such
　　Friends and pilots upon the edge
　　Of the skies of the future—much
You require a bullet's eye of courage
To fly through this age.

The paper brows are winged and helmeted,
　　The blind ankles bound to a white road,
Which streams into a night of lead
　　Where cities explode.
　　Fates unload

Hatred burning, in small parcels,
　　Outrage against social lies,
Hearts breaking against stone refusals
　　Of men to show small mercies
　　To men. Now death replies
Releasing new, familiar devils.

And yet, before you throw away your childhood
　　With the lambs pasturing in flaxen hair,
　　To plunge into this iron war,
Remember for a flash the wild good
　　Drunkenness where
　　You abandoned future care.

And then forget. Become what
　　Things require. The expletive word.
　　The all-night-long screeching metal bird.
And all of time shut down in one shot
　　Of night by a gun uttered.

[1] From *Ruins and Visions* by Stephen Spender. Copyright by Random House, New York.

For the joy that was is hidden under grass,
  Shadows of hawks flicker over.
Buried in cellars is laughter that once was
  Which the pick and shovel endeavor
  Vainly to uncover;
Like a child buried when the raiders pass.

With axe and shovel men hunt among the bricks,
  With lamps and water, for their soul
Of lilac in the city square; they hack with picks
  Amongst the ruins for their love's goal,
  As though a smile frozen at the North Pole
Might take pity on their tricks.

THE SCORE[1]

By Robb White

BOYS are inclined to get into occupations that call for all the qualities they possess. In the following story the question of aviation and submarine duty comes up. Can you think of anything in the way of skill, strength of character, and courage that aviation demands more than submarine service calls for, or the reverse? Does Robb White convince you that he is writing out of first-hand experience?

* * * * *

Lieutenant Joe Gilbert looked with interest at the submarines coming in and tying up at the dock. The ships were painted a dull black all over except for gun breeches and a little brass work. They looked deadly, Joe thought, watching them. And they looked extremely small. They were O-boats which had been out of commission since 1920 and were being put back into service.

"I wouldn't be caught dead in one of those things," Joe said to an ensign who had escorted him into the area.

The ensign glanced down at the submarine insignia—a gold dolphin—on his chest and then, surreptitiously, at the wings on Joe Gilbert's. It was not the ensign's duty to argue with a superior but, like all submarine men, he had no use for these aviators who did nothing but push a little stick back and forth and drew pay-and-a-half for it. Now, submarine men *worked* for a living.

Then, on the O-22, Joe Gilbert spotted a familiar face. An officer in a slicker and battered old uniform cap was conning his ship to the dock. "Isn't that Lieut. Strong?" Joe asked the ensign.

"Yes, sir."

"He was my roommate at the Academy," Joe remarked.

[1] From *Boys' Life*, May, 1942. Reprinted through the courtesy of the author and *Boys' Life*, published by the Boy Scouts of America.

"Haven't seen him for years." He walked closer to the dock and waved. "Hi, sucker," he called.

Bren Strong, from the conning tower of the submarine, looked at his old roommate, so spick and span in his aviator's khaki. "Hi, boy. What are you doing here?" Then he added, to the crew, "Double up, fore and aft."

"Thought I'd come and see how the other half lives," Joe answered. "When are you coming ashore?"

"In roughly five seconds," Bren answered. "I've got a forty-eight hour leave."

Joe snorted and made some crack about the easy life of submarine people. In the meantime he was studying Bren carefully for he had not seen him for two years. There were deeper crow's feet wrinkles at the corners of Bren's eyes now, and he looked tired. But it was the same old Bren except that now he was commanding his own ship and doing it well. Joe could tell that by the way Bren gave his orders and the way the crew obeyed them.

Standing there waiting for Bren to secure Joe thought back over the years and he felt a little warm spot in his heart. He and Bren had had a good time at the Academy—and elsewhere. And as he thought he remembered their old rivalry, a rivalry which had never died and which they had never openly admitted even existed.

Joe felt very peaceful and good as he thought of that. For the score stood, and had stood for two years, Joe Gilbert one up on Bren Strong.

He remembered that on graduation it had been all even, but now it was one up because Bren had not gone into aviation. Joe admitted that Bren's mother, who hated flying, had kept him out, but it made no difference. In this rivalry no quarter was asked or given.

But as he waited, thinking about it, he wondered if Bren could possibly consider the score still even? After all, duty in submarines was plenty tough. Some of Joe's satisfaction died as he considered that. And there was no way of finding out what Bren thought for neither had ever mentioned the fact that they were rivals. But, Joe thought that the score ought to be settled, definitely. If Bren thought it was all even instead of one up for Joe then something should be done about it.

Swift twin-motored fighting ships, the Lockheed P-38's, in formation

And as Bren, in a clean uniform, came toward him across the dock an idea blossomed in Joe's mind. Bren had a forty-eight hour leave and Joe had a brand new airplane.

"Glad to see you, Joe," Bren said. "Loafing as usual."

"My eye." Joe clapped Bren on the back and said, "Hi ya, you sardine sailor?"

"The fearless birdman," Bren said.

Under this there was a great deal of affection and they looked at each other almost shyly, for they liked each other.

"Forty-eight hour leave, eh?" said Joe. "What are you going to do with it?"

"Don't know."

Joe chortled inside. The plan was working out very nicely. "I'll tell you what to do with it. I've got to go down to Norfolk, coming back Tuesday. Come with me."

"Suits me."

"I'll borrow a 'chute for you," Joe said, carefully watching Bren's expression.

" 'Chute?"

Joe could hardly restrain his glee at the way things were working. "Yeh, we're flying."

"Flying?" Bren asked, in just the right tone. Wavery.

"Sure."

Then Bren grinned. "You know, I've never even been *in* an airplane."

"Can't start any younger. Come on."

"Now," Joe thought as he settled himself in the front cockpit and locked his belt, "we'll just decide for sure how the score stands." He glanced back at Bren and noted with satisfaction that Bren's face was tight and a little white showed at the corners of his mouth. "Bren, old man," Joe said to himself, "when you get out of this airplane your knees will be knocking knots on each other and your face will look like a pile of ashes."

He gave the torpedo-bomber the gun and raced down the runway. Trees at the edge of the field slid under his folding landing gear and he began to circle for altitude. At ten thousand feet he flipped on the intercockpit phone and said, "How you lak, boy?"

"Fine," Bren said.

Joe grinned. "Just wait," he said to himself, "just—wait."

In the phone he said, "I'm flying blind to Norfolk. Suppose you handle the radio for me? Might as well learn *something* about navigation."

"Where I navigate," Bren answered, "we don't have the whole earth to steer by. We're under water."

Joe didn't answer as he got on the Washington beam and turned the switch which connected Bren's rear cockpit radio. "Hear that steady buzz?" he asked. "Now, listen to it change to *dit-dah* as I turn." He swung the plane over, hearing the *dit-dah* emerge from the beam. "Now listen for the *dah-dit* on the other side. Got it? The object is to keep on the beam so you listen and let me know whether to swing right or left."

"Okay," Bren answered. "Got it."

Joe noticed then that the sun was setting in an ugly gray mass. Everything was playing right into his hands. He knew from aerology's report that in a few hours there would be a cloud blanket over the earth at three thousand feet. They wouldn't be able to see anything through that. Joe chuckled and said to himself, "Bren, boy, you're in for a bad night."

Then, as the plane swept on through the night sky, they talked, kidding each other mercilessly as they told what they had done out in the Fleet. Joe had finished a stretch as instructor at Pensacola and had come in from a carrier to the new base in Massachusetts. Bren had done a dull two years ashore and then, when he was hoping for duty in the big, fine V type subs, he had been ordered to the ancient O-boats.

They discussed these and Joe realized that submarine duty was plenty hard. Especially in O-boats. Out of commission for twenty years they were not what they should be. Joe could detect in Bren's voice a trace not of fear, of course, but of deep concern for himself and his men.

"Those pig boats are out for you—all the time," Bren said.

Then at last it was time to start really working on Bren, Joe decided, grinning in the darkness. They had passed over Washington and were riding the Norfolk beam. Below there was nothing but a sheet of darkness for the clouds at three thousand covered everything.

Joe reached over and jiggled the switch of Bren's radio listening with satisfaction to the blast of static it caused. After a few seconds of this he let the beam come in again, then went on with the static. At last he switched off Bren's radio entirely.

Bren reacted on the dot. "I can't hear the beam any more. There was a lot of static and then she went off."

In an awestruck voice Joe said, "What? *What?*"

"The radio's dead," Bren said.

Joe put his mouth close to the mike and gasped. Then he leaned forward, jerkily, and pretended to work on the radio. Instead he carefully tuned the Norfolk beam in on his own outfit.

He straightened at last and said in a low, quiet voice, "She's dead all right."

"What do we do now?" Bren asked.

Slowly Joe answered him. "Nothing, Bren. I'll try to keep on a compass course but there's quite a wind blowing."

"Why not go down and look around?" Bren suggested.

Joe almost laughed out loud. Then he said, soberly, "Good idea."

He dove down toward the cloud bank. When he was a few hundred feet above it he slowed up to be sure that Bren appreciated fully what flying inside a cloud meant. Around them the sky was lit with moonlight and the stars. The next instant the cloud folded around them and it seemed as though they had flown into a cave. The lights from the panels were reflected on gray foam streaming past.

Joe left them in there for awhile and then began to climb out again. Making his voice shake a little, he said, "I'm afraid to go any lower. No telling what's inside there—mountains, steeples, power lines."

Bren didn't answer as the plane tore away from the clouds and sailed out into the brilliant night above.

"Nice mess," Bren remarked. "Got any ideas, Joe?"

"Keep your shirt on, we haven't crashed yet," Joe said in a kind voice. "We'll keep on flying in the general direction of Norfolk and maybe we'll find a hole in these clouds."

"And—if—we—don't?" Bren asked.

Joe choked back his glee and said, "I'll go ahead until the gas is almost gone then head due east. If we aren't too far inland we'll crash at sea. It's softer than smacking the ground."

"Yeh," Bren said.

It was getting him all right, Joe decided. He glanced back and saw Bren's face in the panel light. His jaw was set and his face looked pale. Joe noticed that he was holding on to a longeron. He had to turn quickly so that Bren wouldn't see him.

"What do we do if we crash at sea?" Bren asked finally.

"Well, when we come down, if you see that it's water try to get your 'chute off. It may drown you if you don't." Then Joe added slowly, "I'll try to crash her easy."

"See that you do," Bren said.

"If she flips over on her back—which she probably will—try to get your safety belt unbuckled before you drown."

"Good idea," Bren said. Then he added, "Boy, I wish I was back on that safe old submarine of mine."

"Keep your shirt on," Joe said.

"It's on," Bren answered, "even if it is rolling up and down my back like a window blind."

Joe could taste victory as he banked steeply, preparing to land on the Norfolk beam.

Bren's voice said, quietly, "Is this—it, Joe?"

"Don't know," Joe answered, trying to get the right tone in his voice. "But if this is it, well, Bren—"

"Skip it," Bren said. "I'm not fish bait yet."

"I'm going—down," Joe said. "By dead reckoning we should be close to Norfolk. If we aren't I'm turning east—for the sea."

Bren didn't answer as the clouds wrapped around the plane again. Joe settled dead on the beam and went on down. At a thousand feet, knowing that Bren would see the field lights in a moment, he said, quietly, "Bren."

"What?"

"I'm sorry about this."

"So am I, Joe."

"If we strike something try to relax. Okay, good luck, Bren.

"Good—good luck, Joe."

Then Joe saw the faint beads of light marking the runway. He put the landing gear down and rolled down his flaps. He shook with laughter as he remembered Bren saying, "Good—good luck, Joe."

Gray fog writhed on the runway as he put her down and taxied to the hangars.

When he cut the gun Bren said in a cold voice, "This is Norfolk, I presume."

"Yep."

"Joe," Bren said.

"Aye, aye?"

"O—kay," Bren said.

Back at the submarine base Joe was still kidding Bren about
that "Good—good luck, Joe" thing.

"Take it easy," Bren answered. "I'll get you for that, Joe, if I
have to live to be an admiral."

But Joe only snorted with laughter and reminded Bren of
the window blind remark.

At the dock they started to say good bye when Bren suddenly
said, "Why don't you come aboard? We're doing some routine
stuff. You might like it."

"Not on your life!" Joe said. "You're just trying to get back
at me."

Bren looked at him scornfully. "I work for a living. I don't
go around scaring little children and submarine people. Just
thought you'd like to see a pig boat at work."

Joe hesitated, not trusting him too far. "No tricks?" he asked.

Bren waved at the long line of submarines leaving the docks.
"Do they look like they're going out to frolic around like a
bunch of aviators?" he demanded.

"All right, I'll go. But if you pull anything—"

"Forget it," Bren said. "Do you think I'd give the commanding officer a chance to jump down my throat just to have some
fun with you? Forget it."

On board the submarine Joe stood beside Bren as he conned
his ship out into the line of submarines heading for the open
sea. "Outside we'll go below," Bren said. "Why don't you go
down now and change your clothes? Hate to see you get your
pretty aviator's suit all fouled up with grease." He turned to a
sailor and said, "Take Mr. Gilbert below and outfit him with
a suit of coveralls."

In a few minutes Joe, in coveralls, started back up through
the conning tower but met Bren coming down. "We're ready to
dive," he said, passing Joe and going into the crowded control
room. One wall of this was covered solidly with switches and

dials, the other with valves and gadgets, the third with lockers, while on the forward bulkhead were more dials, these with large faces and big indicator needles. In the center of the room was the big column of the periscope, shiny with oil. Joe stood out of the way of the working men and looked around.

He was impressed by the way Bren handled his men, gave his orders. Some skippers Joe had served under believed in rattling off a multitude of orders as though the men were completely unintelligent machines. But Bren said only, "Take her down to thirty feet."

Then he turned and grinned at Joe. "Don't mind if I seem a little nervous, Joe," he said quietly. "Because I *am* a little nervous. Until we get these boats into top shape they're dangerous.

Joe could feel nothing but the throb of the engines. There was no sensation of slipping below the water except that he could no longer hear the slap-slap of waves against the hull. There seemed now no outside noise at all.

"Down periscope," Bren ordered. "Course one six five, speed four." Then to Joe: "Just routine stuff. We'll go out, pick up a destroyer acting as target; fire some fish at her. After that we'll do a few dives and come home."

"Soft life," Joe said. He looked around at the room with the men working in silence at their posts. "How do you know how deep you are?"

Bren pointed to one of the largest dials. Joe watched the needle moving slowly between 25 and 30 feet. The dial registered beyond 300 feet. "Will this thing go down three hundred feet?" he asked.

Bren stared at him. "Man, *no!*" he exclaimed. "At two hundred feet she'd fold up like a paper bag. She might have done it twenty years ago, but I hope I'm not aboard when she does it again."

One of the crew, sitting over a radio affair with headphones on, reported then: "Target bearing six zero."

Bren glanced at his chart board and said, "Starboard motor full ahead, port motor stop. Bow tubes stand by."

The listener kept reporting the target's bearing and Joe watched Bren plotting the course of his ship and the target.

Even though it was only practice Joe could feel the tension mounting, feel the expectancy and the hope among the men. They wanted to do a good job—to score a hit—even in practice. It made Joe feel good to see them.

Then Bren said quietly, "Bow tubes ready. Fire one and two.

Joe felt nothing but he could imagine the torpedoes roaring from their tubes as they sped toward the target.

Then Bren was snapping out orders. "All stop. Down one hundred. Stand by stern tubes."

There was complete silence in the submarine then. Joe glanced at the depth gauge and saw the needle sliding past 50 feet. Bren came over beside him. "If this was real that destroyer or a screen would be dropping depth bombs like a handful of gravel. We're silent now and they can't get any bearings on us. When we get down to a hundred feet we'll sneak away."

"Sounds good," Joe said. Then he wiped the sweat off his brow. "Is it always as hot as this?"

Bren grinned. "Oh, the life of a sailor," he said. "Especially a submarine sailor."

When Joe glanced at the depth gauge again it read 95. He was amused to think that he was now 95 feet below the ocean's surface in a boat which looked, from a plane, like an oversized cigar.

He turned then as a petty officer came and talked in low tones to Bren. Bren stood a moment thinking and then said, quietly, "Put all you've got on them." The petty officer nodded and hurried away.

"What's the trouble?" Joe asked. He could feel just a faint prickle along his spine.

Bren grinned. "Nothing. Little trouble pumping tanks, that's all."

Joe could hear machinery running with a low, annoying whine and he was badly startled when one of the electric circuit breakers on the board went with a flash and crash of juice. Bren stared at it as a man jumped to the board and began throwing the big brass switches.

The petty officer ran back. "She blew, sir," he said, his face serious but not, as far as Joe could tell, worried.

Bren nodded and glanced at the depth gauge. Joe looked at

it, too, and the needle was still moving at 135. He went over beside Bren. "Anything wrong?" he asked.

Bren shook his head. "These old boats are cranky. We'll get her stopped in a minute."

"What's she doing?" Joe asked.

"Sinking," Bren said and went to the switchboard.

The word grabbed at Joe's throat. Sinking? How far? And how far could she sink before she folded up? Joe got his feet working and followed Bren. Looking back over his shoulder he saw the depth gauge at one hundred and eighty feet.

"How's she doing?" he asked.

But Bren only glanced at him and then turned again to the dials on the bulkhead. Joe stared at them but they were all meaningless to him.

Then it suddenly occurred to Joe that this was just a gag of Bren's. Old Bren was just trying to get back at him for that Norfolk business.

Joe laughed out loud and clapped Bren on the back. "Give up, Bren," he said. "I've caught on. And I'm not scaring today."

Bren turned slowly and looked at him. Joe saw that the muscles of his jaws were standing out and there was no smile in his eyes or mouth. Bren did not say a word as he stared at Joe for a moment and then turned back to the dials.

Joe looked at the other men. They were all at their posts and they were not smiling. He went back to the periscope and stood there, waiting. Somewhere in the vitals of the sub a machine began to run again and Joe listened to it eagerly and realized that the sound of it was just like the sight of an open field to a flier when his engine had quit on him and there seemed to be nothing but forest below.

Then the machine stopped. The dead, thick silence started again.

The petty officer came in—running. He and Bren whispered together for a moment then the petty officer ran back.

The machine began to hum again. In a few seconds it stopped. Joe, who was watching Bren, saw him shake his head slowly and speak to the man at the switches.

The depth gauge read two hundred and ten feet! Joe looked at it with horror and went over to Bren. "It says two-ten," he said, and noticed that he, too, was whispering.

Bren whirled around, staring at the depth gauge for a second then whirling back and hurrying toward the small oval door leading into the engine room.

It was then, as Joe walked back to the periscope, that he noticed the thinness of the air. He thought at first that it was just the stinking, oily heat but as he stood there breathing deeply he felt as though his lungs weren't getting anything. The air did not feel solid and good but thin.

Joe stripped the knot of his tie down and unbuttoned his collar. That helped a little and for a few breaths his lungs were all right. Then it began again, the thinness of the air.

Almost gasping Joe fought for air until he felt the dizziness creeping up from his starving lungs. He put both hands down on the chart table to steady himself and was standing thus when Bren came back in. Bren hardly glanced at him as he walked over to the depth gauge and tapped it with his forefinger. The noise seemed loud and clear in the silence. The needle jumped —ahead—to two hundred and thirty feet.

Bren came over beside Joe. "We're still sinking and the pressure's too great for the pumps now. But our rate of sinking is much slower. That's a good sign."

Joe nodded.

"Air's getting pretty thin," Bren said. "But we'll be out of this soon."

Joe, remembering newspaper headlines, said, "Out of it?"

Bren grinned a little. "I've sent up distress flares and smudges. They'll have us on the surface soon."

"Hope so." Then Joe looked at Bren and said, quietly, "Bren, I hope this isn't a gag."

Bren looked at him as he had before and Joe was very sorry that he had said it.

A quartermaster came in. "Bad forward, sir," he reported.

"Have the men stand by the escape hatch," Bren ordered. Then he went to a locker and got a small packet, wrapped in khaki. "Here's a Momsen lung for you, Joe."

Joe took the thing and looked at it. It was somewhat like a gas mask with mouth and nose piece and a flat bladder at the end of the tube.

"If they don't get us up soon we'll have to use them," Bren said.

Joe turned the thing over in his hands. "Are they—any good?" he asked. He heard his voice trembling then and the sound of it seemed to release something for a cold shiver went up his spine and out across his shoulders.

Bren grinned a little and said, "They're like your parachutes, Joe. If they don't work the first time the Navy Department will give you a new one."

Joe was about to laugh when, from forward, there came a long, loud, ringing bang. It sounded as though someone had struck an iron hoop with a sledge. Bren leaped through the door and vanished while Joe stood there not needing to be told that the noise was made by the tons of pressure outside at last cracking the old steel plates of the sub. Now he knew that it wasn't a gag—the submarine was collapsing, its thin walls being crushed inward.

He was standing there, sweat pouring down his face, his throat rasping for breath when Bren came running back. "All hands stand by the escape hatch," he snapped.

Men came running from every direction, the Momsen lungs swinging on their chests. "Go ahead, Joe," said Bren. "They'll show you how to use the lung."

Joe started to argue but Bren gave him a little shove and when he spoke again it was as the captain of the ship. "Go ahead, Joe." Then his voice softened and he said, "I'll be along."

Joe joined the men climbing a ladder. On the ladder they were waiting their turn, going up one by one through a heavy steel door above them.

A man in front of Joe showed him how to inflate the lung and clamp the face piece on. "Just take it easy, sir, on the way up," the man said and climbed up into the escape hatch.

Then it was Joe's turn. He climbed through the door and crawled into a small, circular chamber just about big enough for his body. Above his head was a second door with a huge lever lock. He had been told to let water in then climb out. An automatic pump got the water out for the next man.

For a moment Joe stood motionless, thinking. Then he opened the valve. Water roared in on him. Joe, breathing frantically into the mouthpiece and hearing the panting hollow sound of it in the bladder on his chest, felt above his head for the lever lock. Outside that door, he knew, was the ocean.

Joe opened the door above his head and climbed out of the sub, closing the door behind him. With his eyes shut he felt with his feet and hands until all was ready. Then, with nearly three hundred feet to go upward, he pushed off from the sunken hull. Terror gripped him and he was not ashamed of it and he started swimming. If the lung collapsed under that enormous pressure he knew that he would be crushed to death. Or, if the oxygen gave out before he reached the surface, he would drown.

With this thought driving him he forgot his instructions to take it easy and began swimming upward with all his might. His hands and feet clawed and beat at the water and his breath began to sob into the lung but he went on fighting his way.

He broke the surface with a terrible splash and for a moment went on thrashing around like a bull until he realized that he was safe. Then hands were reaching down for him and he saw that two life boats were there picking up the men.

Tearing the lung off his face Joe collapsed in the bottom of the boat. Now that it was all over an uncontrollable shaking seized him and he lay there trembling like a leaf.

Then, hazily, he saw Bren's face appearing over the gunwale.

Joe stared at it for Bren was grinning like a fool as he climbed into the boat and began squeezing water out of his clothes.

Joe sat up slowly in the bottom of the boat. "What's so funny?" he demanded.

Bren didn't answer as he pointed downward. Joe crawled over beside him and looked down. At first he saw nothing but a mass of bubbles breaking the surface but as he stared he saw a black outline of a submarine in the clear water.

It was about fifteen feet below the surface.

Joe slowly raised his head and looked around. He was sitting in a boat about twenty yards from the dock. A sailor was fishing from the fantail of a subchaser.

Joe turned angrily toward Bren, his fists clenched but Bren only laughed as he backed away.

"I told you, Joe," he said. "It was routine stuff. Just a simulated emergency. We practice them all the time."

Joe slowly relaxed and sat down. Then he looked down again

at the submarine. When he glanced at Bren at last he grinned. "Okay, Bren," he said, slowly.

The score was—all even.

Or, Joe wondered, one up—for Bren?

TOPICS FOR CONSIDERATION AND DISCUSSION

1. Words and phrases you will need to understand. Inquire of your friends or use the dictionary for pronunciations and meanings: gun breeches; ensign; insignia; dolphin; surreptitiously; conning ship to the dock; Academy (Annapolis); khaki; double up fore and aft; score stood one up on Bren; torpedo-bomber; folding landing gear; flying blind; Washington beam; aerology; longeron; "rolled down his flaps"; starboard motor; port motor; bow tubes; stern tubes.

2. Find out what you can about the Momsen lung.

3. Make a list of the things you learned in this story about navigating and flying an airplane.

4. Make a similar list about submarines and their operation.

HERE ARE YOUR WINGS[1]

By Wolfgang Langewiesche

THE following is an article about learning to fly a small
plane for private or business. This is written by one who
has had a great deal of experience both as an instructor
on private air fields and as a popular writer about flying.

*   *   *   *   *

They have put the soul of a Model T into the body of a
glider, and now I've got wings. True, the airplane thus obtained is not the kind of ship that eats up continents overnight; if it were not for customary airport speech, I should not
call it a ship at all; I would call it a sky-going canoe. It is a
slender, two-seated craft with a skin of taut fabric, and very
light. When I am through flying for the day and want to put
it back into its hangar, I don't even bother to start up its engine; I simply take its tail skid on my shoulder and drag it
along behind me like a toy. It is also small; at least for an eye
accustomed to air liners. Once I flew it low over the house of a
girl, to show it off, but afterward I found out that I had
spoiled my show merely by waving to her; the grotesque size
of my hand in proportion to the size of the ship made the
whole thing appear like a clowning act. Compared to air
liners, my ship is also slow; it has less horsepower than your
car, and wallows along at seventy-five mph. Out on the airways, the liners do not merely overtake me, they shoot by me
like sharks and make me feel like a bit of aerial flotsam.

A plaything? Fifteen people have made their first solo flights
on this ship since it came out of the factory a year ago. For,
though I call it mine and fly it, it actually belongs to my old
instructor, who does a thriving business on a former cow pasture in New Jersey by teaching all comers how to fly and rent-
ing or selling them ships. Thus it earns its keep by carrying

---

Army cadets begin their flight training on a cutaway model of an airplane

all sorts of amateur aviators besides myself. The soloists were a carpenter, a minister, two stenographers, a truck driver, a professor of mathematics, a housewife, and a whole bunch of college boys. All of them are now building up their time and skill toward their licenses. Add to that some twenty beginners currently taking dual instruction on it. Then add a dozen fly-yourself renters such as myself—amateurs who have their licenses, but haven't ships of their own. Keep adding.

This country airport boasts a fleet of eight ships, all equally busy; it also hangars three private ones, one owned by a doctor, another by a retired sea captain, and one by a syndicate composed of a building contractor, a store clerk, a garageman and a farmer. Keep adding. You'll find one or several such flying schools at almost every airport in the country, each with its string of ships, its students, its fly-yourself renters, its private owners. Meanwhile, new ships of the $1000 to $2000 class come booming out of the factories at the rate of some 300 a month; about two thirds of them to go into training and rental service, one third to private owners or clubs. Just how many men and women are actually flying in this country nobody knows exactly, for in the first stages, before one's first solo flight, no permit other than a certificate of physical fitness is required. The best estimate is that there are 110,000 of them now, and that, by the year's end, if the present rush continues, there will be a quarter million. Add it all up, and you see that the biggest thing in aviation since the crystallizing, ten years ago, of the regular air lines, is the air flivver, the airplane for the people.

I am one of them. I have flown myself around in air flivvers for seven years now, ever since the first funny-looking prototype went into service at our airport. I have flown some 60,000 miles from coast to coast, from border to border, around the highest mountains and into the deepest canyons, all over beautiful-for-spacious-skies America, and all that time I have been, in my ground life, such meek things as a graduate student, a college instructor, and a writer—that is, neither a professional pilot nor an athlete, and certainly not a rich man. That ordinary folk like me should roar around—well, all right, putt-putt around the country in private airplanes still amazes some people. I landed on a Louisiana plantation the other day, and

the boss himself came running to look. Seeing me in ordinary
street clothes, wearing glasses and with an ordinary hat on, he
peeked inside and asked: "What happened to your pilot?"

And, in fact, I am still amazed myself at those wings of mine,
and how they were Santa Claused' into my life. That first air
flivver's climb and speed were nothing to boast of, but it did
bring the cost of flying down with a bang. Before, the cheapest
airplane you could dream of buying cost nearly $5000; after-
ward, it cost $1400, and today the cheapest is $900. Before, a
two-seat ship cost some twenty cents a mile to operate; afterward, it cost five cents a mile; and today the cost of operation,
including fuel, hangar, maintenance, insurance, and all the
fancier items of accountancy, such as depreciation, is four cents
a mile—no more than that of a car. Before the light plane, my
own flying was a kid's crazy extravagance; since the light plane,
it has made sense.

But of all the things that have brought the airplane and the
common man together, the hardest hitting is this: That you
don't need to buy a ship of your own; that you can walk into
the nearest airport with a few dollars in your pocket, ask for a
ship to fly, and get it, not as a matter of favor but as a matter of
business. Flying costs a little more that way, $4.50 to $7.00 an
hour, depending on the ship, the section of the country, the
class of trade the field caters to, and the size of the "block of
time" you buy. That works out at seven to nine cents per mile.
But it requires no investment at all, not even a deposit. Remember how Lindbergh himself was unable to make his first
solo flight, at the very school that had taught him, because he
could not furnish the required crash bond? Today, all risk of
breakage is borne by the ship's owner. Today, you may be a
complete stranger at a field and still get a ship within a few
minutes, if only you look reasonably sane, and if your Federal
papers are in order. The owner, or his hired instructor, will
merely go up with you on a check-out hop, and he can tell,
after a couple of take-offs and landings, whether you are fit to
go solo, and if so, how far away from the field and in what
weather.

This arrangement may look a bit haphazard, yet it actually
has kept many an amateur out of grief. If he wants to keep his
ships, the commercial operator cannot skimp on maintenance

the way the private owner is often tempted to do; and he must also supervise his customers' flying closely, must cultivate their piloting habits, keep tabs on their cross-country plans, keep them down on mornings after; he must ground the smart alecks, go up on check hops with the dubs, build up confidence in·the jittery; he must gauge their personalities accurately and sometimes remold them, for beyond a reasonable skill, what counts for safety in the air are ordinary sense and maturity, and many a young fellow has been steadied more by his flight instructor's three-word characterization of himself than by years of parental admonition.

It takes only eight hours of dual instruction to be able to take a ship once around the field by yourself, but thereafter it takes some thirty-five hours of closely supervised solo practice, with occasional dual periods, to polish up your wares enough to show them to the awesome Federal inspector who will, or will not, give you a license. From that point on, you may fly cross country with confidence, if you are careful, and can carry nonpaying passengers; but also to get the finer points of piloting into your system so they'll pop up readily when someday you may need them, you can use easily another 100 hours of maneuvering practice. That is why amateur fliers are always talking of time, and why, at present, with most amateurs still in the learning stage, most of the flying is in short hops around the airport.

On a Sunday afternoon, or on a summer evening, after the offices and the schools let out, our field swarms like a skiing site in full swing, with boys and girls in the gaily colored ships climbing all over the invisible slopes of air and sliding down again to short, precise stops. Lots of them cut down all week on meals and movies and parties in order to finance half an hour at the controls; there are high-school kids who start at sixteen—the youngest age for a student permit—and there are lots of week-end fliers who take a couple of years to build up their licenses, who don't get out of sight of the field for months—yet they are happy. Before you do it, you think of flying mostly as a way to get from A to B in a hurry; once you start doing it and for a long time that side is less important and all you want is the feel of a ship under your pants.

For even the routine milling-around, strictly right side up, strictly conservative, that looks so humdrum from the ground is actually a lovely art. It requires more feel and rhythm and a softer touch than does driving. Except that both are powered by gasoline engines, a wing kiting on thin air has nothing in common with four wheels rolling on concrete. If it feels like anything else, it feels like a sailboat. It doesn't simply go where you point it. To manage it, you don't need a thing that the body and soul of the average man or woman hasn't got; but you must wear into your nervous system some new and rather strange grooves. For instance, you must make your feet do what your hand does on the steering wheel of a car in straight-way driving; you have no brakes, and you must etch it into your brain that you get into trouble by slowing up, out of trouble by speeding up; you gauge your flying speed by the feel of the stick in your hand; your climb and descent by the sound of the engine and of the wind. You keep your balance by the seat of your pants; as long as that feels all right, you are all right, even though the world may hang at a crazy angle.

As any amateur pilot will tell you with personal pride, the flivver plane is not foolproof; it is still basically the same device as an Army trainer or an air liner or the Spirit of St. Louis. If you can fly it, you can also fly those glamorous ships; in the same way, no more, no less, in which a boy who can sail a dinghy can also sail a seagoing schooner or an over-canvased racing craft.

A flivver plane will stall and spin and even kill its man, just like the real thing you see in the movies, if its controls are mishandled and the mishandling is timed wrong enough.

But there is a difference of degree here that almost amounts to a difference of kind. "Fool-tolerant" is what airport language calls it. To a pilot accustomed to less friendly craft, it is fascinating and even funny. A certain young air-line copilot sometimes sneaks out to our field on his day off, rents a ship, and for half an hour wallows in aeronautical sin—all the low, slow, sloppy, nose-high flying that he can never do in his hot and heavy air liners.

I myself am not a "hot" pilot, and have almost come to grief on flivver planes several times, but never quite—and that makes all the difference. Here are the actual repair bills I have run up for my owners in seven years: One busted propeller, twenty-five dollars, plus air-express charges to send it to me at the back-

country town where I was marooned. One stove-in wing tip, five
dollars. (I flew that one home across 1200 miles, so you see it
wasn't so bad.) One wing tip slid over the grass while landing
cross wind, one dollar. That was the only damage I ever did in
take-off, flight, or landing; the rest was all by sheer absent-
mindedness in taxiing, the way you crumple your fenders on
your garage door. Various triangles torn in the fabric covering
by sticks and stones while taking ships into rough country,
about two dollars. (You paste a patch over them; it's easier than
getting your pants repaired.) That's all.

What makes flivver ships safer to fly is their uncanny hold on
the air. A "hot" airplane will stall—that is, its wing will lose its
hold on the air whenever the pilot slows it up to seventy miles
an hour. My present ship will hang on merrily at thirty miles
an hour—which, as airplanes go, means practically standing
still. A "hot" airplane, such as a pursuit or an air liner, once
stalled, will go for the ground like a ton of bricks and must fall
hundreds of feet before the wings take hold again. A flivver
plane, once stalled, comes down rather in the style of a leaf
falling from a tree and will catch itself after dozens of feet, instead of hundreds. And it is harder to stall, in the first place. It
used to be that the most difficult part of a pilot-license test was
the precise recovery from stalls and from tail spins, which are
merely a fancy variety of stall. Today, the most difficult part is
often to throw the ship into a complete stall or a spin. Have you
ever felt a fish fighting at the end of your line and wondered
how so small a body can find so firm a hold in so slippery a
medium? That is how an air flivver feels on such occasions. It
won't let go.

How the designers achieve all that holding power, most
pilots, including myself, understand only hazily. Partly they do
it by putting a lot of wing on very little airplane; partly by the
wizardry of wing shapes and curves, profiles, tapers, washouts,
slots, centers of gravity, stabilizing surfaces, angles of incidence
and dihedrals—not gadgets, but inconspicuous fine points about
an airplane's shape that the layman can't even see and that yet
make all the difference. You let an airplane designer whittle
your kitchen table into shape, and you can jump out of the top-
floor window with it and go gliding.

Flivver planes also have a different feel to the pilot, or rather,

they have more of it than "hot" ships have. "Feel" in an airplane means more than merely a nice sensation, as in a car; it
is almost as important in the job of flying as is vision—especially those feels which in slow-flight maneuvering warn the
pilot that a stall is setting in. There are ships whose sticks must
be held lightly, the way a doctor feels for a pulse, and if in such
a ship the pilot is a bit tense—say during a forced landing—it
is only too easy to disregard such faint warning signals and stall
the ship. There are also ships that have almost no feel at all
and must be flown by the help of instruments all the time—a
job for experts. In light planes, on the other hand, those feels
are blatant and pronounced enough to penetrate even the thick
skin of the spare-time pilot. Have you ever tried to milk a cow
from the wrong side, or to put the bit into a horse's mouth in a
noncustomary manner? Those protesting swishings of the tail,
those impatient jerks of the head are exactly the way an air
flivver behaves when the pilot forgets his flying manners.

For an example, let's take a tiny and commonplace incident,
of a kind that would not ordinarily be worth mentioning—
something like the time when you stepped on your marvelous
hydraulic brake and managed just to miss that truck. I hadn't
flown for six months, and was limbering up by shooting landings on our field. During one of them I found myself gliding
in too low. Afraid I might touch the electric wires bordering
that side, I tried to haul the ship higher by simply pointing her
higher. With the engine idling, that is about as effective as lifting yourself by your boot straps; yet it is exactly the instinctive
reaction by which many a pilot has pulled himself into a stall,
at too low a height to recover before striking the ground. If you
want to see the inside of the typical private flying accident,
there you have it.

I didn't realize I was doing wrong, but my fool-tolerant flivver did. She shuddered; she wallowed; she even made strange
noises. She tugged forward against my pull on the stick with
real force; she all but poked me in the ribs. I blushed as I
slammed the throttle to her and lifted her across the wires with
power. I could almost feel the manufacturer's contempt for amateur pilots, and could hear him say to his designer: "Put it on
thick. Fix it so even that absent-minded professor will know
what he's doing."

That first light plane of ours, seven years ago, arrived on a truck. It was never meant to fly cross country. It had only thirty-seven hp, its cruising speed was on the wrong side of sixty, its luggage allowance five pounds, and its last-drop, dead-calm fuel range 180 miles. We soon flew it cross country anyway, and manufacturers soon began to allow for it. My present ship is perhaps fairly typical for all of the low-priced kinds—Cubs, Aeroncas, Taylorcrafts, Luscombes. It still cost about $1400, but the same four-cylinder engine has been stepped up to fifty hp, and that means it picks you out of smaller fields across higher trees with more safety. Its seventy-five mph cruise is slow—other ships in this price class do eighty to eighty-seven—but it has been achieved without increasing its landing speed. Its fuel range is 240 miles—in some kinds, an additional 100-mile tank can be fitted. Its luggage allowance is thirty pounds. Its cabin is draftless, its engine almost vibrationless, its noise slightly muf-fled; there is a heater, a ventilator and comfortable seats: it is really quite a kite.

I admit that there are occasions even now when it seems hexed, considered as a means of transport. The other day, flying against a stiff wind, I found that I would fail to reach my des-tination merely for lack of a measly gallon of gasoline. I landed, and had to hitch-hike to town for gasoline. By the time I had scared up a container to carry it in and had hitch-hiked back, it was too late by a measly ten minutes to make my destination before dark. Next morning there was fog. In the afternoon, warming up to take off, the engine stammered; there had been dirt in the gasoline. I drained it, hitch-hiked to town, scared up a container, and so on. It was too late again to make it before dark. That time I tied the ship to an apple tree, to fetch it later, and flagged down a bus to travel on.

But as a rule, I can now get my trips completed, even against headwinds. Five hours of cruising in this ship no longer leave me tired out for the day. The many new small airports also help, and there are now 25,000 miles of Federal Civil Airways crisscrossing the country, veritable aerial highways with night lighting and closely spaced emergency-landing fields and expert weather stations—all open to the whole piloting public, as well as to the air lines, free of charge. The Airways are a unique na-tional possession of which Americans may be proud. Furthermore, the manufacturers now turn out models with engines up to eighty hp and quite brisk utility, yet still selling for less than $2000. One such ship, for instance, cruises at 105 mph; another carries three people plus luggage; still another has a fuel range of 600 miles. And on the border between air flivvers and de luxe airplanes is the $3300 Stinson that will carry three people at 105 miles per hour for 400 miles and is nearly fool-proof in the bargain.

In short, the light-plane amateur's horizon is today almost as wide as the hot-ship professional pilot's. While the mass of amateur fliers are still in the learning stage and fly mostly for the sake of flying, the light-plane boom has already graduated the first batch of men and women who put their airplanes to the homely uses of ordinary American living—A-to-B-in-a-hurry flights, Sunday-afternoon-with-the-family flights, week-end-fishing flights, daily-commuters' flights, Western-camping flights, love-in-the-moonlight flights. There are hundreds of them, and possibly already thousands—no one quite knows, for they do it privately and, except for myself, with so little shouting that you would hardly realize they are pioneering a new era in American civilization.

Putting the flivver plane to that sort of service will work like a charm if one can allow for its limitations and can make use of its good points. Its most serious limitation is the weather. All questions about cheap ships' performance are yielding to the magic of mass production, but about bad weather nothing can be done so far. On the contrary, there are now weather laws which correspond to the speed laws of the road, and the limits they set are quite a bit more severe than those an experienced pilot on a slow ship over good flat country would allow himself —which may be just as well, incidentally, and has stopped me from doing a lot of the scary treetop flying I used to do. You now need a ceiling of 800 feet—1000 feet if it rains—and a visibility of one mile—three miles near air-line stops. If you break these rules, you get a ticket. Exempt are only ships flown by approved blind-flying procedure such as the air lines use. But for the flivver pilot, blind flying is out, since it requires a skill that one can't keep up in one's spare time and radio and instrument equipment that weighs too much and costs too much.

And that means you wait. Boy, how you wait! I have waited

three days in Pittsburgh for a chance to cross the Alleghenies. By the third night every bed near the airport was taken up by some waiting pilot. I have struggled six days to make the 550 miles between San Francisco and Portland, Oregon, what with Pacific fogs, clouds in the mountain passes and forest-fire smoke. I have run up hotel bills in small prairie towns until I knew everybody on main street, had lunched with Rotary, dined with the Lions, and addressed the high-school assembly, a bit half-heartedly, on the speed and convenience of flying one's own.

The flivver plane's strongest point is its landing. It can land in less space than any other conventional airplane, however expensive, however laden with gadgets. My present ship will touch down at thirty mph if the air is calm; if there is a wind, one lands against it, and the landing is correspondingly slower. On an average day, on a sod surface, my landing run is about forty paces. That means even more to the pilot than appears at first glance; here again, the difference of degree amounts almost to a difference of kind, and the light plane actually stands halfway between the heavy airplane and the autogiro. The thing that counts here is the size of the average parcel of farm land in most parts of the United States. For a ship landing at fifty, sixty miles it is too small, and such a ship can make a riskless landing practically only at airports, but unless it is surrounded by high trees and there is a dead calm, there is almost always a parcel big enough for the air flivver to slip into—though I want to add that the pilot must know his stuff. Nor does the flivver pilot, with his doughnut-shaped soft wheels, worry overmuch about softness; even in wet weather, anything that has wagon tracks or cows on it is hard enough, and anything that has been worked by agricultural machinery is level enough.

And that flavors every single minute of flight, for it takes the sting out of the dangers of the air. When in trouble, you simply sit down. I can remember worlds of trouble I never had because I simply sat down. Once, a bungled job of navigation left me far out over Nebraska, uncertain of my position in the gathering darkness, with nothing much to distinguish below but those dark and light stripings, plowed soil and stubble field, characteristic of dry farming. I picked one of the light stripes, groped my way down onto it, and spent the night.

Once, short of gasoline, I plunked myself into an Iowa corn-

and-hog farm. Once, to let a thunderstorm pass over, I even landed on one of those deep-furrowed cotton patches of Mississippi, touching down crosswise to the furrows, which is the next most lively sensation to being inside a cocktail shaker. But the landing gear took it. Or take the possibility of engine failure, always present, though no longer very real; the air flivver saves you a lot of wear and tear on your nerves. Some military ships land so "hot" that if the engine quits over strange terrain, you simply give up and jump; in an air flivver, you don't even wear a parachute, for even if the engine should quit over mountains or over a forest, the ship itself, with its firm-holding wings, will let you down about as gently as a 'chute would. And over ordinary farm country, on long, high, monotonous cross country, when it is lonesome and one's ship and engine become one's almost-living companions, I have often said to my engine: "Go ahead and quit. I wish you would." But the flivver-souled little putt-putt never has.

Flying an airplane cross country is not a spur-of-the-moment, free-as-a-bird sort of thing, but rather a methodical art, much like seamanship, that must be learned. You may interpret this as proving that the airplane is not yet quite ready for the common man. Most of us see it differently; we think of cross-country flying as the keenest adventure of our time, and are glad that its costs and its risks have become so manageable. We are glad there is still something to it, glad to learn it; and here is how it goes:

With your instructor-owner watching over your shoulder, you pencil your course on your map, measure your direction, your allowance for cross wind, your compass reading. Then you go up and follow your compass across the landscape for two hours and so many minutes, and it works. You hit a town that you have never seen before, right on the nose. That was a cinch, you think—in fact, a bit dull. You get gassed up and go to the Government weather office for your weather and your "winds aloft," and on the airport lunch counter you plot your next hop. Then you go up again. Ship handling is nothing on a cross-country flight; in most kinds of air you can sit most of the time with your arms folded—only your feet must keep up a continual slight play to keep your flight on the course.

Half an hour out, you raise your first big landmark, a town, not exactly on the nose. The wind has changed a bit, you think, and you make a correction that will bring you out exactly over that town. You note with indignation that the Government flight map shows the river bending the wrong way round. An hour out, you pass over that Federal emergency field at the confluence of those two rivers, and you note with amazement that it has been WPA'd into truck gardens.

An hour and a half out, you are deep in the Pennsylvania mountains, all of which look like all others, and you are waiting for that valley with the double-track railroad. It turns up about ten minutes late, and the second track has been sold for scrap iron.

You barge ahead for ten more minutes, and then, with a slow shock that seeps all the way down to your knees, you realize that you are lost.

Thus begins the seasoning of a cross-country flier. Actually, now, you can't be more than a couple of dozen miles to one side or the other of your course, at the very worst. But the first time it takes real fortitude not to think that you are over Timbuktu. Believe me. Strange as this may sound, the most disturbing thing about it is that you are up in the air; the first impulse is to go down and ask somebody. One pampered boy with an airplane for a plaything could think of nothing but to circle low over a crossroads filling station and shout down questions —tearful ones, I imagine—before he finally let himself go into an apple orchard. He cracked up his ship and contracted a nose bleed. You, yourself, of course, collect your wits, start doing the several things your instructor has told you to do, the first or second of which will probably work, and proceed to a safe landing.

In memory, my first fifty hours or so of cross-country flight seem all to have been a bit frantic. You put a bond salesman or a college prof into a pilot's seat and he feels sort of far from home at first. That first time a layer of cloud closes in under you—you ghost around up there and think you have lost the world forever. The first rain squall you bore into gets you as nervous as a lady with a new hat. The first time I had to pick my own field and make an outside landing—I had won several spot-landing contests on our home field—I found my precision was all shot, and I had to make three passes at it before I could even sit down. And on top of those first-time crises there is a whole new feeling to get used to, unconscious and yet quite strong—that impersonality of the air. The clouds don't care what happens to you, and neither do the forests and the farms, and as for the people whose houses and automobiles you see, they think you know your way around. But you don't, at first.

If my own early experience adds up to anything, it is not that cross-country flying is dangerous, but merely that most of us are at first almost incredibly deaf, blind and numb to the things of the air. I once took a ski champion walking in New York. For him, New York was dangerous. Unless I held him back by main force, he would walk straight into all sorts of traffic. After two days of this, it turned out that he had never discovered the traffic lights. Similarly, I am now often amazed how ground men simply can't see things which to a pilot are big, solid, important realities. While visiting with a passenger of mine at his office the other day, I pointed out of the window and said, "Look at that."

"Look at what?" he asked, searching all over and finding nothing to look at. Yet the flags on the buildings were strung out one way while the clouds were drifting the opposite way, showing an opposite wind aloft—just the thing to set an unsuspecting novice twenty miles off his course in an hour.

Common sense has something to do with it too. Perhaps the noise at first drowns it out. Once I followed a railroad in bad weather. It went into a small town, and, on the other side, it refused to come out again. My railroad wasn't supposed to do that; I had followed the wrong one; *ergo,* I was lost. I spent a full quarter hour circling over that town, trying to identify it. I circled low, my passenger pale behind me, trying to read its name on some sign; I circled high, my passenger clutching my shoulder, and we frantically searched the map—quick now, something to fit this place below. Could it be X-borough? Could it be Z-ville. No, X-borough had a big lumber mill and Z-ville straddled a river. Fifteen minutes of real, soul-chilling air drama. Lost in the air, weather bad, ground too rough for a landing, and the gas gauge coming down all the time. And all the time it failed to click in my mind that the dead-end railroad itself, being a rare thing anywhere and easy to find on a map, was, of course, the most unmistakable "fix" of my position!

Different pilots might give you different figures, but it probably takes a couple of hundred hours of cross-country flight, at least once, to meet all the most important combinations of weather and terrain and make all possible mistakes. I can list some more of them right here, so you can see there is no mystery to them, and let me add that there are things to do about each one of them, both preventive and remedial. You are tired from a long flight, your mind reverses the meaning of the airport wind sock, and you come in to land downwind at terrific speed. Or you have taken off in noonday heat from a high-altitude airport in the West, and your engine develops even less power than you were prepared for, and the ship refuses to climb. Or you have taken off without checking the weather reports, and a thunderstorm or a fog forces you to make a landing right now, right here. Or a head wind keeps you out after dark, and you make your first night landing. Or, in perfectly clear weather and almost out of gas, you arrive at your destination just as a blanket of sea fog rolls in and cuts you off. So it goes, and half the time, as you have probably figured out for yourself, the best and simplest remedy is: "Don't."

Eventually, at any rate, you feel at home in the air, and find your way about almost by instinct. Looking over the side and watching the way the ground slides along under you slantwise, you can tell within a few miles per hour the exact strength of the wind and how much to allow for drift. Your senses get keen for aeronautically important things. You can tell a lake long before it is actually in sight—by a certain luminous quality of the horizon where the water reflects the light back into the haze. You can look down at some Midwestern farm region and can sense the direction of the nearest big city, even though it may be a hundred miles away. And you can find your way to a landing field as surely as a horse can find its way to a water hole.

Of all the practical uses of the light plane, the most convincing is touring. At twenty-two miles to the gallon of gas, a ship such as mine will carry two people across the continent for fifty dollars westbound, into the teeth of the prevailing wind; for forty dollars eastbound, with the prevailing wind on her tail.

Touring in a light ship has almost nothing in common with air-line travel. With no wing under you and free forward vision over the nose, you can really see; and where air liners fly at, say, 6000 feet, the flivver plane will safely float at 2000, much closer to things. The pilot has, of course, all the fun of making his way cross country, and believe me, you will never know how great the Great Lakes really are and how rocky the Rockies until you have piloted a ship across them. But even the passenger will usually take his spell at the controls and help keep track of navigation with watch and note pad, and help pick distant landmarks out of the haze.

And in a light plane, any time you are tired of the long-range overview of things, you can come down and take a close-up look. I have circled low and slow many a time merely to watch something, such as a herd of elk, or a fishing boat at work, or cranes winging along, or an oil-well crew drilling offshore in the Gulf. And I have landed on the beach at the foot of a lonely lighthouse, on the polo field of a dude ranch, on cattle ranches and oil fields, on Indian reservations and on the athletic track of a campus; on golf courses, stretches of road, sand bars in the Mississippi River, and once, unknowingly, on the secret retreat of a film star. Once, on the wide plains of Texas, I noticed a man under me on a tractor plowing a field, and for no better reason than that I felt talkative, I landed beside him. We ate lunch together, sitting on the wheels of my ship, and discussed the working of our respective machines. Once, following a highway and getting hungry, I landed on the prairie behind a roadhouse that had curb service, managed to taxi around to the front without hooking a wing on a telephone pole, blasted my throttle in lieu of a horn, and had lunch from a tray hung outside my cabin window in regular automobile fashion. Afterward, I rolled back into the prairie and flew away.

Of the things I have seen while touring the American air, some have been so breath-taking, some so peculiarly aerial, some so big that I can't hope to make you see them in written words, though I shall catalogue a few. Take only one trip, a three months' tour of the West. I had a good look at the Mississippi River, every inch of it from its source to its very mouths —four days of it, cutting straight across its grotesque bends as you might draw the lines across the S of a dollar sign. I flew

down 7900 feet into the Salmon River Canyon and the Snake
River Canyon, the deepest in North America, and landed at
the former's bottom, on a gravel bank, to spend a week with the
gold miners. I soared under a young thunderstorm over the
Sierra Nevada, riding the upsurge of air in near silence, with
my engine ticking over at idling speed. I chased a herd of wild
horses across a Nevada sagebrush plain. I flew close to a forest
fire that had a whole mountainside burning. I flew from Montana down to Minnesota in one night when the northern lights
were shooting all the way up to the zenith. And there was the
time when I met Mt. Shasta.

"Met" is the only word that describes it, though it was more
like meeting a ghost. I was flying at no mean altitude myself
and was looking for the mountain among the clouds. I expected
it high. I had an idea it would be even higher than I expected,
and I had already discounted that surprise. And then, while I
was still searching for it in the distance, I realized it had been
looking down at me for quite a while—a snow-white specter,
disembodied, floating above the blue haze in which the mountain's own understructure was swallowed up. As is always the
case with very high mountains seen from an airplane, we were
in a way alone with each other at our altitude, and the effect
was as scary as if you had come upon a god in his habitat.

In all, that 21,000-mile trip was probably as tough a test of a
touring ship as one could devise. It was roughly equivalent to
four transcontinental round trips; much of it was high-moun-
tain work requiring wide-open throttle for long stretches. I
landed in some of the strangest places, and some of the rough-
est. I burned too-powerful air-line gasoline, and tractor gasoline, and automobile regular, fetched sometimes in rusty, dirty
cans.

For a total of two months, I left the ship staked down in the
open day and night, exposed to fierce mountain sun, ice, dew,
gales, frost, rain, salt air, dust storms, blowing sand, and also
prying fingers.

And here is an account of trouble and expense, fuss and
bother. I spent about $300 for gasoline and oil. For hotels, taxis
and hangars I spent little, for I carried my own camping equipment in the ship. I did no work on the ship myself—in fact, I
didn't carry any tools, not even a screw driver. What's more, I

never gave thought to having no tools. I spent twenty dollars for the periodic inspections prescribed by law; they showed no defects. I gave a free ride to a fellow for fixing a slow leak in my tires, caused by cactus barbs. I spent sixty cents on a new tail-skid shoe, the old one having worn away; two dollars on rechargings of the battery for my red-and-green wingtip lights. I did one thing the auto tourist might not do—that is, staked down my ship overnight with pegs and ropes, so it wouldn't blow away. Each morning I started the engine without a helper, and it never took more than a minute. When I finally brought the ship back to that New Jersey cow pasture, my home field, there was no perceptible wear; I had barely time to yank out my luggage, when a bank clerk piled in with his fiancée and took it up again.

If one wants to put the light plane to work, a rented ship won't do, and one needs one of his own. Then that mechanical toughness comes in handy. To many of us, a new ship is still a bit too stiff financially, even with the new eighteen-month installment plan. But a secondhand ship can be bought at half price, and with confidence, for the light plane has no clutch, gear, transmission, radiator, water pump, generator, starter, and frequently no lights, battery, wiring and no wheel brakes. The engine is good for 2000 to 4000 hours, with overhauls every 500 hours or so. The ship itself, given a new fabric covering every few years, is good for from six to ten years.

For business use, the light plane is not so reliable as ground transport or the air lines, though some business travelers find it advantageous when they can land near their objectives. But there are some fields in which the flivver has proved itself. There's the Kansas farm boy who flies his little brother to school every day, the Florida flying newsboy who delivers papers to the coastal resort islands by light plane, the Texas cattle broker who lands near his clients' herds, the Wyoming rancher who supervises an upper and a lower ranch by air, the businessman who has leveled a landing strip behind his country house and commutes.

The light plane is also handy where there are barriers to jump, hard-to-get-at places to reach. One aerial commuter claims to save more in bridge tolls than it costs him to run his ship; a CCC official, way out in the forest, flies to town for week ends;

a young highway engineer who works on remote locations maintains a ship to keep in touch with his wife and children. And the other day, flying low over Matagorda Island, a desolate strip of beach and scrub off the swampy Texas coast, I came upon three men on horseback, driving a herd of cattle along the beach. I landed near by, a writer in search of local characters, thinking they must be lonely on their island and thrilled to have an aerial visitor. And sure enough, one of them came trotting over eagerly. But when I climbed out, he seemed disappointed.

"I thought you was the boss," he said, and turned his horse around. "I thought you was bringing our grub," and rode away without another look.

WIND, SAND AND STARS [1]

By Antoine de Saint Exupéry

IN 1939 we Americans became acquainted with a new pilot author, the French Antoine de Saint Exupéry. He started his career as a mail pilot flying planes from Toulouse in the south of France to Casablanca on the North African coast and thence across the Sahara to Dakar, the farthest point on the west coast of French North Africa. He served as an airline pilot for eight years and had become a well-known pilot-author before his books became widely known in America. The first of these was *Night Flight*. Then came *Wind, Sand and Stars*. And since World War II began he has written another with the same poetic and philosophic qualities of the earlier books. The title is *Flight to Arras*.

The following selection is from an early part of *Wind, Sand and Stars*.

*   *   *   *   *

THE CRAFT

The night came when it was my turn to be called to the field manager's room.

He said: "You leave tomorrow."

I stood motionless, waiting for him to dismiss me. After a moment of silence he added:

"I take it you know the regulations?"

In those days the motor was not what it is today. It would drop out, for example, without warning and with a great rattle like the crash of crockery. And one would simply throw in one's hand: there was no hope of refuge on the rocky crust of Spain. "Here," we used to say, "when your motor goes, your ship goes too."

An airplane, of course, can be replaced. Still, the important thing was to avoid a collision with the range; and blind flying through a sea of clouds in the mountain zones was subject to the severest penalties. A pilot in trouble who buried himself in the white cotton-wool of the clouds might all unseeing run straight into a peak. This was why, that night, the deliberate voice repeated insistently its warning:

"Navigating by the compass in a sea of clouds over Spain is all very well, it is very dashing, but—"

And I was struck by the graphic image:

"But you want to remember that below the sea of clouds lies eternity."

And suddenly that tranquil cloud-world, that world so harmless and simple that one sees below on rising out of the clouds, took on in my eyes a new quality. That peaceful world became a pitfall. I imagined the immense white pitfall spread beneath me. Below it reigned not what one might think—not the agitation of men, not the living tumult and bustle of cities, but a silence even more absolute than in the clouds, a peace even more final. This viscous whiteness became in my mind the frontier between the real and the unreal, between the known and the unknowable. Already I was beginning to realize that a spectacle has no meaning except it be seen through the glass of a culture, a civilization, a craft. Mountaineers too know the sea of clouds, yet it does not seem to them the fabulous curtain it is to me.

When I left that room I was filled with a childish pride. Now it was my turn to take on at dawn the responsibility of a cargo of passengers and the African mails. But at the same time I felt very meek. I felt myself ill-prepared for this responsibility. Spain was poor in emergency fields; we had no radio; and I was troubled lest when I got into difficulty I should not know where to hunt a landing-place. Staring at the aridity of my maps, I could see no help in them; and so, with a heart full of shyness and pride, I fled to spend this night of vigil with my friend Guillaumet. Guillaumet had been over the route before me. He knew all the dodges by which one got hold of the keys to Spain. I should have to be initiated by Guillaumet.

When I walked in he looked up and smiled.

"I know all about it," he said. "How do you feel?"

He went to a cupboard and came back with glasses and a bottle of port, still smiling.

"We'll drink to it. Don't worry. It's easier than you think."

Guillaumet exuded confidence the way a lamp gives off light. He was himself later on to break the record for postal crossings in the Andes and the South Atlantic. On this night, sitting in his shirtsleeves, his arms folded in the lamplight, smiling the most heartening of smiles, he said to me simply:

"You'll be bothered from time to time by storms, fog, snow. When you are, think of those who went through it before you, and say to yourself, 'What they could do, I can do.' "

I spread out my maps and asked him hesitantly if he would mind going over the hop with me. And there, bent over in the lamplight, shoulder to shoulder with the veteran, I felt a sort of schoolboy peace.

But what a strange lesson in geography I was given! Guillaumet did not teach Spain to me, he made the country my friend. He did not talk about provinces, or peoples, or livestock. Instead of telling me about Guadix, he spoke of three orange-trees on the edge of the town: "Beware of those trees. Better mark them on the map." And those three orange-trees seemed to me thenceforth higher than the Sierra Nevada.

He did not talk about Lorca, but about a humble farm near Lorca, a living farm with its farmer and the farmer's wife. And this tiny, this remote couple, living a thousand miles from where we sat, took on a universal importance. Settled on the slope of a mountain, they watched like lighthouse-keepers beneath the stars, ever on the lookout to succor men.

The details that we drew up from oblivion, from their inconceivable remoteness, no geographer had been concerned to explore. Because it washed the banks of great cities, the Ebro River was of interest to map-makers. But what had they to do with that brook running secretly through the water-weeds to the west of Motril, that brook nourishing a mere score or two of flowers?

"Careful of that brook: it breaks up the whole field. Mark it on your map." Ah, I was to remember that serpent in the grass near Motril! It looked like nothing at all, and its faint murmur sang to no more than a few frogs; but it slept with one eye open. Stretching its length along the grasses in the paradise of that emergency landing-field, it lay in wait for me a thousand miles from where I sat. Given the chance, it would transform me into a flaming candelabra. And those thirty valorous sheep ready to charge me on the slope of a hill! Now that I knew about them I could brace myself to meet them.

"You think the meadow empty, and suddenly bang! there are thirty sheep in your wheels." An astounded smile was all I could summon in the face of so cruel a threat.

Little by little, under the lamp, the Spain of my map became a sort of fairyland. The crosses I marked to indicate safety zones and traps were so many buoys and beacons. I charted the farmer, the thirty sheep, the brook. And, exactly where she stood, I set a buoy to mark the shepherdess forgotten by the geographers.

When I left Guillaumet on that freezing winter night, I felt the need of a brisk walk. I turned up my coat collar, and as I strode among the indifferent passers-by I was escorting a fervor as tender as if I had just fallen in love. To be brushing past these strangers with that marvelous secret in my heart filled me with pride. I seemed to myself a sentinel standing guard over a sleeping camp. These passers-by knew nothing about me, yet it was to me that, in their mail pouches, they were about to confide the weightiest cares of their hearts and their trade. Into my hands were they about to entrust their hopes. And I, muffled up in my cloak, walked among them like a shepherd, though they were unaware of my solicitude.

Nor were they receiving any of those messages now being despatched to me by the night. For this snowstorm that was gathering, and that was to burden my first flight, concerned my frail flesh, not theirs. What could they know of those stars that one by one were going out? I alone was in the confidence of the stars. To me alone news was being sent of the enemy's position before the hour of battle. My footfall rang in a universe that was not theirs.

These messages of such grave concern were reaching me as I walked between rows of lighted shop-windows, and those windows on that night seemed a display of all that was good on earth, of a paradise of sweet things. In the sight of all this happiness, I tasted the proud intoxication of renunciation. I was a warrior in danger. What meaning could they have for me, these flashing crystals meant for men's festivities, these

lamps whose glow was to shelter men's meditations, these cozy
furs out of which were to emerge pathetically beautiful solici-
tous faces? I was still wrapped in the aura of friendship, dazed
a little like a child on Christmas Eve, expectant of surprise
and palpitatingly prepared for happiness; and yet already I
was soaked in spray; a mail pilot, I was already nibbling the
bitter pulp of night flight.

It was three in the morning when they woke me. I thrust
the shutters open with a dry snap, saw that rain was falling
on the town, and got soberly into my harness. A half-hour later
I was out on the pavement shining with rain, sitting on my
little valise and waiting for the bus that was to pick me up. So
many other flyers before me, on their day of ordination, had
undergone this humble wait with beating heart.

Finally I saw the old-fashioned vehicle come round the
corner and heard its tinny rattle. Like those who had gone
before me, I squeezed in between a sleepy custom guard and a
few glum government clerks. The bus smelled musty, smelled
of the dust of government offices into which the life of a man
sinks as into a quicksand. It stopped every five hundred yards
to take on another scrivener, another guard, another inspector.

Those in the bus who had already gone back to sleep responded with a vague grunt to the greeting of the newcomer,
while he crowded in as well as he was able and instantly fell
asleep himself. We jolted mournfully over the uneven pave-
ments of Toulouse,* I in the midst of these men who in the
rain and the breaking day were about to take up again their
dreary diurnal † tasks, their red tape, their monotonous lives.

Morning after morning, greeted by the growl of the custom
guard shaken out of sleep by his arrival, by the gruff irritability of clerk or inspector, one mail pilot or another got into
this bus and was for the moment indistinguishable from these
bureaucrats. But as the street lamps moved by, as the field
drew nearer and nearer, the old omnibus rattling along lost
little by little its reality and became a grey chrysalis from which
one emerged transfigured.

---

* *Toulouse* (tōō lōōz'): a city in the south of France.
† *diurnal* (dī ŭrn al): daily; of a day.

Morning after morning a flyer sat here and felt of a sudden, somewhere inside the vulnerable man subjected to his neighbor's surliness, the stirring of the pilot of the Spanish and African mails, the birth of him who, three hours later, was to confront in the lightnings the dragon of the mountains; and who, four hours afterwards, having vanquished it, would be free to decide between a détour over the sea and a direct assault upon the Alcoy range, would be free to deal with storm, with mountain, with ocean.

And thus every morning each pilot before me, in his time, had been lost in the anonymity of daybreak beneath the dismal winter sky of Toulouse, and each one, transfigured by this old omnibus, had felt the birth within him of the sovereign who, five hours later, leaving behind him the rains and snows of the North, repudiating winter, had throttled down his motor and begun to drift earthward in the summer air beneath the shining sun of Alicante.*

The old omnibus has vanished, but its austerity, its discomfort, still live in my memory. It was a proper symbol of the apprenticeship we had to serve before we might possess the stern joys of our craft. Everything about it was intensely serious. I remember three years later, though hardly ten words were spoken, learning in that bus of the death of Lécrivain, one of those hundred pilots who on a day or a night of fog have retired for eternity.

It was four in the morning, and the same silence was abroad when we heard the field manager, invisible in the darkness, address the inspector:

"Lécrivain didn't land at Casablanca † last night."

"Ah!" said the inspector. "Ah?"

Torn from his dream he made an effort to wake up, to display his zeal, and added:

"Is that so? Couldn't he get through? Did he come back?"

And in the dead darkness of the omnibus the answer came: "No."

We waited to hear the rest, but no word sounded. And as the seconds fell it became more and more evident that that

---

* *Alicante* (ăl ĭ kăn'tĕ): a city in Spain.

† *Casablanca* (kă sä blănk'ä): city on the west coast of Morocco (Africa).

"no" would be followed by no further word, was eternal and without appeal, that Lécrivain not only had not landed at Casablanca but would never again land anywhere.

And so, at daybreak on the morning of my first flight with the mails, I went through the sacred rites of the craft, and I felt the self-confidence oozing out of me as I stared through the windows at the macadam shining and reflecting back the street lights. Over the pools of water I could see great palms of wind running. And I thought: "My first flight with the mails! Really, this is not my lucky day."

I raised my eyes and looked at the inspector. "Would you call this bad weather?" I asked.

He threw a weary glance out of the window. "Doesn't prove anything," he growled finally.

And I wondered how one could tell bad weather. The night before, with a single smile Guillaumet had wiped out all the evil omens with which the veterans overwhelmed us, but they came back into my memory. "I feel sorry for the man who doesn't know the whole line pebble by pebble, if he runs into a snowstorm. Oh, yes, I pity the fellow." Our elders, who had their prestige to think of, had all bobbed their heads solemnly and looked at us with embarrassing sympathy, as if they were pitying a flock of condemned sheep.

For how many of us had this old omnibus served as refuge in its day? Sixty? Eighty? I looked about me. Luminous points glowed in the darkness. Cigarettes punctuated the humble meditations of worn old clerks. How many of us had they escorted through the rain on a journey from which there was no coming back?

I heard them talking to one another in murmurs and whispers. They talked about illness, money, shabby domestic cares. Their talk painted the walls of the dismal prison in which these men had locked themselves up. And suddenly I had a vision of the face of destiny.

Old bureaucrat, my comrade, it is not you who are to blame. No one ever helped you to escape. You, like a termite, built your peace by blocking up with cement every chink and cranny through which the light might pierce. You rolled yourself up into a ball in your genteel security, in routine in the stifling conventions of provincial life, raising a modest rampart against the winds and the tides and the stars. You have chosen not to be perturbed by great problems, having trouble enough to forget your own fate as man. You are not the dweller upon an errant planet and do not ask yourself questions to which there are no answers. You are a petty bourgeois * of Toulouse. Nobody grasped you by the shoulder while there was still time. Now the clay of which you were shaped has dried and hardened, and naught in you will ever awaken the sleeping musician, the poet, the astronomer that possibly inhabited you in the beginning.

The squall has ceased to be a cause of my complaint. The magic of the craft has opened for me a world in which I shall confront, within two hours, the black dragons and the crowned crests of a coma of blue lightnings, and when night has fallen I, delivered, shall read my course in the stars.

. Thus I went through my professional baptism and I began to fly the mails. For the most part the flights were without incident. Like sea-divers, we sank peacefully into the depths of our element.

Flying, in general, seemed to us easy. When the skies are filled with black vapors, when fog and sand and sea are confounded in a brew in which they become indistinguishable, when gleaming flashes wheel treacherously in these skyey swamps, the pilot purges himself of the phantoms at a single stroke. He lights his lamps. He brings sanity into his house as into a lonely cottage on a fearsome heath. And the crew travel a sort of submarine route in a lighted chamber.

Pilot, mechanic, and radio operator are shut up in what might be a laboratory. They are obedient to the play of dial-hands, not to the unrolling of the landscape. Out of doors the mountains are immersed in tenebrous darkness; but they are no longer mountains, they are invisible powers whose approach must be computed.

The operator sits in the light of his lamp, dutifully setting down figures; the mechanic ticks off points on his chart; the pilot swerves in response to the drift of the mountains as

---

* *bourgois* (bŏŏr'zhwä): middle class business man.

quickly as he sees that the summits he intends to pass on the left have deployed straight ahead of him in a silence and secrecy as of military preparations. And below on the ground the watchful radio men in their shacks take down submissively in their notebooks the dictation of their comrade in the air: "12:40 A.M. En route 230. All well."

So the crew fly on with no thought that they are in motion. Like night over the sea, they are very far from the earth, from towns, from trees. The motors fill the lighted chamber with a quiver that changes its substance. The clock ticks on. The dials, the radio lamps, the various hands and needles go through their invisible alchemy. From second to second these mysterious stirrings, a few muffled words, a concentrated tenseness contribute to the end result. And when the hour is at hand the pilot may glue his forehead to the window with perfect assurance. Out of oblivion the gold has been smelted: there it gleams in the lights of the airport.

And yet we have all known flights when of a sudden, each for himself, it has seemed to us that we have crossed the border of the world of reality; when, only a couple of hours from port, we have felt ourselves more distant from it than we should feel if we were in India; when there has come a premonition of an incursion into a forbidden world whence it was going to be infinitely difficult to return.

Thus, when Mermoz first crossed the South Atlantic in a hydroplane, as day was dying he ran foul of the Black Hole region, off Africa. Straight ahead of him were the tails of tornadoes rising as a wall is built; and then the night came down upon these preliminaries and swallowed them up; and when, an hour later, he slipped under the clouds, he came out into a fantastic kingdom.

Great black waterspouts had reared themselves seemingly in the immobility of temple pillars. Swollen at their tops, they were supporting the squat and lowering arch of the tempest, but through the rifts in the arch there fell slabs of light and the full moon sent her radiant beams between the pillars down upon the frozen tiles of the sea. Through these uninhabited ruins Mermoz made his way, gliding slantwise from one channel of light to the next, circling round those giant pillars in which there must have rumbled the upsurge of the sea, flying for four hours through these corridors of moonlight toward the exit from the temple. And this spectacle was so overwhelming that only after he had got through the Black Hole did Mermoz awaken to the fact that he had not been afraid.

I remember, for my part, another of those hours in which a pilot finds suddenly that he has slipped beyond the confines of this world. All that night the radio messages sent from the ports in the Sahara concerning our position had been inaccurate, and my radio operator, Néri, and I had been drawn out of our course. Suddenly, seeing the gleam of water at the bottom of a crevasse of fog, I tacked sharply in the direction of the coast; but it was by then impossible for us to say how long we had been flying toward the high seas. Nor were we certain of making the coast, for our fuel was probably low. And even so, once we had reached it we would still have to make port—after the moon had set.

We had no means of angular orientation, were already deafened, and were bit by bit growing blind. The moon like a pallid ember began to go out in the banks of fog. Overhead the sky was filling with clouds, and we flew thenceforth between cloud and fog in a world voided of all substance and all light. The ports that signaled us had given up trying to tell us where we were. "No bearings, no bearings," was all their message, for our voice reached them from everywhere and nowhere. With sinking hearts Néri and I leaned out, he on his side and I on mine, to see if anything, anything at all, was distinguishable in this void. Already our tired eyes were seeing things—errant signs, delusive flashes, phantoms.

And suddenly, when already we were in despair, low on the horizon a brilliant point was unveiled on our port bow. A wave of joy went through me. Néri leaned forward, and I could hear him singing. It could not but be the beacon of an airport, for after dark the whole Sahara goes black and forms a great dead expanse. That light twinkled for a space—and then went out! We had been steering for a star which was visible for a few minutes only, just before setting on the horizon between the layer of fog and the clouds.

Then other stars took up the game, and with a sort of

dogged hope we set our course for each of them in turn. Each
time that a light lingered a while, we performed the same
crucial experiment. Néri would send his message to the airport
at Cisneros: "Beacon in view. Put out your light and flash three
times." And Cisneros would put out its beacon and flash three
times while the hard light at which we gazed would not, in-
corruptible star, so much as wink. And despite our dwindling
fuel we continued to nibble at the golden bait which each time
seemed more surely the true light of a beacon, was each time a
promise of a landing and of life—and we had each time to
change our star.

And with that we knew ourselves to be lost in interplanetary
space among a thousand inaccessible planets, we who sought
only the one veritable planet, our own, that planet on which
alone we should find our familiar countryside, the houses of
our friends, our treasures.

On which alone we should find . . . Let me draw the picture that took shape before my eyes. It will seem to you childish; but even in the midst of danger a man retains his human
concerns. I was thirsty and I was hungry. If we did find Cisneros we should re-fuel and carry on to Casablanca, and there
we should come down in the cool of daybreak, free to idle the
hours away. Néri and I would go into town. We would go to a
little pub already open despite the early hour. Safe and sound,
Néri and I would sit down at table and laugh at the night of
danger as we ate our warm rolls and drank our bowls of coffee
and hot milk. We would receive this matutinal * gift at the
hands of life. Even as an old peasant woman recognizes her
God in a painted image, in a childish medal, in a chaplet, so
life would speak to us in its humblest language in order that
we understand. The joy of living, I saw, was summed up for
me in the remembered sensation of that first burning and
aromatic swallow, that mixture of milk and coffee and bread
by which men hold communion with tranquil pastures, exotic
plantations, and golden harvests, communion with the earth.
Amidst all these stars there was but one that could make itself
significant for us by composing this aromatic bowl that was its
daily gift at dawn. And from that earth of men, that earth

---

* *matutinal* (măt ū tīn'ăl): of the morning.

docile to the reaping of grain and the harvesting of the grape, bearing its rivers asleep in their fields, its villages clinging to their hillsides, our ship was separated by astronomical distances. All the treasures of the world were summed up in a grain of dust now blown far out of our path by the very destiny itself of dust and the orbs of night.

And Néri still prayed to the stars.

Suddenly he was pounding my shoulder. On the bit of paper he held forth impatiently to me I read: "All well. Magnificent news." I waited with beating heart while he scribbled the half-dozen words that were to save us. At last he put this grace of heaven into my hands.

It was dated from Casablanca, which we had left the night before. Delayed in transmission, it had suddenly found us more than a thousand miles away, suspended between cloud and fog, lost at sea. It was sent by the government representative at the airport. And it said: "Monsieur de Saint Exupéry, I am obliged to recommend that you be disciplined at Paris for having flown too close to the hangars on leaving Casablanca."

It was true that I had done this. It was also true that this man was performing his duty with irritability. I should have been humiliated if this reproach had been addressed to me in an airport. But it reached me where it had no right to reach me. Among these too rare stars, on this bed of fog, in this menacing savor of the sea, it burst like a detonation. Here we were with our fate in our hands, the fate of the mails and of the ship; we had trouble enough to try to keep alive; and this man was purging his petty rancor against us.

But Néri and I were far from nettled. What we felt was a vast and sudden jubilation. Here it was we who were masters, and this man was letting us know it. The impudent little corporal! not to have looked at our stripes and seen that we had been promoted captain! To intrude into our musings when we were solemnly taking our constitutional between Sagittarius and the Great Bear! When the only thing we could be concerned with, the only thing of our order of magnitude, was this appointment we were missing with the moon!

The immediate duty, the only duty of the planet whence this man's message came, was to furnish us accurate figures for our computations among the stars. And its figures had been false. This being so, the planet had only to hold its tongue. Néri scribbled: "Instead of wasting their time with this nonsense they would do better to haul us back to Cisneros, if they can." By "they" he meant all the peoples of the globe, with their parliaments, their senates, their navies, their armies, their emperors. We re-read the message from that man mad enough to imagine that he had business with us, and tacked in the direction of Mercury.

It was by the purest chance that we were saved. I had given up all thought of making Cisneros and had set my course at right angles to the coast-line in the hope that thus we might avoid coming down at sea when our fuel ran out. Meanwhile however I was in the belly of a dense fog so that even with land below it was not going to be easy to set the ship down. The situation was so clear that already I was shrugging my shoulders ruefully when Néri passed me a second message which, an hour earlier, would have been our salvation. "Cisneros," it said, "has deigned to communicate with us. Cisneros says, '216 doubtful.'" Well, that helped. Cisneros was no longer swallowed up in space, it was actually out there on our left, almost within reach. But how far away? Néri and I talked it over briefly, decided it was too late to try for it (since that might mean missing the coast), and Néri replied: "Only one hour fuel left continuing on 93."

But the airports one by one had been waking each other up. Into our dialogue broke the voices of Agadir, Casablanca, Dakar. The radio stations at each of these towns had warned the airports and the ports had flashed the news to our comrades. Bit by bit they were gathering round us as round a sick-bed. Vain warmth, but human warmth after all. Helpless concern, but affectionate at any rate.

And suddenly into this conclave burst Toulouse, the headquarters of the Line three thousand miles away, worried along with the rest. Toulouse broke in without a word of greeting, simply to say sharply: "Your reserve tanks bigger than standard. You have two hours fuel left. Proceed to Cisneros."

TOPICS FOR DISCUSSION

1. Find passages in which the author emphasizes his philosophy.

2. Use a large map or a blackboard sketch map to show his flying course from Toulouse to Dakar. What obstacles such as mountains, rivers, seas, and desert stretches do you see?

3. Select some paragraphs in which the language itself attracts attention by its beauty or suitability. Read these aloud.

THE AIR MOUSE[1]

By A. Capwell Wyckoff

THE story that follows is a good one, but it deals with an unusual phase of aviation. The pilot is not in the Army or the Navy, nor is he carrying passengers in a luxurious airliner. He is using a plane to spread insect poison over cotton fields.

* * * * *

Bucky O'Mara stopped a moment with his hand on the knob and read the gold letters on the glass portion of the door. Inside, he could hear the choppy clicking of a typewriter and somebody coughed sharply. The words on the ground glass office door were the same as those on the letters he had been getting.

"NAPIA AIR SERVICE," Bucky read. "CROP DUSTING, SWAMP SPRAYING, INSECT CONTROL. J. Edward Napia, Pres." He went in.

The office was small with greasy-looking furnishings stippled with cigar ashes. A man sat at the desk facing him, an individual with graying hair and a stern face. Just beyond him a thin man with piercing black eyes was punching the typewriter. On the walls were pictures of planes, and farms that Napia Air Service had crop-dusted; also there was a model of a Bellanca on an ebony base. The afternoon sun glared on the dingy water cooler.

"What can I do for you?" the man at the desk asked, nodding crisply. His sweeping glance catalogued Bucky swiftly. A little short, stocky, firm jaw, mild gray eyes. Might make a flier.

---

[1] From *Boys' Life,* January, 1941. Copyright by the author. Reprinted through the courtesy of the author and *Boys' Life,* published by the Boy Scouts of America.

"I'm Bucky O'Mara," the boy said. "We've been having some correspondence lately, and you offered me a job with Napia Air Service."

"Oh, yes!" The man at the desk smiled suddenly and the thin typist showed a little interest. "I'm the president of this company," the man at the desk went on. "We expected you to get here a little earlier, so as to go out on a job this afternoon. Glad to meet you, son." He held out his hand.

Bucky didn't take it. "I spent a little time looking into things," the young pilot said. "After I found out a few facts, I didn't want the job, and I thought it was fair to tell you so. Thanks for the offer, though." He laid a contract on the desk.

Both men looked at him hard, and the cordiality was gone. "What's the matter with our contract?" J. Edward Napia rapped.

"Something I wasn't smart enough to see by myself," Bucky answered. "No provision for your pilots if anything happens to them while flying for you. And the kind of planes you buy and wire up won't go long without something going wrong."

"Been talking to somebody pretty wise, haven't you, kid?" the lanky typist sneered.

"I did a little looking around for myself first," Bucky retorted.

The president was studying him from under lowered lids. "We take care of our fliers," he said.

"No, you don't," Bucky contradicted, flatly. "Over in the hospital you've got one now, badly injured while flying one of your crates. You refused to pay the bill, and the first question asked was how badly the ship was damaged. I don't want to fly for an outfit like that."

Concentrated venom was in the look that the thin man gave him. "Listen, kid, nobody around here is begging you to fly for Napia. And if you're wise, you'll keep your mouth shut, understand?"

"I'm not a reporter," Bucky reminded him.

The president turned back to his papers. "O.K., son, it's just with you. If you want to pass up twenty-five dollars a week on a five year contract, go to it. Maybe you've got jobs waiting for the picking."

"I haven't," Bucky shook his head. "But I happen to know

that your pay is pretty poor in comparison with what the top-notchers put out. The best dusting companies pay a base of three hundred a month, plus a cent an acre for the job. And they carry insurance for their pilots."

"Maybe you've forgotten that they pick the best pilots, too," the typist put in. "I bet they'll fall all over themselves when they see you coming!"

Bucky gave him a level glance and turned away. "I'm not so dumb as to think I rate with them," he said. "Just wanted to let you know that I had been doing a little thinking of my own. Thanks for your offer, gentlemen."

He was gone and for a moment there was silence in the office of the Napia Air Service Company. J. Edward looked across to his partner and his jaw was grim.

"Somebody talked plenty to that kid," he said.

John Gilbert got up and pulled on his coat. "Must have been Larry Powers, over in the hospital," he growled. "I'll go see about it. Maybe we ought to pay some of his bill and keep him quiet in the future." He went out, and the president picked up Bucky's contract and after a glance at the empty line where the signature should have been, he filed it carefully away. It wasn't easy to get a job with any of the crop dusting companies just then, and the cocky kid might come back and eat his words yet.

The thin man got into a car and drove rapidly to the hospital, going up to the ward. There was a nurse near the bed where the broken flier was slowly mending. Gilbert put on his best smile and took Larry's hand for a brief squeeze.

"Not too long," the nurse warned. "He had another caller today."

When she had moved away, Gilbert came to the point. "You had another visitor," he said. "Some kid wanting to know about your accident, eh?" His piercing eyes were boring into Larry's.

"Yes," Larry replied. He was still hoping for some help from Napia in his doctor bill, and he decided to be cautious.

"What did you tell him?"

"Not much," the injured pilot said. "I didn't have any idea what he wanted to know those things for, I mean details about my crack-up. He asked if the company was going to pay my bill, and I said I hoped so." The boy looked anxiously at Gilbert, who shifted the subject.

"Don't worry about things like that now, Larry! What I'd like to know is how he knew enough to come see you."

"He said that Spark Kane was a friend of his, and had told him about me," Larry said.

"Oh-ho!" The thin man's breathed exclamation was a whole story in itself. "So Spark Kane of Regis Air Company put him on the track, eh? I see some things now that are plain as the nose on your face."

Back in the office again, Gilbert explained briefly to J. Edward Napia. "Spark Kane put that kid wise to us," he said. "Seems to be some friend of his."

The president of the company narrowed his eyes so much that he seemed to be asleep for the moment. "So Regis Air Company doesn't lose a chance to hurt us, eh?" he murmured. "We'll see if we can't pay them back with interest and then some."

Blissfully unaware of what a hornet's nest he had stirred, Bucky O'Mara took a bus out to the Regis Airfield. Sitting back in the seat of the old vehicle, he sent his mind rambling over the series of events which had made up the day. Although it seemed a long time ago, it was only this morning that he had met Spark Kane by accident on a Greyhound bus and for miles they had travelled along without speaking. Then their attention had been attracted by a passing plane, and Bucky had made a remark, which he had since forgotten, to his companion. One thing led to another and at last Kane had looked at him keenly, his newspaper forgotten.

"Say, are you a pilot?"

Bucky tapped his pocket. "I've got a contract here to sign with the Napia Air Service," he said. "Going to dust crops and spray insects."

"I know all about it," the other said. "I'm Clark Kane, of Regis Air Company, mostly known as Spark. My outfit and the Napia aren't exactly buddies."

"Rivals, huh?"

Spark Kane curled his lip. "We don't even want to be called competitors with a bunch like that," he said.

"Why? What's the matter with Napia?"

Spark looked at him a moment and then turned abruptly

back to his paper. "Kid, I'm talking too much. After all, you're going to work with them."

"But look here," Bucky protested. "Maybe I'm heading into the wrong corral, and you ought to head me off. Anything you tell me won't influence me until I've checked on it myself. So spill it."

Spark Kane did. Bucky had the feeling that Spark wasn't doing it to be vicious, but only because he hated to see men like the Napias and their stripe in a game that sometimes held the lives of good pilots as the price of a mistake. "They're a gyp concern, one of a shoestring group getting by to make a few dollars," Spark told him. "They buy up wrecked planes and rebuild them as cheaply as possible, knowing that someday the things have got to give way. Now, I'm not telling you all this because we've got anything to offer you, and I don't want to talk you out of a job."

As a result of this encounter, Bucky O'Mara had walked around the trap before going in. He knew enough about planes to spot several weaknesses in the few that were on the runway at the Napia hangars, and his conversation with Larry Powers at the hospital had settled some things in his mind. At the office of the hospital he had found out that Napia Air Service had refused to pay the bill of the injured pilot. His contact with the two in the office had showed him conclusively what kind they were.

"And I came within an inch of signing up with that outfit!" he reflected, as he got off the bus and made for the gate at Regis Field. "Spark Kane really did the big brother act on that."

Of course, things were still pretty tough. He had to have a job so that he could eat and have a place to sleep nights. It hadn't been easy to turn Napia down, even with what he knew. In the end, it had been his frank dislike of such commercial vultures and not fear which had cast the decision for him.

The man at the gate let him through, and he found Kane tinkering with a ship over near the first hangar. The Regis flier was only a year or two older than Bucky, but he had a streak of swell-head about him that secretly irritated the boy from Oklahoma. No matter what he did or said, though,

Bucky wasn't going soon to forget the good steer that Spark had given him.

"Hello, kid," Spark greeted him. "All signed up with the enemy?"

"Not a chance," Bucky told him. "I went down the line checking up, and found out that what you told me was the right number. So I'm out of a job, and don't think I'm blaming you, or coming around here to cry or beg."

"That's all right," Kane nodded. "I told you to look me up. Go over to the office and see Leo Walsh. He'd like to talk to you."

Walsh was interested in Bucky but not too encouraging. "Just now there's nothing doing, but if you want to hang around awhile, something may turn up," the manager said. "We can give you a place to sleep and food to put under your belt for a few weeks. Spark thinks he talked you out of a job and he wants to do that much for you. In return, we'll want some work out of you. What's your flying time?"

"Over a thousand hours," Bucky answered. "Did quite a bit of barn-storming out on the edge of the Oklahoma Ozarks."

"Barn-storming, eh? We like to get men who have done that kind of work, because the dusters have to handle a ship fast in a pinch."

When Bucky went back out on the field, Kane was standing in a group talking to two pilots and two mechanics. Bucky started to back off, but Spark looked inquiringly at the newest and unofficial member of Regis Air Company.

"I just wanted to tell you I got on, at least for a few weeks, or until something turns up," Bucky told him. "Thanks to you, and maybe someday I may be able to help you out of a jam."

Kane and the others grinned, and Bucky stiffened as the import of it hit him. "Oh, I might get a chance to do something even for the great Kane!" he asserted. "There is a story about a mouse getting a lion out of a net, don't forget that."

"All right, mouse," Spark grinned. "Shake hands with Ike Colson and Jim Morgan, old stick-pushers from way back. The two greaseballs are Trig Runyon and Abe Banter."

And from that time on, Bucky was Mouse. In the days that

followed he worked over the Regis planes, and whenever anybody wanted him they just yelled, "Hey, Mouse!" He took it with a grin and they liked him and accepted him as part of the outfit.

There were small jobs all the time. One time Kane took him along while he sprayed a fair-sized cotton field. They took off before dawn in a plane built especially for dusting, with cantilever wings that wouldn't fold up when the branch of a tree hit a strut. The sky was gray and the shadows were still in the low places when the ace crop duster started his work.

"We have to start early, because when the sun gets up and burns the dew off of the plants, there's nothing to hold the insecticide," Spark explained, as he sent the ship down low to the ground. He watched his distance from the edge of the woods and then gave the engine full throttle. A surge of power blasted the poison back to the edge of the trees from the sprayers under the plane. This was important, he explained to Bucky, because the boll weevils live in the underbrush and begin destroying cotton at the edge of the field first.

Bucky watched all operations with intense interest. Kane was flying not more than three feet above the cotton, and his speed was around a hundred miles an hour. The cloud of dust covered a swath of cotton about forty feet wide, and at that rate it wouldn't take many hours to do the whole field. He began to get an idea of what it had once meant to dust it all from ground machines.

"One of the things you've got to learn about this business is how to turn without losing time," Kane said. "Here we go!"

Even with all his barn-storming experience, Bucky had never seen anything like the way Spark handled his plane at the turn. The pilot zoomed almost straight up until the ship lost speed, and then he kicked it into a sharp turn and dived back on his new course. Grimly, Bucky figured out what it would mean if engine failure or a puff of wind hit them at the wrong time. But the chief crop duster was safely on his course again, flying tail high so that the pilot could look over his engine at the ground below.

When the big bin was empty, they headed for a nearby field, and Spark set the ship down expertly. A truck had been dispatched to the place and in a few minutes six hundred pounds of insecticide had been loaded, and they were in the air again.

Bucky learned a lot from Spark that day. Calcium arsenate was used to kill out the boll weevil. Swamp jobs called for paris green to control the malaria mosquitos. Spark had worked at dusting grapefruit and broccoli and fruit in general.

By ten o'clock the day had turned hot and they had to wait until four in the afternoon before starting in again. During that time they loafed and napped and got better acquainted. Bucky mentioned possible interference from Napia, because Spark had had some hot words with John Gilbert upon a recent visit to the city.

"They won't come out in the open and do anything," Spark was confident. "Just a big bluff. I keep wondering how they ever found out that I talked to you. Or do they just give a good guess at it, because you're with us?"

"Maybe I was dumb in telling that pilot at the hospital that you were a friend of mine," Bucky said. "I did that to get him talking shop with me."

"Well, it's O.K.," Spark said, lazily. "Someday Napia will have a big crash and go out of business. The competition is keen and in time only the concerns that keep good ships and reliable pilots will be able to hang on."

As the days passed, Bucky found himself in a peculiar position. Everybody at Regis was nice to him and nothing was said about his leaving, but the feeling was growing on him that he was just a sponge and ought to go elsewhere. Here he was, waiting and hoping for a job, but in order to get one, a pilot would have to leave or get hurt, and Bucky certainly didn't want the latter to happen. And he found himself liking Colson and Jim Morgan so much that he didn't want them to leave.

There was one big plantation down in the delta country toward which the heads of all the dusting companies looked with eager eyes. Old Preston Ray owned the big farm and for a long time he had opposed anything so radical as crop dusting from the air. But there were reports that he was weakening and had sent out feelers.

"The company that gets that job will cut a juicy melon," Kane told the other pilots, in Bucky's presence. "He's got thou-

sands of acres that could take the poison. Leo Walsh is court-
ing him."

Word got out that Ray had decided to ask Napia and Regis
for bids. Days followed, and then Walsh came out on the field
and waved a letter excitedly. "We got it!" he yelled. "By jumping jupiter, we got it!"

Regis had won the bid over Napia. But it wasn't to be a
straight job yet. The manager explained it to them.

"He's a doubting Thomas and has to be shown. He wants a
thousand acres salted down and then he'll watch it for results.
If the job is a good one, he'll open the whole place to us. It's
a conditional contract."

Things swung into action for that. The Regis fliers were
confident that they could put the job over. Colson and Morgan
were sent to finish a swamp assignment so that they could be
in readiness to help on the big contract. Spark was to dust the
preliminary thousand acres, which would take him a full day.
Bucky helped the mechanics check planes and equipment and
Leo Walsh ordered additional poison. Everything was in readiness.

Late that afternoon a truck loaded with the arsenate came in
and delivered it to the storeroom. Walsh sent Bucky down
there to check it in and sign for the stuff. There was no firm
name on the green truck and the men who unloaded didn't
have much to say. Bucky locked the storeroom and went back
to the bunkhouse.

Spark left long before daybreak, with one load of poison in
the plane bin and a truck with extra dust followed, to be there
by the time the flier was ready for more. The mechanics had
the day off and at dinner time Walsh came out and hunted
for Bucky.

"I've just had a wire saying that my brother is pretty sick,
over in Calhoun County," he said. "So I'll get on over there
and see him. Spark won't be in tonight; he's flying on to the
swamp where the other stick-pushers are working and will give
them a hand. You can handle things around here until I get
back tomorrow morning."

"Me and that old ship in the hangar!" Bucky grinned.

Late in the afternoon somebody hobbled into the yard, and
from his chair at the office window Bucky saw him coming. It

was Larry Powers, one-time flier for Napia, a thin, wasted-looking shadow of his former self. Bucky greeted him cheerfully and they sat down to talk.

"I thought Leo Walsh might be in," Larry said. "He's a good friend of mine, and I wanted to tip him off to something I heard. I'm glad I told you what I did when you came to the hospital, and if I had known then what I know now, I'd have told you a lot more."

"You helped me miss getting into a bad mess," Bucky nodded. "Not to be too personal, but I'd like to know whether or not they paid your hospital bill?"

Powers snorted. "They didn't pay anything!" he cried. "And because it wasn't in my contract, I couldn't hold them to it. But they had told me at the start that all injuries would be taken care of."

"Same way with me," Bucky nodded. "Well, I'm sorry Mr. Walsh isn't in, so you can pass on that tip, but you can come in again tomorrow."

Powers shook his head. "I expect to be a long way from here tomorrow. But I don't mind telling you. Yesterday morning I went up to the Napia offices to have a last round with those guys about paying my bill, and just as I got outside the door, I could hear them talking, Napia and Gilbert. Did Regis just beat them out of some big contract?"

"We got a chance to dust the Preston Ray plantation, over Napia's bid," Bucky nodded.

"Well, that's what had worked them up, because they were in a sweet temper about the whole thing. I don't mind admitting that I stood there in the hall a minute to listen. Mr. Napia said, 'We'll break that outfit yet and get that Ray contract ourselves. Let me see that stuff.' Just then somebody came along the hall and I didn't want to be seen standing there listening, so I pushed the door open and went in."

"See anything of the stuff they were talking about?" Bucky asked.

"Yes, but only for a second and it didn't seem to be important. Mr. Napia had a square of brown paper with some powder or dust on it, and Gilbert was bending over the desk looking at it. When they heard me they both looked like kids caught stealing jam, and they slipped the paper into the top drawer. That's all I saw or heard, but I know they'll take a whack at Regis as soon as they can."

"I've felt that coming for a long time," Bucky nodded. "But I don't see how they can get the Ray plantation contract away from us. Spark Kane is over there salting it down right now."

"I don't know, but I thought I'd let you know what I heard," Powers said, getting up to go. "As far as flying goes, take it from me, I'm all washed up."

After his visitor was gone, Bucky sat thinking with intense concentration about the whole thing. He didn't put it past the Napia bunch to do something to cripple Regis, but he couldn't figure out what it would be. Funny thing that they should talk about getting the Ray contract away from them, because Spark was already on the job.

About ten o'clock the truck came back and Bucky was glad to check it in. From the driver he learned that Spark had had no trouble with his job and everything had gone off smoothly. Three sacks of the arsenate had been sent back.

The truck pulled away and Bucky stood in the storeroom, his hand on the electric light switch button. Maybe Napia would get the Ray contract, but he couldn't see how, now that Spark had dusted the preliminary thousand acres. There was nothing to stop that, for weevils in that field were doomed.

Something like a flash of lightning went across Bucky's mind as he thought of what Larry Powers had told him. Turning away from the switch, he cut open the top of one of the bags of arsenate and carefully wrapped some of the poison in a piece of paper. Then he examined the sacks in the storeroom.

After that, he moved fast. The light went out with a click and the door was locked in a hurry. Bucky closed up the office and hurried outside the gate to the main road. It seemed as if a bus would never come along, but one finally did, and he was off to town, his mind working rapidly.

At a small house near the university Bucky knocked on the front door. A tall man in a bathrobe answered, looking anything but pleased.

"You are Professor Barret, head of the chemistry department, aren't you?" Bucky asked.

"Yes. What can I do for you at this hour?" the chemist demanded.

"Something very important," Bucky answered, fishing out the paper from his pocket. "I'm from the Regis Air Company and we need some expert help. What is this stuff?"

Professor Barret looked closely. "It looks like calcium arsenate," he said.

"Mind stepping over to the laboratory a few minutes?" Bucky requested.

On the following afternoon Spark Kane set his plane down on the Regis field and walked over to the office. The swamp job was about finished and he had come in a little ahead of the other pilots. In the main building he found Walsh in a highly emotional state. He fairly exploded at the ace flier.

"Spark, why didn't you take care of that preliminary job at the Ray plantation? Great Scott, don't you know how important it is that we don't bungle that assignment? What's the idea of sending a kid like O'Mara to do it? He's not even employed here!"

"What the dickens are you talking about?" Spark yelled back. "I did the whole blooming thing myself, yesterday!"

"That kid took the old duster and pulled out of here sometime in the night," Leo Walsh said. "He left a note on my desk. Look it over."

Spark snatched it out of the manager's hand. Bucky had been brief. "I'm spraying the Preston Ray thousand acre field and will be back when it is done," he had written in his schoolboyish scrawl.

Spark slammed the note down on the desk in fury. "Why, the fresh little pup, I'd like to twist his neck!" he cried. "I did that job and it doesn't need to be done again. Of all the—"

"You didn't by any chance make a mistake and do the wrong field, did you?" Walsh asked.

"Mr. Ray was there and showed me the field, so I couldn't very well salt the wrong one," Kane retorted. "What about dust? He couldn't work without more poison than his hopper holds. Have you sent him any?"

Walsh jumped up. "No. I thought all the time that you had fallen down on the job or part of it, and didn't check on that. Let's see."

In the storeroom things were undisturbed as far as their

hasty glances could determine. No dust had gone out. Walsh looked at Spark and his mouth was grim.

"Spark, that kid has jumped this outfit, with one of our planes."

"Maybe so," Spark answered. "But I'm going to shoot down to that delta farm and see if he is anywhere around. I just don't see why he would leave a note like that if there wasn't something behind it."

Spark Kane gave his big plane full throttle all the way to the Preston Ray plantation, his jaw set but his mind vainly trying to puzzle things out. Faint dusk was beginning to settle over the landscape when he reached the place, and a glance at the earth below caused him to boil up inside again. Over the thousand acre field a plane was flying back and forth, a trail of white dust trailing in the rear. Most of the area had been covered.

"Well, blast his nervy hide, he is doing my job over!" Spark gritted. He dived down close to the dusting plane, and Bucky looked up and waved carelessly, grinning at Kane's angry face. Spark lifted his wings, circled, and finally set his ship down on an open, uncultivated field, close to where a truck was parked. At the same time, Bucky headed in for a landing.

"Whose truck is this?" Spark asked, addressing the two men, who seemed to be eyeing him suspiciously.

"You keep away from it, buddy," one man began, but the other interrupted him, pointing to the lettering on the plane.

"It's O.K. He's from Regis. O'Mara's coming in; he'll handle everything."

Spark was boiling again. "He'd better handle something," he said. Then somebody laughed, and Spark swung around, to see Preston Ray on the other side of the truck. The white-haired old planter started for the big house, making one comment as he went.

"You're a good flier, Kane, but no better than that kid in the old plane."

Spark strode across the field and was beside the ship when Bucky climbed out. "All right," Kane barked. "Let's have the story. What's the answer?"

"I've got the answers," Bucky said, brushing the back of his hand over his mouth. He looked all in, and his clothes were dirty. "Naturally, you're wondering why I'm doing your job over. You—"

"I'll say I'm wondering," Spark cut in.

"You sprayed this field with a worthless powder that wouldn't kill a single boll weevil," Bucky told him. "Napia saw to that. When Walsh telephoned in for real poison, Napia called our supply company and cancelled the order, pretending it was Leo talking. They saw to it that fake powder that looked just like what we needed got to us for this job. You can figure it out for yourself."

"I'm beginning to get it!" Spark cried. "The weevils would have eaten up this field and Ray would have been through with us forever. Then Napia would have dickered for the job. Of all the—"

"Sure," Bucky nodded. "I haven't got time to tell you all the details now, but I got onto it and had the powder analyzed. It's worthless. The bags they sent aren't even marked in any way. I was busy all night, getting in touch with our supply company and having the right truck sent here to meet me today." He motioned toward the squat plane. "And I've had a swell time with this piece of junk. The hopper has jammed a dozen times."

"But what did Preston Ray think of this duplication?" Spark asked, anxiously.

"I laid the whole thing before him, using no names, but he's a smart man and can do his own thinking."

In the gathering dusk Spark looked hard at the tired Bucky. "I'm going to see to it that you get a regular job as one of our pilots, after this stunt. And you've taken me down a peg, Mouse!"

Bucky grinned. "Shove a load of the dust into your bin and we'll both do the last two rows and finish the job before it gets dark," he said. "Let's go, Lion!"

Topics for Discussion

1. What are some of the things you like about this story? Some you do not like? Do you like the author's choice of names for his characters? Why or why not?

2. Do you like that typist in the first five minutes of the

story? Why? Of the two men, which at the beginning makes the best impression?

3. Are you prepared at the first for the villainy of the Napia men that comes out at the end of the story? How?

4. Does the phrase "heading into the wrong corral" indicate to what part of the country this story belongs? Do you find any other bits of the language to support this first impression?

5. Did you find this industry of crop-dusting to be something new to you?

6. What do you know about boll weevils?

Suggested Film

The United States Department of Agriculture distributes a film illustrating this phase of aviation. It is called *Winged Warfare* and can be obtained by writing the Department of Agriculture in Washington. The film is not very new but, nevertheless, it gives a good idea of how crop-dusting is done by airplanes.

ADVENTURE WAS THE COMPASS[1]

By Alma Heflin

ONE would like to believe that two office girls could decide to spend a vacation in Alaska, buy a plane, and, after a few days of instruction and practice, fly off through the blue sky to fun and adventure. Alma Heflin in her gay story makes that seem possible, but it was not so in her own case. After school and college she worked some months in the shops of an airplane company and then went into the publicity department. When she and her friend, Margie McQuinn, decided upon the Alaska vacation she was head of the publicity department and a licensed pilot. After her book was written she became one of the few women to hold a license as a commercial pilot and actually the first woman test pilot. She was not, you see, a mere amateur, irresponsibly dashing here and there across the map.

The selection which follows is from Chapter X of *Adventure was the Compass*. "Mr. Shrdlu" is the familiar name the girls gave their plane.

*   *   *   *   *

I should have learned about Nenana from Montana's Hell Gate, and someday no doubt when I'm an old, old lady I'll approach the lee side of canyons with plenty of altitude. But that will happen only when I've lost the last vestige of my girlish trust, the last treble note of my girlish laughter. And Nenana Canyon in the heart of Alaska will have helped.

Not that we knew Nenana was a canyon when we started, or course. Alaskan maps are Alaskan maps, and no one told us.

We left Fairbanks the morning after our visit with James Barrick. It was 3 A.M. and therefore presumably dawn even though the sky had blazed with sunlight all night. Mt. Mc-

Kinley, though, lay southward where there was an authentic, if brief, night and, someone told us, there were only three days out of the year when McKinley could be photographed and then only at daybreak. The rest of the time there was a misty veil over the peak that added to its beauty but made photography difficult. There was no way of knowing which three days he would unveil his hoary head. It behooved us to be there early on a far chance that this was the day.

We set Shrdlu's nose dead on the pale peak that dreamed on the horizon, sailed over Nenana Village, droned along over more than a hundred miles of tundra, and started circling back and forth along the foothills. There was some mist, but it was not heavy and we snapped a dozen pictures, reloaded the camera, pointed it optimistically at some mountain sheep plunging down a slope, and turned back toward the railroad.

Alaska has only one railroad except for a short loop of narrow-gauge stuff near some of the coastal cities. It stretches four hundred and seventy miles between Anchorage on the sea, skirting through the edge of McKinley National Park, and Fairbanks. Our map showed it cut through the mountain range along which we flew between two little towns, Healy and Mt. McKinley Station. Presumably there was a valley there to slide through without taking time to climb. We had used three hours' gasoline already—more than we had planned—but about forty-five minutes should bring us safely to Healy where we could refuel if really necessary and McKinley Station was only ten miles down the railroad.

The wind was rising by the time we reached the river a little far north, and when we turned our backs on the sun and roared south it suddenly hit us like a tide. We measured our ground speed uneasily between two check points. According to it and our air-speed indicator, the wind was howling full in our face at forty-five miles an hour. Landing would be more than difficult. It would be dangerous. But to turn back to the town of Nenana, much less to Fairbanks, was impossible. Gasoline was too low. Sand bars in the river back in the area of low velocity had looked either muddy or boulder-strewn. There was one hope. If Nenana Pass, ahead of us, was quite narrow this high wind could be the result of a Venturi-like force, a compression that would have stepped up its velocity on this side of the mountains. Once over the range on the windward side we should probably find only a gentle wind. We climbed for as much altitude as we could gain before reaching the pass.

Either we had started climbing too late, or the down-currents were stronger and surging higher than usual. Ahead two mountains towered, leaning toward each other. Between them the railroad ran and there lay our course flanked by their scabby rusty shoulders. To our right the river turned away into another course, and carved its valley on two levels, a high flat shelf on the southern side down which the wind boiled, a deep flat groove where the river flowed on the northern side in the shadow of another mountain range.

The wind hit us here not like a tide, but like an avalanche forcing us inexorably down. Altitude spurted away like blood from an artery. Shrdlu pitched, bucked, scrabbled for a wing hold. Two thousand feet, fifteen hundred, a thousand, four hundred. . . . We wheeled over, fled down the valley to our right. Along the northern edge, perhaps where the wind had to make its leap over the ridge before it flattened out over the tundra basin, we could ride up on the waves and make another pass at the canyon.

Margie frowned at the map.

"The way I read the map," she said, "you're off course. You're nearly ninety degrees off. We were supposed to go straight ahead."

I had no time to answer. Shrdlu was bucking in the high seas of the wind currents. I clenched the stick, relaxed consciously. Careful, careful, Alma. Not too tense . . . feel for it . . . hold it! Nose down . . . get the nose down . . . flatten the angle of the wings . . . grab all the lift in sight . . . raise the nose a little . . . a little . . . Come on, Shrdlu old hoss, CLIMB!

"I said you're on the wrong course!" said Margie. "We should be over the railroad. And it's behind us!"

"We'll go back," I gasped. "Hush! I can't fly and talk. Hush!"

"But . . ." she said. Whump went Shrdlu. The cover of the baggage compartment unlatched, flopped up. The typewriter bounced toward the ceiling.

"Catch it!" I yelled.

"Darn typewriters," said Margie.

"It'll land on our heads. It'll break our necks," I wailed. "Hold it down!"

She twisted around in the seat. It isn't easy with a belt cinched tight over your thighs to squirm pretzel-fashion to hold down a baggage cover directly behind you. She put both hands hard on the lid. We hit another williwaw.* Shrdlu dropped, tipped, did a tango on one wing tip. Margie ducked. The baggage cover flipped open again, something hurtled out.

"Camera!" cried Margie desperately.

"Catch it!" I yelped. But she had it. She was pulling things out of the compartment. Everything loose: camera, ropes, tie-down stakes, flashlight, film. She hauled the typewriter out last, piled the junk in her lap, weighted it down with the typewriter. She looked at me, wide-eyed, over the pile, her arms stretched around the load, her knees hunched up to keep her lap concave. The baggage lid flapped, banged.

"Now what?" she said.

I didn't know. The air was so rough that I dreaded going over the edge of the shelf to hunt the rising current on the opposite side of the valley, but we were getting steadily lower. Ahead the valley narrowed. It would soon be another Nenana Canyon. Another Hell Gate. "Hold on," I said. "Here we go."

We wheeled out over the valley. Under us were the buildings of the coal mine that furnishes heat and power for interior Alaska. They weren't big but they looked big. They loomed. Behind them the exposed veins of shiny black coal striped the cliffs. If the current didn't rise here, we might go through the roof of the buildings or splatter on the cliff behind.

But it did. It had to. There was no place else for the tide to go. There was a mountain there, and the wind must climb it. It roared up it at forty-five miles an hour or more. We rode its plunging surface to the mountain crest, turned back toward Nenana Canyon.

I hadn't seen any building at all at the mouth of Nenana when we fled from the avalanche, but riding the waves above

---

* *williwaw:* down draft.

the northern ridge there was time to look for the Healy that
the map said lay there, and for the airport. With the extra ex-
cursion toward the coal mine, with the time spent climbing
as we had first approached the pass, with the extra fuel con-
sumed fighting down-currents with wide-open throttle, gas
was too low to spend more time scrabbling for altitude only to
go into a canyon with an unknown floor and without gas to
retreat if need be. Wind or no wind, we needed to land. At
any rate, with the proper wind technique, a pilot can neu-
tralize a good deal of the danger in such a landing.

We located Healy suddenly. There was a little green building, a railroad station probably. There was a tall squarish affair that was probably a coal bunker. There was a decrepit
building with a high false front with HOTEL sprawled across
it in peeling paint. That was all. There was no airport. I
looked at the map again. It said there was an airport.

"Do you see an airport?" I asked Margie.

She peered over her lapful of baggage. No, she didn't see
any.

The shelf curled around here, a high bluff toward the mountains with a ravine bisecting it at right angles to the canyon.
The buildings lay at the foot. But what price landmarks? This
was no CAA* map.

"But do you see a wind sock † or anything?" I couldn't.

"I see some white crosses," Margie said.

The white crosses were really white boards laid like a carpenter's square, almost buried in the rioting green growth on
the shelf. The ravine paralleled the line they made just to
their south. Towards Fairbanks another ravine lay parallel to
them, and there . . . no . . . yes . . . there were two more
white carpenter's squares.

"Do you suppose that can be an airport?" I said.

"Nothing else looks as much like one," she said dubiously.

There would be no wind technique needed here. What we
needed was a horseshoe and a four-leaf clover. We flew down
its length. The green might be the high bushy plants we had

---

* *CAA:* Civil Aeronautics Administration.

† *wind sock:* the long open-ended bag flying from a pole at an airport to
show wind direction.

seen in the swamps when we were fossil hunting. Or they might be bushes. Or stunted tundra willow. The plane might squash down . . . if we landed slowly. If . . . But it looked as if the white boards might be airport markers all right, and suddenly we spied the tattered remains of a wind sock on a tall pole.

All right. If other planes could land, we could. We turned into the wind, half closed the throttle, approached.

"The sand bar?" said Margie. That's what I was wondering myself. The field looked worse as we came lower. Would it be better to land on the bar down at the foot of the cliff? But the rocks on it looked boulderish even from the air. And how would we cross the boiling river to shore? I shook my head.

Margie put the typewriter in the baggage compartment. Clear the decks, girls . . . we may go over. She slammed down the lid, faced front, braced.

They were bushes, not weeds, not trees. Shrdlu hit with a whoosh, squashed, stopped. The wind shrieked. One wing tipped up, slowly . . . agonizingly. I tore at my belt, got it unfastened, tumbled out of the cabin, fell full length on the wing strut. The plane, wavering with the wing high, its left wheel well off the ground, slowly edged back to level. Margie jumped out the other door, sat on the right wing struts. The plane shuddered, strained. Take-off speed for a Cub is about forty miles an hour. The wind under the wings at that or a higher speed might lift it any minute. I looked across at Margie, panting.

If we could get it turned around, tailed into the wind so that the gusts hit on top of the wing instead of under the up-tilted leading edge, we might get it tied down safely. "Margie," I yelled across at her, "you hold it down and I'll turn it around. Look! If your wing goes up, pull down on it. If my wing starts up, push up on your wing. Get it?" She nodded grimly.

I raced to the tail, slipped my hands under the longéron tube, lifted. My insides cracked, hardened. My face burned and ears roared. I couldn't lift it, I couldn't. I . . . did. The tail inched up from the ground, the tailwheel turned. I shoved. Slowly, slowly nudging through the clogging bushes, mashing them flat, the tail began to swing around. The wind caught Margie's wing, lifted. I raced back to mine, shoved up on the struts; the plane settled back.

Back to the tail. Shift, shove, lift. Crush down the darned bushes. Never mind that cut on your leg. Wipe off the blood later. Darn the bruise. Forget it. Two thousand dollars' worth of airplane and radio here. Don't let it blow away. Shove, lift, shove. It's the first hundred years that are the hardest, the last three feet that kill. SHOVE! Race back and grab that wing. Hold ON . . . what if your feet are lifted from the ground . . . it won't turn over . . . you won't be crushed under it . . . hold ON . . . leverage . . that's it . . . you'll settle back . . . there . . . your feet are down, the plane is quiet. Hurry, grab the tail . . . just a little farther now . . . There!

The times you need most to cry there is never time for it. There wasn't time now. Every muscle was water. Hearts were pounding. So what? We set the parking brake, jammed crushed bushes under the wheels to keep the plane from rocking, scrabbled for ropes and stakes in the cabin, for the axe. Margie would drive in her stake first. I could guard the wing struts.

The stake must be ahead of the wing, must slant forward so the rope could not slip loose. She set it in the ground, started pounding. The soil was matted with roots, but inch by inch it slid into the earth. She tied the rope to the strut, pulled its wind-whipped length firm, knotted it to the stake.

I drove in a stake at my side, tied down the left wing. We staked the tail. Now for a second set, driven in at a vee angle with the first; now for a second set of ropes. We broke the axe handle driving the second wing stake. The tail rope on the first stake might hold alone. To make sure, we tied the second around a bush. Now . . . what?

"It's a long ways down the cliff," said Margie, "and the wind is getting worse. Let's rest until the wind goes down. We'll be in an awful mess if Mister Shrdlu blows away four thousand miles from home."

But the plane was not even shivering now. It sat firmly, tied to withstand a gale, we hoped. And it was after seven o'clock. We had been out from Fairbanks well over four hours. If we were tired enough to die, we were twice that hungry. Breakfast would be heaven. We started the long dusty trek down to the building marked "Hotel."

We stepped into a big barren room and looked around. On the farther side was a counter with some notions and knick-knacks. There were rough chairs. A bleary-eyed drunk staggered up from a box leaning against one wall and weaved over to us. "N . . n . . new girrrrlsh come vishit!" he announced. Margie and I drew back, stared at him with our backs plastered against the wall. A thin woman came out of a door opposite. She looked at us.

"Get out of here," she snapped at him. He grinned vacantly, amiably, stumbled outside. "He wouldn't hurt you. What do you want. Where are you from." She wasn't asking. She was daring us to answer.

"F-from Fairbanks." She looked unbelieving. No train had come through for days. "In an airplane," I added. Her eyes labeled us plainly as two of the Ladies that are known as Lou. That . . . that . . . ! But you don't flounce out of a restaurant when you're starving and the next nearest food is more than a hundred miles away. No, wait . . . that was an exaggeration. There would be food in the Park. Ten miles away. I clenched my teeth.

"Can we get some breakfast here? Coffee?"

"No," she said.

"But the sign says it's a hotel."

"But it isn't," she snapped. "It's my home."

Margie's face had that peculiar waxy look that meant she was going to be desperately sick . . . the look she gets when it's terribly hot or the air is rough or she is completely exhausted. "But can't we get coffee anywhere?" she asked in a small tearful voice.

"I don't know," the woman said. "You might try the railroad station."

We got out. Tall grass tugged at our dragging feet. We went over to the railroad and walked down the ties. Like a couple of bums. We looked like bums. Our dresses were wrinkled and dusty and Margie's was torn. Our legs were scratched and cut and bleeding above our ankle socks. The leather was torn off the heel of one of my shoes. Our hair was mussed and tangled, our faces—judging by Margie's and the way mine felt —looked as if a horse had trampled over them. The drunken man sat on an empty oil drum and leered at us happily.

"And we didn't even ask about gasoline," Margie said. We could get it from the station, maybe. There was a little gasoline speeder upended over by the coal bunker.

We stumbled up the steps of the little green station. A tall good-looking man sat at a telegraph key. He looked over at us, his eyes widening.

"For gosh sakes!" he said. "Where did you drop from?" We explained that Mister Shrdlu was up on the . . . er . . . airport, tied down until the wind should die. "But no one lands there any more," he protested. "Didn't anyone tell you in Fairbanks? It's too dangerous. Too much wind through the pass. Too much bush. They fly over here at ten thousand feet. Did you crack up?" We told him we hadn't. We wanted gasoline.

He looked at us quizzically, twinkling. "Have to wire Anchorage," he said. "Got any money?" We bristled. "But if you have any money," he said, "they may set any price down in Anchorage. Now if you're a little broke maybe we can get it for seventy-five cents a gallon." Okay. We were broke. He clicked the telegraph key. Anchorage chattered back. He clicked at them again.

His wife came out of the living room and stared at us. Where were we from? Pennsylvania? My DEARS! How did we get to Healy? Did she hear us tell Bill we flew in? In our OWN plane? We flew it OURSELVES? We smiled sickly. Could we get some coffee? I didn't know about Margie, but I didn't really want it any longer. My stomach shivered. Mrs. Greene looked at me sharply. "My dear," she said, "you're sick."

"Just tired," I said, and suddenly felt a thousand years old. "We hurried to get our work done so we could start, and we got tired flying to Seattle, and we didn't get enough sleep in Juneau, Skagway, Burwash, or Tanacross. In Fairbanks it never gets dark and we kept forgetting to go to bed, and last night we took the KFAR staff flying to take pictures of the midnight sun and then went to a breakfast party at one A.M. and took off at three. We didn't get to bed at all. We're tired."

"You look dead and ready for burial," she said. "Coffee, and then you're going to bed."

I think we had breakfast. I have a dim memory of coffee and waffles and orange juice, and of Mrs. Greene pulling my clothes off and pulling bedcovers up under my chin and patting my cheek. And then I was asleep. I don't even remember Margie. She had much the same program, I suppose.

I woke standing on my feet at the end of a plunge halfway across the room. The building was rocking under the buffeting wind. Mrs. Greene ran out of the kitchen. "The plane," I wailed, "the plane . . ."

"It's all right!" she said. "Calm down, child. Bill went up as soon as I tucked you in, and put another set of ropes on the plane and retied your knots. It will ride out the wind. Everything will be calm in a couple of hours. There's time for a bath and dinner. Will you call Margie?" How long had we slept? Nine hours? NINE hours!

"And not a murmur out of either of you," said Mrs. Greene, "except you cried a little when the wind was the worst. It really worries you, doesn't it? But there. Get dressed now. Bill has gone after lettuce. Dinner will soon be ready."

The Greenes had a little greenhouse on the hillside. We had crackling crimson radishes, thin crisp crinkled lettuce. We had beefsteaks an inch thick. We had stories of their last visit Outside. They worked three years, took six months off. Last year they had gone to Hollywood. Bill had danced with movie stars. Mrs. Greene looked at him adoringly. No man in Hollywood was as good-looking as Bill Greene, and the stars knew it!

The soft purple almost-dusk was kind to our eyes, wearied by two solid weeks of never-ceasing sun. We climbed the long hill in the gentle sweet breeze. The Greenes didn't know where the Savage River field might be, on which we had been told to land, and it wasn't on the map, but there was a field at Mc-Kinley Station. Bill Greene had telegraphed through to see if it were usable, and they said the Road Commission workers were having a baseball game on it. They would get off when we came in sight. We filled the main tank, examined the bush-grown field.

Over to one side, the bushes were lower and scantier. We

walked a couple of hundred feet, chopped away the tallest, turned the plane around into what wind was left. Margie held the controls. I flipped over the prop. The motor sang. I climbed in. We waved good-bye at the Greenes, opened the throttle, stood on the brakes until Shrdlu shivered with accumulated power, released them.

Shrdlu leaped ahead, plunged into the air. The sparse bushes reached up, tugged at the wheels. Shrdlu dropped, dragged his wheels, broke free again. This time . . . this time . . . I eased back on the stick a little. The motor howled for heaven . . . up . . . up . . . up . . . bushes pulled us down again, wheels touched with a sickening bump, broke loose, swished through a ragged tree-top . . . and were free. Ahead was the ravine. Beyond the farther edge, the shelf surged upward to the mountain. The air speed was still low. Raise the nose to clear the shelf, lose six miles an hour and we would spin into the ravine . . . heaven, heaven, be kind. . . .

The ravine emptied to the left into the river valley. Down with the left wing, over . . . nose low, Alma . . . you're losing lift in the bank . . . nose LOW . . . dive . . . DIVE down the ravine . . . DIVE down over the railroad station . . . level out . . . don't hit it! . . . Level out . . . not too fast . . . not enough speed yet . . . nose down a little . . .

The air speed crept up and up and up . . . sixty . . . seventy . . . eighty . . . ninety . . . hundred and ten . . . twenty. The river boiled beneath our wheels but the way was clear. We lifted our nose, climbed. Safe.

We climbed to a cautious eight thousand feet before we tackled the canyon, but now the air was calm. Serenely we sailed over its vee cleft. Here it widened out into a broader valley. There to our right the railroad wormed along the ledge. There to our left it dropped to a deep basin with a silver horseshoe of a lake shining among the pines a mile and a half below us. Ahead was the long beautiful government hotel for tourists, a small green railroad station with the bare frame of the new station, a few parked freight cars, a heap of caribou horns piled carelessly, the green Road Commission cookhouse and machine shop with a few tents.

I didn't want to land. The runway was short. One end butted against the cookhouse. The other end dropped five hundred sheer feet into a canyon. Between these two hazards, it humped its short length like a caterpillar with cramps. But we had little choice. WHERE was Savage River field? Joe Crosson landed tourists in there with a Lockheed Electra airliner, safely. But it wasn't on the map. The pilots we had asked in Fairbanks didn't know where it was. Joe was in Seattle. Well . . . Haken Christensen landed here safely, from time to time. We cut the throttle, sideslipped with a whoosh over the roof of the cookhouse, straightened out, and landed. The baseball players ran to meet us.

CLASS ACTIVITY

Get a fairly large and accurate map of Alaska and from Appendix II, p. 282 of the book trace the journey of the girls on their vacation. Sketch the trip on a map drawn on the blackboard.

SMOKE OVER THORBY[1]

By Hammond Inness

THIS selection is the final chapter of a thrilling war
novel by a young English lieutenant who had been a
newspaper man before the war. At the time of writing
he was an artillery sergeant twenty-seven years old located at
one of the defense bases near the English coast across from
Calais. "*Attack Alarm* was scribbled," he says, "during warning
periods and long alerts in ammunition shelters and at night
amidst the remains of supper and the noise of men talking.
Chapter by chapter it went home to my wife to be typed."

The attempt at invasion was made in the summer of 1940.
The book was written in the winter of 1941. The pictures of
events are real but are woven into the pattern of an imagined
story. A young sergeant came to suspect the base librarian of
fifth column activities. He reported his suspicions to superior
officers and was disciplined for throwing suspicion upon Mr.
Vayle, a highly respected and very useful man. The whole novel
is the sergeant's attempt to verify his suspicion. He discovers at
last that Vayle has been in charge of the fifth column arrange-
ments on the English side to prepare everything for the invasion. His final act was to hide smoke shells on an abandoned
farm and on the night before the attack to have them distributed over the several airdromes, and to set up markers to
guide the attacking fighter, bomber, and troop transport planes.

At the end of the preceding chapter the narrator of the story,
Barry Hanson, and his pal, the cockney Micky Jones, had just
made their way in a stolen truck back to the base and were trying to pass the sentry to get to their gun emplacement. They
jump out of the truck and let it coast into the embankment. It
is three A.M. of the night before the expected attack.

*   *   *   *   *

---

[1] From *Attack Alarm*, Macmillan Co., New York. Copyright 1942 by the
author.

The crash of the lorry * as it hit the bend seemed surprisingly loud. Automatically we halted, listening. The trees whispered amongst themselves, stirred by a faint breeze. There was no other sound. We crossed the trench where we had stumbled into each other only just over three hours ago. A ghostly pallor filtered through into the wood so that everywhere was shadow. We went stealthily, flitting from tree to tree. Reason told me that it was all right. A sentry would not leave the path without cause and, if he were anywhere near, his attention would be drawn towards the lorry. But reason could not still the flutter of my nerves. So much was at stake. We had to get back to the site without being caught. To be frustrated at the last moment by the obtuseness of a Guards' corporal would be bitter in the extreme. And I knew that the wood was the easiest part. Beyond was the slope up to the barbed wire. It was bare of all cover and would be lit by the moon. Finally there was the barbed wire itself.

We reached the path, a broad white swath in the moonlight, and crossed it without mishap. At last the trees thinned and their leafy boughs stood out against the white of the hillside. We pushed through the low-hanging fringe of the trees and paused, gazing up at that pale grassy slope. There was the dannet wire, a dark streak against the grass, and along it a figure moved slowly. At every step the man's bayonet caught the moon and glinted white.

"Cor!" said Micky. "This ain't 'alf going to be a job."

I nodded. "I'm afraid the odds are against us," I said. "We'd better split up."

"O.K., mate. But what do I do if I get through and you don't?"

"Go to Gun Ops.† and get in touch with any one in authority. Tell them what you've heard and seen. And if a sentry challenges you, don't try and get away. Good luck!" I said. "If we both get through we'll meet in the hut."

"See you in the 'ut, then."

"I hope so," I replied. And we parted company, advancing into the open and moving obliquely up the slope. The sentry was going away from us along the wire.

---

* *lorry:* British word for truck.
† *Gun Ops.:* Gun Operations Headquarters.

There was no retreat now. I reached the wire and parted the near side of a coil with my gloved hands. I did not even glance in the direction of the wood. If he were standing there watching me, there was nothing I could do about it. My whole attention was concentrated on getting through that wire in the quickest possible time. Had the slope been down instead of up, I am certain I should have risked jumping it. As it was I had to follow the more laborious procedure of climbing through it. And the angle of the slope made it more difficult.

I slipped into the gap I had made in the near side of the coil and then, pressing the farther side apart, swung my right leg high over the wire into the gap.

"Halt! Who goes there?"

The challenge rang out clear and startling in the stillness. I froze, the barbs of the wire cutting into the flesh between my legs. Instinctively I looked in the direction of the wood. But before my eyes had seen that there was no one there, I had realised that the challenge had come from the opposite direction. As I turned my head I heard the sound of a man running. He was coming along the wire, up out of the dip, as fast as his equipment would allow him. His rifle, its bayonet gleaming, was held at the ready.

For an instant panic seized me. I wanted to run. But I was still astride the crossed coils of the wire. Before I could get clear he would have ample time to pick me off. I waited. There was nothing else I could do. The sweat broke out on my forehead with the sense of frustration that overwhelmed me. There was the hut and the gun pit. They were not more than fifty yards away and so plain in the moonlight that I could almost believe myself there. Just fifty yards between success and failure. It was heartbreaking. But perhaps Micky would get through.

"What are ye doing?" The man had halted a few yards from me and I saw his thumb on the safety-catch of his rifle. He was a Scots Guard, big and heavily built, with a flattened nose and large hands.

"Trying to get through the wire," I said. "Do you mind if I get my other leg over. It isn't very comfortable in this position."

"All raight. But dinna play ony tricks. If ye du I'll no hesitate to shoot."

"I won't play any tricks," I said. I pressed the wire down and swung my other leg over. I managed it better this time and did not lose my balance.

"What are ye doing creeping into the camp like this?" he demanded.

"I broke camp," I replied. "That's my gun site over there. I had a good reason for doing so."

"Och, mon, it willna du." He shook his head. "Ye've got yerself in an awfu' mess."

"Look," I said. "Be a sport. I had my own reasons for breaking camp."

"Ye canna wheedle me. I know my duty. Ye're under arrest."

Out of the corner of my eyes I saw Micky creeping up on the wire. I moved a little farther along so that the sentry had to turn away from Micky in order to keep facing me. "Stand still!" The rifle jerked threateningly.

"Give me a break," I said. "We've been in this place more than a month without leave. We haven't even had any local leave." Micky was at the wire now. "I had to see someone. It was urgent. The only way I could do it was by breaking camp. I bet you haven't been long in this place. You'd understand if you had." I was scarcely thinking what I was saying. Anything would do so long as it kept his attention away from Micky, who was now clambering through the wire.

"That sort o' talk willna get ye onywhere." The man was ruffled. I felt he would like to have let me go, but he didn't dare. "Ye'll have to see the corporal. Ye might be a German parachutist for all I ken. Come on, now. Get going."

At that moment there was a dull thud along the wire. Micky had lost his balance and fallen flat on his face.

The sentry swung round. Instantly his rifle was at his shoulder. "Halt!"

Micky had just got to his feet again. His head jerked quickly in our direction. His face looked very pale in the moonlight. I could even see his eyes. They were narrowed and shifty-looking. His momentary hesitation was obvious. In a flash my mind wondered how often he had looked at a policeman in that same indecisive manner. Suddenly he dived forward. He looked like a little rabbit scuttling to cover towards the hut.

"Halt, or I fire!" The sentry's thumb pressed the safety catch forward.

I jumped forward. "Don't fire!" I said. "He's my pal. Don't fire!"

Micky might think he had a chance, but he was not a fast runner and he was not attempting to zigzag. To a good marksman he was an absolute sitter.*

"Micky!" I yelled. "Micky! Stop!"

He glanced over his shoulder. I waved to him. "Come over here," I called. "Quick!" And in practically the same breath I said to the Guardsman, "Hold your fire. He's all right—only scared of being caught."

Micky had stopped, doubtful what to do. "Come over here!" I called to him again. Reluctantly he began to walk in our direction.

The sentry lowered his rifle. He turned to me. "Will ye tell me what's going on here? Are there ony mair of ye?"

"No," I replied. "There's only the two of us. And I didn't break camp to meet my girl friend. We broke camp to get certain vital information from men we knew to be Nazi agents."

"It willna du." He shook his head. "Ye'd best tell the truth when ye see the corporal. Come on now. March!" By changing my story I had lost his sympathy. It was a pity. But it couldn't be helped. Pray God the corporal wasn't a fool. The sentry fell in behind me. "Gang straight for that pill-box oop yonder."

Micky joined me. He was still panting slightly. "Why the hell did you call me?" he demanded gruffly, as he fell into step beside me. "I could 'a' made it."

"You could not," I told him.

"I thought this information was important. It was worth the risk, wasn't it?"

"It wouldn't have helped to have you shot," I said. "He couldn't have missed at that range."

He didn't reply to that and we walked on in silence. We climbed the final slope of the hill. The pill-box, which was about a hundred yards to the north of our hut, looked squat and menacing in the moonlight.

"Corporal! Corporal!" called our guard as we approached the low concrete and brick structure. "Corporal!"

---

* *sitter:* as easy to hit as a sitting rabbit.

The corporal in charge came out, crouching to get through the low entrance of the pill-box. He blinked the sleep out of his eyes as he came up to us. He was short for a Guardsman, and he had reddish hair and a sharp, rather bitter face. This was going to be difficult.

"What's all this?" he demanded. There was only the faintest trace of a Scotch accent.

"A' caught these two getting into the camp over the wire, Corporal." Our guard nodded in my direction. "First this laddie says he broke camp to meet his lassie. Then when I challenge the other laddie he says they broke camp together in order to get some information aboot Nazi agents. They say they belong to the gun over yonder."

The corporal looked us up and down. His eyes were sharp and close-set. "Name and number?" he demanded.

"Hanson," I said, and gave him my number. Micky also gave him the information he wanted. He then checked our papers and aerodrome passes.

"Right," he said. Then, turning towards the pill-box, "Guard, turn out!"

They tumbled out, bleary-eyed and half awake, putting their tin hats on as they came.

"McGregor and Baird, march these men down to the guard-room."

I cleared my throat—I felt nervous "Excuse me, Corporal," I said, "but—"

I got no further. "Anything you have to say, say it to the duty officer when you come on charge in the morning."

"I would like to see my sergeant before going to the guard-room."

"I will see him. If you really belong to the site, I will let him know that you have returned."

"But I must see him. It's of vital importance—"

"Don't argue. March 'em away."

"God in heaven, man," I cried, "do you want the Germans to land on the 'drome without any one having a chance to prevent them?"

"Speak when you're spoken to, Gunner," he barked. "You're under arrest. Try to remember that. You'll have a chance to think up all your crazy excuses for breaking camp in the guard-room. You," he said to the two Guardsmen detailed as escort, "take 'em away."

I broke free of them as they closed in on me. My sense of frustration was so great that I lost control of myself. "Listen, you fool!" I began.

"Don't adopt that tone with me," he cried.

"Shut up," I spoke quietly. And perhaps because there was a ring of authority in my voice, he did not interrupt me this time. "If you don't let me see Sergeant Langdon, I can almost certainly guarantee that you will pay for your denseness with your life. At dawn this morning this and other fighter stations are going to be invaded from the air. Normally a landing on the 'drome wouldn't succeed. At this moment three, possibly four, R.A.F. lorries manned by Nazi agents are approaching Thorby. They carry smoke containers. The wind is north-east." I glanced at my watch. "The time is now three-forty. At any moment now those lorries will enter the camp and drive along the tarmac * here. They will take up a position somewhat to the north of us. A smoke screen will then be laid across the 'drome. Under cover of that smoke screen troop-carriers will land. And under cover of that smoke screen the ground defences will be stormed."

I had shaken him. I could see it in his face. In my desperation my voice had probably carried conviction. "And how would the troop-carriers land if the runways were screened by smoke?"

"They will land blind," I said. "The start and finish of the runways will be marked by captive balloons flown at a definite height. Probably they will carry lights. There's very little time if the other 'dromes are to be warned. That's why I want to see my sergeant."

"Why don't you want to see the ground-defence officer—eh?" He was still suspicious.

"Because by the time I had got him out of bed and convinced him that I wasn't crazy, it might be too late to stop the smoke screen." I didn't tell him that I was afraid the ground-defence officer might not believe me and that I wanted sufficient proof to leave him in no doubt of the position. "All I

---

* *tarmac:* paved road.

want to do is to have five minutes' talk with Sergeant Langdon.
That's not an unreasonable request, surely?"

He hesitated. "Well," he said, "it can't do any harm." Then,
with a resumption of his previous sharpness: "All right. March
'em over to the hut yonder. Lance-Corporal Jackson, take
charge."

We were half-way to the hut when I heard the sound of
engines approaching from the direction of the square. A sudden
excitement surged through me. An instant later the first of
four R.A.F. lorries appeared from behind the low bulk of the
hut. They lumbered past us along the tarmac, dark, cumbersome shapes against the moon. I turned to the corporal. "That's
them," I said.

"They look all right to me," he said. But I could see that he
was impressed.

I went in by the back entrance of our hut, the corporal following close on my heels. The door of the sergeant's room was
on the right. I went straight in. A hurricane lamp turned low
stood on a table beside Langdon's bed. I shook his shoulder.
He mumbled and turned over with his eyes tight shut. I shook
him again. "What is it?" Unwillingly he opened his eyes.

"Good God, Hanson!" He sat up in bed with a jerk. "Where
have you been? Is Micky with you?"

Before I could say anything the Guards' corporal said:
"This is one of your men, is he, Sergeant?"

"Yes."

"We caught the two of them entering the camp over the wire
just below your site."

"What's going on here?" It was Bombardier Hood's voice.
He pushed past the corporal into the room. "Oh, so you're
back, are you? I just came in to wake my relief and heard voices
in here," he added by way of explanation. He was fully dressed
with gas mask at the alert and he carried a rifle and bayonet.

"Sergeant Langdon," I said.

"Yes?"

"I want you to give Bombardier Hood instructions to get
every one up and dressed as quickly as possible."

"But why?"

"What the devil are you talking about?" cut in Hood. "Do

you realise that you've done a very serious thing, breaking camp. Your absence was reported to Mr. Ogilvie."

"There's no time to waste," I told Langdon urgently. "There's going to be an air invasion of the 'drome at dawn. Four lorries carrying smoke containers have been got into the camp. They passed the site just before I woke you. The smoke will screen the landing."

"What the hell are you talking about?" demanded Langdon, swinging his feet out of bed. "How do you know this?"

"I've just watched Vayle superintending the loading of the lorries and issuing his instructions. It was at an isolated place called Cold Harbour Farm in Ashdown Forest. They caught us, but we killed two of the guards and got away." I pulled the revolver I had taken from our guard out of my pocket and tossed it on to the bed. "There's a revolver we took off one of them. I'll give you the details as the others are getting dressed."

Langdon hesitated. His face wore a puzzled frown. Suddenly he glanced up at Hood. "Have four lorries passed the pit?"

"Yes, just before I came in to wake my relief," he replied. "But they were perfectly ordinary R.A.F. lorries. You're surely not going to take any notice of this ridiculous story. Personally I think Hanson is trying to screen his own rather peculiar activities. You remember, just after he arrived here there was that business of a plan of the ground defences being found on a Nazi agent. Then he talked with that German pilot and later he was identified—"

"Give a 'Take post *'," Langdon cut in.

"But it's a ridiculous story. R.A.F. lorries with smoke containers! It's—"

"Give the 'Take post'," Langdon ordered. "We'll soon find out if there's any truth in it."

Hood went out sullenly. A second later came his shout of "Take post." It was followed almost immediately by the sound of men scrambling out of bed and into their clothes. The thin partition wall only slightly muffled the noise, and the hut itself shook to the sudden burst of activity.

---

* *Take post:* an order for each man to take his position at the gun.

"Now then, tell me the whole story," said Langdon as he slipped his trousers on over his pyjamas.

Briefly I outlined the events of the night with some reference to the things that had led up to them.

"And what do you suggest this detachment does?" he asked when I had finished.

"Surround the lorries," I replied. "No officer is going to send out an urgent warning to all the other fighter 'dromes unless this ridiculous story of mine is backed up by some concrete evidence. If you find those lorries are harmless, I don't care what happens to me. Anyway, I know they're not harmless."

"All right. We'll do that. Are you willing to leave these two men in my charge, Corporal? I'll make myself personally responsible for them."

"Very good, Sergeant."

"Oh, just a minute, Corporal," said Langdon as the other was leaving the room. "Hanson here expects the lorries to be parked somewhere on the north-east side of the landing field. Will you notify all Guards' posts along this side of the field that in the event of rifle fire being heard they are to close in on four R.A.F. lorries. The personnel of these lorries are dressed in R.A.F. uniforms.

"Verra good, Sergeant. I'll do that."

As he went out, Micky appeared in the doorway, looking rather sheepish. "And I'll bet you didn't go out after fifth columnists," said Langdon as he put on his battle top.

Micky looked uncomfortable, but said nothing.

"All right. Go and get your rifle," said Langdon.

A sudden glint of eagerness showed in Micky's eyes. "An' bay'net, Sarge? Cold steel! That's the stuff to give them."

"All right." Langdon turned to me. "I don't know whether it has any bearing on the position, but Squadron-Leader Nightingale drove up to the pit at about twelve-thirty. There was an alarm on at the time. He asked for you. When I told him that you were missing, he ran back to his car and drove off at a terrific lick. He had that Waaf * of yours with him."

"He knows the situation," I said. "He got in touch with a

---

* *Waaf* (wŏf): Woman's Auxiliary Air Force.

fellow on my paper for me. He may have got some fresh information."

Bombardier Hood came in. "Well, they're all dressed, Sergeant. And I've kept them in the hut." His tone conveyed his complete disagreement with the arrangement.

"All right. Come on, then, Hanson. And I hope to God this doesn't prove to be a fool's errand." Langdon led the way out of the room and into the hut, where one hurricane lamp was all that lit the gloom of the blackout.

Every one was crowded round Micky. They fell silent as we entered. Every face was turned towards us. "Get your rifles," ordered Langdon. "Issue twenty rounds per man, Bombardier Hood. Fuller, you will remain as sentry." Whilst the rounds were being issued, Langdon said: "Hanson has returned to camp with a story of an air invasion at dawn. Four lorries have arrived on the landing ground which he says are manned by fifth columnists whose job it is to put a smoke screen across the 'drome at the appropriate moment. I intend to investigate these lorries. We will surround one of them and I shall go forward and examine it myself. It will be your job to cover me. And if there's any truth in Hanson's story I shall rely on you to cover me properly. Micky, Chetwood, Helson and Hood, you will carry hand grenades. You'll find them under my bed. Right, let's get going."

Outside, the moon, though low in the west, was bright by comparison with the gloom of the hut. A faint pallor showed in the eastern sky. I glanced at my watch. It was past four. "Dawn will soon be breaking," I said.

"Will they attack before it's light or after?" Langdon asked me.

"I don't know," I replied. "I should think about half light. They would want to get the troop-carriers in before it was light enough to make them an easy target for our fighters."

As we passed the pit, the stocky barrel of the three-inch lifting darkly against the moon, Langdon said: "Helson, my bike is over there. Will you bring it along? I may want you to act as runner if anything happens."

"O.K., John. Shall I bring the gun as well?"

The laughter that greeted his remark was derisive. Kan's rather high-pitched laugh and Chetwood's deep bellow rang out

clear above the others. I glanced back. The detachment was
following us in a ragged bunch, and I noticed that Kan and
Chetwood were walking on either side of Hood. He was talking
and they were listening intently. I couldn't hear what he was
saying, but for a second his eyes met mine, and I knew that if
by any chance the lorries turned out to be harmless it would go
ill with me.

Half unconsciously I quickened my pace as we reached the
tarmac edge of the landing field. Langdon and I walked in
silence. For myself, I began to feel uneasy, almost frightened.
The events of the night seemed more like a dream than the
reality I knew them to be, and now that I had persuaded Langdon to action I had an unpleasant feeling that I might be
wrong. All my self-confidence seemed to have been expended in
my effort to obtain this positive action. Langdon, too, was
anxious. If I were wrong, he would look a fool in the eyes of
his detachment and would have some awkward questions to
answer when I came up on charge in the morning.

We passed the dispersal point to the north of our site. We
were half-way to the next dispersal point when Hood joined us.
"Where are your lorries?" he asked.

The question was pertinent, but the way he put it was almost
exultant. In that moment I came as near to hating any one as I
have ever done. Dimly I could now make out the trees and scrub
at the north end of the 'drome. The tarmac roadway, a ribbon
of white in the moonlight, curved away to the left as it followed the perimeter * of the landing field. Nowhere could I
see any sign of the lorries. I felt a sudden sinking sensation inside me. The gravel pit by Cold Harbour Farm seemed so far
away and unreal. I felt scared. "We'll cut down behind the next
dispersal point," I said. "They've probably spread out along
the slope in order to cover as much ground as possible with the
smoke."

Hood grunted. His disbelief was quite unmasked. I sensed
that Langdon was feeling uncomfortable and ill at ease.

We struck off the tarmac on to the dry, coarse grass. We
passed the crumbling sandbags of what had once been a Lewis
gun pit. In places the grass gave way to bare, baked earth. The

---

* *perimeter* (pẽr ĭm′ĕt ẽr): boundary.

grass became thicker and more plentiful, however, as we reached
the slope and passed behind the great bank of the dispersal
point. We threaded our way between two bomb craters, relics
of Friday's raid, stumbling over heaps of loose clay that were
hard like bricks.

At last we came in sight of the wire that stretched like a
dark snake across the grass half-way down the slope. Two men
moved along it, carrying a heavy cylindrical object between
them. They were in R.A.F. uniform. I touched Langdon's arm.
I had a sudden feeling of triumph. My relief was so great that
I could hardly speak. "That looks like one of the smoke cylinders," I said.

We had stopped, and for a moment we watched the two men
moving along the wire with their burden. The others crowded
up behind us. They had stopped talking, sensing some development. "All right," Langdon said. "Leave your rifle, Hanson,
and come on with me. The rest of you get down in the grass and
don't make a sound."

Langdon and I went forward alone. We did not attempt to
conceal ourselves. We walked diagonally along the slope and at
every step more and more of the wire came into view. Two more
men in R.A.F. uniform appeared, carrying another cylinder between them. And then at last we sighted an R.A.F. lorry parked
close against the wire at a crazy angle. Four men were busy
unloading the cylinders from it. One of the Guards' sentries was
leaning on his rifle watching them.

"Good enough," said Langdon. "So far as it goes you're right."

We turned and retraced our steps. "What do you mean—so
far as it goes?" I asked.

"Well, I've got to satisfy myself that they shouldn't be doing
what they are doing."

"But surely you believe what I have told you now?"

"Yes. But it's just possible you may have been mistaken. God
knows, I hope not for your sake. But it is possible that they may
be R.A.F. and that they may have orders to put those cylinders
out along the wire. You see my point?"

"What are you going to do, then?" I asked.

"Try and bluff them into showing their hand."

"We had reached the others now. "Get back to the road as

quickly as possible," Langdon ordered. "Go quietly and keep low."

I picked up my rifle and followed him. As soon as we were out of sight of the wire he broke into a trot. We rounded the end of the dispersal point and reached the tarmac. On the roadway we increased the pace. After doing about three hundred yards at the double, Langdon stopped. When the whole detachment had come up with us, he said: "There is an R.A.F. lorry almost directly below us down the slope of the hill. That is our objective. I want you to spread out about twenty yards apart in a long line. We will then move forward. As soon as you come within sight of the lorry, get down and try to creep forward without being seen. I want you to finish up in a big semi-circle round the lorry. That means the two flanks will close in. Your final position must not be more than two hundred yards from the lorry. You'll have five minutes from the time we move forward to get into position. I shall then go forward on my own. You will not open fire until either I give the order or they open fire. If I give that order or if they fire on me, I shall rely on you to take the lorry in the quickest possible time. It will mean that they are there for the purpose of assisting an invasion of the 'drome, and there will be very little time to spare. Is that understood?" No one said a word. "All right, then. Spread out on either side of me at the double *."

As soon as the detachment had spread out in a line along the edge of the roadway, Langdon waved his hand and started forward. Langdon, Hood and myself were together in a little bunch. Micky was twenty yards to the left of us, and Helson, who had left his bike on the edge of the roadway, was on our right. The line was not very impressive, there being only four men on either side of us. But it advanced with some pretensions of a line, and as a result looked reasonably like an infantry section in extended order.

We soon topped the brow of the hill, and before we had gone thirty yards down the slope we sighted the lorry. Langdon had judged it nicely. We ourselves were directly above it. We crouched down, moving forward more cautiously. The moon

---

* *at the double:* double-quick march.

was low enough now for the sharper slope of the hill near the brow to be in shadow. This shadow completely swallowed up the detachment, so that, looking to either side of us, I could scarcely believe that we were not alone.

The slope gradually eased off and the shadow ended abruptly. We were less than a hundred yards from the lorry and we halted here. I touched Langdon's arm and pointed along the wire to the north. The slope spread out here in a shoulder, and on it, close against the wire, was parked a second R.A.F. lorry. Here, too, men dressed in R.A.F. uniform were carrying cylinders along the wire.

Langdon looked at his watch. "The five minutes is up," he said. "I'll go and see what they're up to."

"It's suicide," I said. "If you force them to show their hand you'll get killed. This is too big a thing for them to have any scruples."

"Well, at least I shall have died to some purpose," he said with a boyish laugh which sounded brittle and false to my sensitive ears.

"Let me go," I said. "It's my show."

"No, this part of it's mine," he said. "You've done enough." His tone was quiet but final. He was, after all, the detachment commander.

"Well, whoever you talk to, see that you don't get in my line of fire. I used to be something of a shot when I was at school. I'll keep him covered the whole time."

"Thanks." He rose to his feet and went down the slope, his slim figure suddenly showing up in the slanting light of the moon. Beyond him the eastern sky was paling.

It all seemed so strangely ordinary. And yet there was a difference. The slope down which John Langdon was walking and the line of dannet wire—I knew it all so well. In the stillness of the evenings I had walked along this hillside. And my rifle! It had just been something to take on night guards. Now all these familiar things took on a new significance. This hillside might suddenly become a miniature battlefield. My rifle was suddenly a weapon. And yet there was no visible indication of a change. Everything looked much the same.

Langdon had reached the lorry now. A man in the uniform of an R.A.F. sergeant jumped out of the back of it. Langdon

moved slightly so that he did not screen the man. Quickly I
cocked my rifle and raised it to my shoulder. It seemed rather
unnecessary. The man was unarmed. I could see no sign of
hostility.

Hood probably sensed my feeling, for he suddenly said:
"Mind that thing doesn't go off. You don't get away with
murder just because you're in uniform."

I made no reply. I felt distinctly uncomfortable.

The Guards' sentry had continued on his beat. Langdon was
alone. Two men were watching him from the tail-board of the
lorry. I wished I had brought a pair of glasses with me. Langdon
nodded in our direction. The R.A.F. sergeant glanced at the
slope above him.

Then suddenly the whole atmosphere of the scene changed.
The man had produced a small automatic from his pocket. I
saw it glint in the moonlight as he waved Langdon towards the
back of the lorry.

Automatically my forefinger had taken the first pressure on
the trigger. Langdon moved slowly towards the lorry. The man
covering him pivoted but did not actually move. The foresight
came up into the U of the backsight. I squeezed the trigger. The
recoil was pleasantly reminiscent of the ranges at Bisley. There
was no sense of killing. The man was just a target. He jerked
forward with the force of the bullet's impact, stumbled and
slowly crumpled. I reloaded automatically without removing
the rifle from my shoulder.

Langdon hesitated for a second, watching the man fall. It was
like a "still" from a film. The two men on the tailboard of the
lorry gazed at their leader, fascinated, momentarily incapable
of action. The men carrying the cylinders along the wire halted.

Then suddenly like puppets, they all came to life. Langdon
dived for the slope. The men along the wire dropped their cylinders and ran for the lorry. The two men on the tail-board disappeared inside. They reappeared, a second later, with rifles.
Two more came out from behind the lorry, they also had rifles.

Langdon had reached the steepest part of the slope. He was
running hard and zigzagging at the same time. I fired at the
men on the tail-board. As I reloaded I heard the crack of Hood's
rifle just to the left of me. I fired again. Sporadic fire had now
developed along the whole of our short line. One of the men on

the tail-board toppled to the ground. The other disappeared inside. I turned my fire on the four men who were coming up along the wire. They were spread out, and though little spurts of earth were shooting up all round them, they made the lorry without being hit.

"They've got down behind the wheels of the lorry," Hood said. Little spurts of flame showed in the dark behind the bulk of the lorry. I could hear the thud of bullets as they lashed into the grass at Langdon's feet. I concentrated my aim on the pin-points of flame, firing rapidly. Others were doing the same. I don't know whether we hit any one, but our fire seemed to put them off their aim, for Langdon reached the shadow and slumped down beside us, panting heavily.

I stopped firing. I had only six rounds left. "What do we do now?" I asked.

"Send a runner back," Langdon replied breathlessly. "Helson!" he called.

"Yes, Sergeant," came his voice from the right of us.

"Get back to the bicycle. Ride to the pit and 'phone Gun Ops. Tell 'em what's happened. We want reserves to put these lorries out of action. Tell 'em to issue an Attack Alarm, have all ground defences manned—to prepare for an air invasion of the 'drome within the next half-hour. O.K.?"

"Right." Vaguely his form loomed up out of the grass as he scrambled to his feet and started back up the slope.

"What about the armoured car over by Station H.Q.*?" said Hood. "It's just the thing for this job."

"You're right. When you've done that, Helson," Langdon called after him, "go down to Station H.Q. and rout out the R.A.† lads who run that armoured car. Bring it back here."

"O.K." He disappeared from sight, merging into the shadow of the hillside.

"They're getting a Bren gun ‡ out," Hood said, and his rifle cracked. One of the men, who had appeared on the tail-board again, ducked. I raised my rifle and fired. I had the satisfaction of seeing his legs give under him. But he still continued to hand down first two guns and then four boxes of ammunition. I

---

* *H.Q.*: headquarters.
† *R.A.*: Royal Army.
‡ *Bren gun*: type of machine gun.

fired again at the men on the ground. Fire crackled out along the hillside once more. But they got the two guns into cover behind the lorry.

"Hold your fire!" Langdon yelled.

There was no alternative. Every one's ammunition was getting very low. We had to keep some reserve until reinforcements came up.

Langdon nudged my arm. "The Guards are coming up, along the wire. See?" Two men were running along the wire with bayonets fixed and others were moving along the slope of the hill in extended formation.

I suddenly felt sorry for the poor devils behind the lorry. They were doing their job as they saw it, just as we were doing ours—and they hadn't a hope, unless the time fixed for the landing was very near indeed. The sky was perceptibly lightening. I glanced at my watch. It was nearly four-twenty. I began to feel anxious. There were those other three lorries. So far we had done nothing about them. And though the cylinders which had been carried out along the barbed wire to the south of us were useless, this lorry could still contribute to the smoke screen with the cylinders that had not yet been removed from it.

"We must do something about those other lorries," I said to Langdon.

"Yes, but what?" he replied. "The armoured car is the only thing that will fix them."

"But that may be too late."

"Yes, but what can we do? We'll have to wait for that."

The paling night had become quiet again. It seemed like the lull before the storm. How long would this quiet last? I had a vision of those big Ju. 52's * coming in through the smoke, disgorging their hordes of field grey. Two a minute, we had been told, was the speed at which they could land. Something had to be done.

The quiet was shattered by the ugly chatter of a Bren gun. The fire was not directed at us, but at the line of Guards advancing along the slope.

In a flash inspiration came to me. "My God!" I said to Langdon. "The Bofors.† Number Five pit has a field of fire right

---

* *Ju. 52:* Junkers 52, troop-carrying planes.
† *Bofors:* anti-aircraft gun.

down the slope. It should be possible to bring it to bear on one of the lorries at any rate."

"You're right," he said. "Take charge, will you, Hood. Hanson and I are going up to Number Five pit."

"Wait," Hood said. We checked, half standing. "He'll never make it!" Hood's voice was a tone higher than usual in his excitement.

We both crouched, breathless. I felt a horrible sick sensation inside me. At any moment I expected that small figure to double up and pitch headlong down the slope.

It was Micky. He had jumped to his feet and was running down the slope like a mad thing. His rifle, complete with bayonet, was slung across his shoulders. "What the hell is the fool up to?" I muttered.

The Bren gun was chattering away. But its fire was still concentrated on the advancing Guards. Apparently they saw Micky too late, for when they checked their fire in order to train their gun on to him, he was already at the foot of the steep part of the slope and within some thirty yards of the lorry. He suddenly stopped and swung his right arm back. For an instant he stood poised like a javelin thrower. Then his arm came forward and a small object curved lazily through the air. At the same instant the Bren gun set its rat-a-tat again, and Micky checked and staggered.

I lost sight of the Mills bomb he had thrown. But it must have been well aimed, for he had barely fallen to the hail of bullets that bit into the turf all round him, when there was a sudden flash beneath the lorry, followed by the sound of an explosion; not loud, but sharp. The lorry rocked slightly and several pieces of wood were flung into the air.

Complete silence followed the explosion. Then quietly, menacingly, smoke began to rise out of the back of the lorry. At first I thought it must be on fire. But the stuff began to pour out in a great cloud, thick and black like funnel smoke. Then I knew that the smoke cylinders had been hit.

Micky was on his feet again now and running rather jerkily towards the lorry. He made it just as one of the Bren gunners staggered out from behind it. Micky had unslung his rifle. The fellow tried to dive back into the cover of the lorry. But Micky was on him before he could turn. I saw a flash of steel in the moonlight and the man fell, pinned to the ground by the force of Micky's lunge. The last I saw of Micky as the smoke enveloped the lorry, he was tugging to get his bayonet out of the poor wretch.

The smoke lay close to the ground like a thick amorphous blanket, gathering volume with every second. In an instant the lorry was lost to sight as the breeze rolled the smoke up the slope towards us.

"Come on," said Langdon. "Let's get to the Bofors."

We scrambled up the slope and struck northwards along the brow of the hill. As we ran I asked Langdon what had made the fellow he had spoken to produce a revolver. "He said he was acting under instructions from Winton," Langdon replied. "They were going to test smoke as a means of defending the 'drome against heavy air attacks. I asked to see his instructions. When he said they had been given to him verbally, I told him he would have to get the cylinders back into the lorry and return to Station H.Q. for written instructions. We argued for a bit, and when I made it clear that I suspected him and that I was determined to prevent the cylinders from being set off, he showed his hand."

We were now in sight of Number Five pit. The slender barrel of the Bofors showed above the sand-bagged parapet. Tin-hatted figures were moving about inside the pit and other members of the team were standing about outside their hut, fully dressed. The pit was perched just on the brow of the hill. One of the lorries was almost directly below it and another was just visible about seven hundred yards farther north along the wire.

When we arrived at the pit the sergeant in charge was at the 'phone. We were challenged, but the guard recognised Langdon and let us enter the pit.

"Sergeant Guest." Langdon's interruption was met by a silencing wave of the hand. Langdon went over to the fellow and tapped him on the shoulder.

The sergeant turned impatiently. "Keep quiet," he said. "This is important. They're expecting an invasion at dawn."

"I know, I know," Langdon said. "It's one of my fellows reporting to Gun Ops. Put that 'phone down and listen a minute."

Guest handed the receiver to his bombardier. "What do you mean—one of your fellows? What's happening? There's been firing—"

"That was us," Langdon interrupted. Briefly he outlined the situation.

When he came to the point of our visit—that the Bofors should open fire on the two R.A.F. lorries visible from the pit, Sergeant Guest said: "I can't very well do that without an officer's permission. I mean, how am I to know that they aren't really R.A.F. lorries?"

"Well, get your men on to tearing down the sand-bags so that we can lay on the lorries while we talk the matter over," Langdon said.

We had barely convinced him of the need for opening fire by the time sufficient parapet had been taken down, and then it was only with great reluctance that he gave the order to load and lay on the lorry immediately below the pit. He didn't like it. I must say I couldn't blame him. He had only our word for what was going on. I don't think he would have done it at all if he hadn't seen the dense blanket of smoke creeping over the brow of the hill to the south and spreading across the landing field.

"All right," he said at last. "Layers on*. Load! Lay on that R.A.F. lorry. Vertical zero,† lateral zero."

"On, on," came from the two layers.

"Set to auto.‡ One burst.§ Fire!"

The pit shook to the sudden utterances of the gun—Umm-pom, umm-pom, umm-pom. The flame guard belched fire and the barrel thrust backwards and forwards at each shot. The tracer shells flew through the air like little flaming oranges chasing each other to the target. They hit the lorry square amidships and burst with soft plops. Five shots and the lorry had disintegrated into a great billow of smoke that poured out from its shattered sides, and began immediately to creep up the hill, hugging the ground.

---

* *layers on:* aim at.
† *vertical zero,* etc.: direction for aiming.
‡ *auto:* automatic.
§ *burst:* round of three.

"Langdon, you're right," cried Guest excitedly. "It is smoke."

"Get that other lorry," shouted Langdon. "This stuff will be on top of us in a moment."

The gun traversed left. More sandbags had to be removed from the parapet before the layers could get on target. The smoke rolled up the hill, thick and black and strangely menacing. The vanguard of it topped the hill to the south of us, putting a dense screen between ourselves and the dispersal point below which we had attacked the first lorry. It was clear we should miss the bulk of it, but the fringe of the wretched stuff was only a few yards from us when the layers reported "On, on."

A moment later the Bofors spoke. It was like the sound of tom-toms in a mountain gorge, steady and angry. The first two little balls of fire hit the slope in the foreground. The layers elevated slightly and the fourth shell registered a direct hit on the cabin.* Two more shells and Guest ordered "Cease fire!" The last shell so shook the wreckage that it slowly toppled over on to the wire. Great volumes of black smoke poured lazily from it just as it had from the other two.

"Nice work," I said. I had a horrible feeling of exultation. "Now there's only one left and the armoured car ought to be able to deal with that."

"If it can get through all this smoke," said Langdon.

"No matter," I said. "One lorry won't make much of a smoke screen."

"Yes, but supposing they came over now." He looked anxious. "The whole field will be covered with smoke. The ground defences couldn't do a thing."

"It doesn't matter," I replied. "They couldn't land. Don't forget the whole thing depends on their having balloon markers at each end of the runway to guide them in. Besides, they won't come yet. It must have been worked out to an intricate timetable. The cylinders wouldn't have been distributed for at least ten minutes. And they would have had to allow some slight margin. I should say we have got another quarter of an hour. But we must warn other aerodromes."

----

* *cabin:* cab of the truck.

At that moment the Tannoy* sounded faintly from the depths of the smoke, wisps of which were beginning to curl over the pit: "Attention, please! Attention, please! Attack alarm! Attack alarm! All ground defences to report immediately to their action stations. Crews to stand by at dispersal points. All other personnel to take cover. Anti-aircraft defences will be fully manned. All personnel throughout the camp will put on gas masks immediately." The message was repeated.

And then: "Tiger and Swallow-tail Squadrons to readiness immediately."

"Thank God for that," I said. "Helson has persuaded someone to take action."

The 'phone rang. Sergeant Guest answered it. Then he put his hand over the mouthpiece and turned to us. "It's the C.O. Thorby† on the 'phone. He wants to know if any one in this gun pit has any accurate knowledge of what's going on."

"I'll talk to him," said Langdon.

He took the receiver. "Sergeant Langdon here, sir. The position is this: There was a plan to land troops on the aerodrome at dawn this morning under cover of a smoke screen. Four R.A.F. lorries entered the camp at roughly three-fifty hours, carrying smoke cylinders and manned by fifth columnists in R.A.F. uniforms. Gunner Hanson of my detachment saw a large number of these lorries being loaded up in a gravel pit in Ashdown Forest. Mr. Vayle was in charge. Yes, Vayle. The four lorries that entered Thorby distributed themselves along the wire to the north-east of the landing field—that is, to windward. My own detachment dealt with one of them and two more have just been destroyed by Bofors fire from Number Five pit. Yes, sir, as far as we know it's only smoke. Gas would hamper their own troops as much as ours. Well, the cylinders must be fairly well shot to pieces. It shouldn't take long to clear. No, they were to be guided in by balloons flown at a fixed height at each end of the runway. The last one must be practically at the north end of the 'drome. The wind is north-east, you know. Yes, the runner who reported to Gun Ops. has gone on to get the armoured car. You'll come out with it, sir? Very good. I'll wait here at Number Five pit. Well, we think in about quarter of an

---

* *Tannoy:* the loud speaker.
† *C.O. Thorby:* Commanding officer at Thorby. This was Winton.

hour. Can you send an urgent warning out to all 'dromes in the south-eastern area? Yes, there isn't much time. Very good, sir. I'll be here."

He put down the receiver. "He's sending out a warning to other stations right away," Langdon told me.

"Is Winton coming out here?" I asked.

"Yes—and the ground-defense officer."

"Aren't you two going to put your gas masks on?" came Guest's muffled voice. He already had his on, and I suddenly realised that the whole of his detachment had put gas masks on. The smoke was curling into the pit and it smelt acrid and dirty. I had a moment of panic as I discovered that I hadn't got mine with me. Langdon hadn't got his either. In the excitement of the moment I don't think any of our detachment had taken their masks with them. Langdon sniffed at the air and then shrugged his shoulders, as much as to say, what will be will be. We examined the pit gas detectors. They were unmarked though the smoke was thickening all round us. To the north it was still light, but visiblity was too bad for us to make out any details. To the south, however, it was pitch black.

It gave one an unpleasant feeling of being choked. At the same time I began to feel that expectant void in my stomach. Time was slipping by. In a few minutes it would be zero hour. I began to wonder what would happen. They might not have the smoke screen to help them, but that did not necessarily mean they wouldn't land. And if they landed—well, on paper it should be a massacre. But—I wasn't sure.

"I think we'd better get out of here whilst we can still see our way," Langdon said to me. "Winton will never get as far as the pit in this stuff. We'll meet him on the road."

Smoke from the lorry to the north of us was now pouring over the brow of the hill and rolling in a thick, low-lying cloud across the landing field. It didn't spread much, however, so that there was quite a well-defined lane of pale light, part moon, part dawn, between this bank of smoke and the one behind us. The latter was already beginning to thin out, for the cylinders, having been shattered, had not much staying power.

We had barely reached the roadway when a pair of headlights nosed out of the smoke. At first I thought it was the armoured car. But when it cleared the smoke, it turned out to

be a small sports car. As it drew up alongside us I recognised it
for Nightingale's. Three people were sitting in it. They looked
strangely impersonal, for they had gas masks on. The two in
front were in Air Force uniform. But the one behind was a
civilian.

I knew who the two in front were before they removed their
gas masks. The driver was Nightingale, and it was Marion who
sat beside him. "Where have you been, Barry?" Her voice was
quiet. For a momen I thought her eyes looked reproachful,
anxious. But there was a smile on her lips—a smile that made
my heart race—and it spread from her lips to her eyes. Her
whole face was suddenly lit up by that smile.

It was an exquisite moment, shared between us there in the
pale light of the dawn with the trappings of war all round us.
It was an oasis in that grim, exciting desert of useless action. All
that she had to offer a man was in her eyes as the smile overwhelmed the anxiety in their depths like sunlight. And both
were for me. I felt pain in my heart, pain that was yet pleasure;
pain that I had found beauty, but could not grasp it firmly for
all time; pain because our moment was fleeting. Life is full of
this ache for moments that cannot be held. War makes it
greater, because there is a futility and not an inevitability about
the immediate cause of one's inability to hold one's moments.

Well, war has separated us now. And of all the things that
make me love her, it is Marion's smile, spreading from lips to
eyes and lighting her whole face, that I remember most clearly,
with that hungry longing that makes a separation almost sweet.

I am sure I should have stood staring at her long oval face
framed in her dishevelled page-boy's hair and those sweet smiling eyes with no other thought till the troop-carriers came
flocking to the 'drome. But the spell was broken by the civilian
in the back. "Well, you old dog, Barry—what have you been
up to?"

I jerked my gaze from Marion. The fellow had removed his
gas mask. It was Bill Trent. "What are you doing here?" I said.
I fear my tone was bleak. He had broken the spell. And any one
who breaks the spell of that first discovery of love given and
offered freely must surely expect a cold welcome.

"I got back here from a forced landing near Redhill to find

him waiting for me," John Nightingale explained. "He had tried to see Winton without any luck."

"He's proved that Vayle's a spy," Marion cut in, her voice sounding surprisingly matter-of-fact.

"How do you know, Bill?" I asked.

"Because he's not Vayle at all, old boy," Bill Trent replied. "Vayle * was last seen in Dachau concentration camp in 1936. That was two years after the Vayle who is librarian here returned to England."

"Yes, but how do you know?" I asked.

"After I'd got your message I did everything I could to find out Vayle's background. I got details about the family, but all his relations seemed to be dead. I could unearth very little information about him prior to 1934. In desperation I combed through my refugee acquaintances. I knew a man who was one of the very few to escape from Dachau. He said he had been with Vayle for nearly two years in that camp. I knew he was telling the truth because he gave me Vayle's life history, which tallied with what I had been able to discover. He said that when he escaped Vayle was still there, slowly dying of T.B."

"I got Winton † to see Trent," John Nightingale put in. "It was a bit of a shock for him. Vayle is a very brilliant man and he had done a great deal for the Fighter Command in working out tactics. A guard was sent to bring him in for questioning. But he had left the camp. That scared me. I told Winton everything that you had told me. He sent me out to your site to fetch you. It was then past midnight. You were missing. Miss Sheldon was on night duty at Ops. She told me which Cold Harbour Farm you had picked."

"And we went there and we found a dilapidated old farmhouse and a dear old gentleman in a night-cap and gown," Marion put in. "But you weren't there. He spoke of two soldiers he'd given a meal to. We came back here. We were in Ops. when all this started, and then Winton spoke to your sergeant. What happened to you, Barry? You did find something there, didn't you?"

---

* *Vayle:* the real Vayle had been a teacher years before in a school attended by Nightingale, Trent, and Hanson.

† *Winton:* was the C.O. who had stood up for Vayle against Hanson.

Briefly I told them of the gravel pit and the lorries—and
Vayle. I explained the plan to them. And I was just beginning
to tell them how we had destroyed the three lorries when out
of the thinning smoke came the armoured car, followed by two
R.A.F. cars. Langdon stepped forward and waved to them. They
drew up just short of us.

Winton jumped out of his car, and Major Comyns and
Ogilvie got out of the other. They had just taken their gas
masks off and they were stuffing the face pieces into their haver-
sacks as they came up to us.

Langdon stepped forward and saluted. In a few words he
explained the situation. When he had finished, the C.O. turned
to a young artillery lieutenant who was standing by the
open door of the armoured car. "Ross," he called. "There is an
R.A.F. lorry somewhere along this wire to the north. It must
be put out of action at once. If possible, I want it captured
intact. And I want prisoners. I'll be at Ops."

"Very good, sir." His voice was muffled in his gas mask. The
iron door of the armoured car clanged to, and the great lum-
bering vehicle roared off along the tarmac and disappeared into
the smoke to the north of us, which was also beginning to thin
out now.

Winton turned to me. "Good work, Hanson," he said. "I'll
not forget it. I'd like you to stay with me. Sergeant Langdon,
get your detachment together and your gun manned as quickly
as you can. Gun Ops. will keep you informed."

"Yes, sir."

As Langdon disappeared, Winton nodded to me, and I followed him to his car. He paused with one foot on the running-
board. "Mr. Ogilvie, will you go round the gun sites. See that
everything is all right, and above all see that they all know
what their fields of fire are for action against 'planes landing on
the 'drome. They must stick rigidly to those fields. I don't want
them duelling with each other across the landing field. Comyns
will take you in his car. You'll be going round the ground defences, Major, won't you? Excellent! Good luck!" He climbed
into the driving seat. "Come on, Hanson, jump in."

I got in beside him and the big car shot forward, dipping
sharply as he swung it round. The smoke was no more than a
few thin wisps now, and in front of us the familiar shapes of

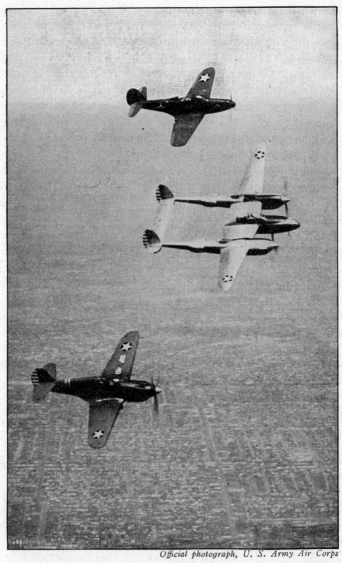

Three of the Army's finest—the Bell P-39, the Lockheed P-38, and the Curtiss P-40

the station showed dimly in the cold grey light of dawn. We made a half-circle of the landing ground and swung in at the barbed-wired gates of Operations. Winton had driven fast, and all the time he plied me with questions. But as we descended the ramp to Operations he was suddenly silent.

His was a big responsibility. And in the minutes that followed I came to admire him greatly. He was conscious of the weight of that responsibility. It was a weight that could not be carried lightly. But he carried it calmly and without fuss. I think he was one of those men who are at their best in action. He was cool and he used imagination.

The first thing he did on entering Operations was to order two Hurricanes to be loaded with smoke and to send a dispatch rider to the meteorological tower for two balloons. "Tannoy!" he called. "Give the All Clear for gas."

Faintly from somewhere outside that big subterranean room came the echo of a voice that spoke quietly into a microphone in one corner: "Attention, please! Attention, please! Gas all clear. Gas all clear. You can show your faces again, boys. It's all clear for gas."

The room was confusing at a first glance. There were so many girls sitting at telephones and so many officers and Waafs standing about, apparently doing nothing. And everything centered on a large table, the top of which was a map of southeastern England and the Channel.

I suddenly found Marion at my elbow. She squeezed my arm and I looked down to find her eyes bright with excitement. "It's all yours," she said. "Your show. I hope it goes well."

"Where's Nightingale?" I asked.

"Gone to dispersals. In a few minutes he'll be leading his squadron up."

"And Trent?" I asked.

"Oh, I left him at the entrance. He's trying to get permission to come in here." She squeezed my arm again and crossed the room to a vacant desk on which was a telephone and a pad.

I stood there, bewildered and alone. I felt conscious of my dirty oil-stained battle dress, so out of place here where there was nothing but Air Force blue. I wished I could have been going up with a squadron to fight invasion. Action! I wanted action; to be on the gun—anything rather than the suspense of waiting with nothing to do.

Winton called me and handed me a message. On it was scrawled: "Mitchet * report four smoke lorries captured." After that, one by one, the fighter 'dromes of the south-east reported lorries containing smoke either captured or put out of action.

All at once my sense of bewilderment vanished. I no longer felt out of place down here in this strange room. It was like being suddenly transported back to journalism. Here was action and I was watching it. My brain would record impressions of it, and some day I'd use this material. God! What wouldn't some Fleet Street † boys give to be on the inside of this story. I felt the thrill of pride that comes of achievement.

A Waaf came up to Winton. "Mr. Ross reports lorry captured intact, sir," she said. "He's got seven prisoners."

"Good. Tell him to fetch the lorry and the prisoners down here at once."

So much for Vayle's attempt to help German troops to land at Thorby. I remembered how he had sent those lorries off. He had been so calm and so assured. Well, he had had every right to be. It had been a clever plan. His luck had been out, that was all. And what would he do now? It seemed such a strange anti-climax for him to be arrested and shot as a spy. Yet that was what would probably happen. And Winton would, of course, have to be present at the court-martial.

Telephone buzzers sounded. The Waafs at their desks began writing furiously. Others took the slips of paper to the table. The whole room suddenly sprang to life. Everything was confusion; but it was the ordered confusion of a job being carried out.

Little wooden markers with arrows began to appear on that section of the table that represented the Channel. All the arrows pointed one way—towards the south-east coast. And the wooden markers had swastikas on them. They also had numbers. There were several thirties and one or two forties and fifties plotted within the space of a few seconds. Each marker meant a forma-

---

* *Mitchet:* another airdrome nearby.
† *Fleet Street:* the London newspaper section.

tion of enemy 'planes. I counted three hundred and forty plotted already.

"Get both squadrons up," Winton ordered. And a moment later came the faint sound of the Tannoy: "Both squadrons scramble! Tiger Squadron scramble! Swallow-tail Squadron scramble! Scramble! Off!"

I heard a Waaf on a telephone just near me saying: "Several large formations of hostile aircraft approaching from the south-east. They are believed to be troop-carriers with fighter escorts. Heights range from fifteen to twenty thousand feet. Guns are to hold their fire."

The movement of the enemy air attack began to take shape as the markers were moved steadily forward with every observa-tion report that came in. Other markers also appeared. These had the red, white and blue roundels * of the R.A.F., and they were mainly inland from the coast.

The young artillery officer, Ross, came in. He went straight up to Winton. They conversed in low tones. Suddenly the C.O. said: "Balloons? With lights? Excellent. A green at the start of the runway and red at the end, eh?"

"No, the other way about, sir. And it's a red light and a white light."

"Sure the fellow isn't trying to put one across you?"

"I don't think so, sir. He's pretty badly hurt and very frightened."

"What height are they to be flown at?"

"I don't know, sir. I didn't ask him."

Winton turned to me. "Do you know what height these bal-loons are to be flown at, Hanson?"

"Vayle said fifty feet, sir."

"Good. That means about thirty feet above the smoke. Get the balloons blown up and the lights attached. The red light will be above the hangars just east of Station H.Q., and the white one above the main gates. Fly the balloons at eighty feet. Can you get them in position in five minutes?"

"Yes, sir."

"Very good. I'm giving orders for the smoke screen to be laid right away. It will be between thirty and fifty feet. See that

---

* *roundels:* circular wing markings of R.A.F. planes.

the balloons are up by the time the smoke screen is finished."

"Yes, sir." He dashed out of the room.

Winton went over to a switchboard. "Give me Number Two dispersal," he told the Waaf telephonist. "Hallo! Marston? Are those two Hurricanes ready with smoke? They're to take off at once and lay a smoke screen along the eastern edge of the 'drome from the Thorby road to the north edge of the landing field. The smoke must not be loosed at less than thirty feet or more than fifty feet, and they must cut off at the limits given. They will continue until the smoke is exhausted or they receive instructions to cease. Right. Tell 'em to scramble."

Winton had a number of ground-staff officers round him now. He was issuing orders to them in a quiet, precise voice. I only caught a few words here and there. From above ground came the faint murmur of engines revving up*. On the table the swastika markers had moved forward over the coast. The attack was taking shape. Formations of about fifty bombers and a hundred fighters were closing in on each of the fighter stations. Two of these formations were heading in our direction.

An officer came to the telephone just beside me. "Gun Ops.? Warn the guns that the two Hurricanes just taking off will be laying a smoke screen about fifty feet above the 'drome. They are only to fire on enemy 'planes landing on the field. They will not open fire at aircraft that crash. Any survivors will be mopped up by ground defences."

Before he had finished speaking the Tannoy announced: "Attention, please! A smoke screen is being laid over the 'drome by two of our own machines. Hostile troop-carriers may be expected to attempt a landing. Some of these will probably crash. Ground defences will ensure that no hostile troops are allowed to take offensive action after their 'planes have crashed. Care should be taken to avoid getting in the field of fire of the guns which have instructions to open fire on any hostile 'planes that succeed in landing on the 'drome. Off."

"Hanson!" It was Winton calling me. "I think you had better report back to your gun site now."

---

* *revving up:* "tuning up."

"Very good, sir."

"Any points that have not been covered?"

"I don't think so, sir."

"Right. Thank you for your help—and good luck."

"And to you, sir." I saluted and hurried out of Operations. Bill Trent was outside. "Look after yourself, Barry," he said. "I'll want a story out of you when the show is over."

"You'll be lucky if you're allowed to print it," I said. And jumping on the first bike I saw, I rode up the ramp and out on to the tarmac. I could just make out our gun pit almost on the other side of the 'drome. It stood out against the dull glow of the eastern horizon. The moon had set and the flying field looked pale and flat and cold. Tin hats—blue and khaki—showed above the ramparts of the ground-defence trenches. Soldiers stood waiting, their rifles ready, at the entrance to pill-boxes. There was an unpleasant atmosphere of expectancy.

As I crossed the tarmac in front of the hangars one of the Hurricanes made its first run along the eastern edge of the field. It was just a vague, shadowy thing in the half light, and it flew so low that I felt it must pile itself up on the first dispersal point. And it left behind it a thin line pencilled across the dull grey of the sky. The line spread and grew, a dark, menacing cloud. It ceased at the northern edge of the 'drome. I could just make out the shape of the 'plane as it banked away for the turn.

By the hangar nearest to Station H.Q. men were busy about a balloon that looked like a miniature barrage balloon. Just below it was fixed a red light. As I passed the hangar the balloon rose gently and steadily into the air.

Soon I was cycling down the roadway on the eastern edge of the field. It was getting very dark now. The smoke was overhead, a great billowy cloud that moved slowly south-west over the station. It was so low that I felt I must be able to touch it by putting my hand up. Here and there a stray wisp reached down to the ground, curling gently, and as I rode through them my nostrils filled with the thick, acrid smell of the stuff. As I passed the dispersal point just to the south of our pit the second Hurricane zoomed overhead. It was so close that instinctively I ducked. Yet I could not see it. The darkness increased as its smoke trail merged with the rest, and I almost rode past the gun site.

As I entered the pit my eyes searched the faces that I could barely see: Langdon, Chetwood, Hood, Fuller. But Micky wasn't there. Nor was Kan. "What's happened to Micky?" I asked Langdon. "Is he . . ." I hesitated.

"No," he said. "He's got a bullet through the shoulder and another shattered his wrist. It's a light let-off, considering the risk he took. We got him to the sick bay." *

"What about Kan?" I asked.

"Dead," Langdon said. The baldness of his statement shocked me. "He leapt up to follow Micky and took it in the stomach."

He didn't add any details and I didn't ask for any. I could well imagine how he had died. I could see him swept into the maelstrom of a fight by his sense of the dramatic. He would have leapt to his feet, a young Raleigh, a Hotspur, a d'Artagnan, imagination cloaking him in the swaggering fineries of the Chivalry. And then a searing pain in his stomach, making him stagger and collapse as he had so often staggered and collapsed heroically for an audience. Then the sordid reality of blood on hard unyielding earth, of pain and finally of death. Poor Kan.

The silence in the pit that had followed Langdon's words was shattered by the roar of a Hurricane as it passed just above our heads laying its smoke screen. The wind sang past its wings. It was unpleasantly close, yet we could see no sign of it. Over us was nothing but a dark fog of smoke, and every now and then a wisp curled into the pit, making us cough.

"What the hell is the smoke for?" Bombardier Hood asked me.

I started to explain, but the Tannoy suddenly blared out: "Mass formation attack alarm! Mass formation attack alarm! Two large formations of troop-carriers, escorted by fighters, are approaching the 'drome from the south-east."

The telephone rang. Langdon answered it. When at length he had put back the receiver, he said: "They're mostly Ju. 52's.

---

* *sick bay:* dressing station or hospital.

They're at eight thousand feet and coming lower. Gun Ops. say that fifty are expected to attempt a landing on the 'drome."

"Fifty!" said Chetwood. "Good God!"

There was a stunned silence.

Then Hood exclaimed: "How the hell are we expected to fire on them when this blasted smoke screen has made it so dark that we can barely see the hut over there?"

"You don't need to for the moment," I replied. "The idea is that they pile themselves up against the hangars." And I explained about the balloons and how they should mislead the Jerries.

"Yes, but suppose they do manage to land?" Hood insisted.

The 'phone rang. I shrugged my shoulders. I didn't know the answer. That worried me. I hadn't realised how dark it would be after the smoke screen had been laid over the 'drome.

Langdon put down the receiver. "That's the answer to your question," he told Hood. "As soon as they start coming in, the searchlight on Station H.Q. will be switched on."

"Won't that give the game away?" asked Chetwood.

Langdon hesitated. "I don't see why it should. After all, suppose this was their own smoke and they were feeling their way in, they would surely expect us to try to pierce the smoke with what lights we had available."

"Listen!" cried Fuller.

For a second all I could hear was the steady drone of the two Hurricanes. The drone grew to a roar as one of them swept over us. The noise of its engines gradually lessened. Then suddenly behind that noise I thought I heard a steady throb. For a moment I was not sure. The other Hurricane swept over the pit. And when the sound of its engine had dropped to a distant drone, I knew I was right. Faint to the south was a low throb, deep and insistent. My inside seemed to turn to water. The moment had arrived.

The sound grew till it beat upon the air, drowning the engines of the Hurricanes except when they were very close. Like the ripping of calico came the sound of machine-gun fire. Two bursts. The sound of the German 'planes seemed to fill the heavens. I had a horrible sense of claustrophobia*. I longed

---

* *claustrophobia:* dread of being hemmed in.

to tear that curtain of smoke away so that I could see what we had to face. More machine-gun fire. Then the high-pitched drone of a 'plane diving to the east of us. It rose to a crescendo of sound like a buzz-saw. And when I thought the noise of it could not rise any higher there was a tremendous crash.

"Attention, please! Attention, please! Troop-carriers are now circling to land. They will come in from north to south. Gi' 'em a reet gude welcome, lads. Off!"

The throb of their engines had passed right over the 'drome. But the sound had not then gradually faded. It seemed to split up. All round the 'drome was this deep, persistent pulsing. I must admit I felt scared. I think we all did. The menace was unseen. There was only the sound of it. And the sound was all about us.

The gun was laid * on the landing field. Chetwood and Red were in the layers' seats. Two sandbags on the parapet marked the limits of our field of fire. Shells fused at a half and one † stood ready in the lockers behind the gun.

One particular engine became noticeable above the general throb that filled the air. It was coming in from the north. "Right. Fuse a half. Load!" Langdon's voice was clear and calm, and I recognized that boyish note in it that had struck me before.

The searchlight on Station H.Q. flickered and blazed into life. The great beam produced a queer effect. It was diffused by the smoke so that the landing ground was lit by a sheen of white and not by a beam. It was rather like the moon seen through thin cloud. And above it the banks of rolling smoke looked inky black.

The throb of the approaching 'plane grew nearer. The beat of it was slower now, and I could almost hear the screws ‡ ploughing their way through the air. The throb became more and more sluggish. The sound crossed the 'drome in front of us. It seemed as though it was feeling its way through the smoke.

Then suddenly landing wheels and a vague spread of wings showed white through the smoke. The moment of its appear-

---

* gun was laid: was sighted toward.
† a half and one: this gives the fuse-length. These are very short fuses.
‡ screws: propellers.

ance in the light of the searchlight seemed an age. It was dropping gently, searching with its wheels for the runway that
should have been there. The whole 'plane was visible now,
like a huge silvery moth flying into the light of a street lamp
on a misty night. There was an iridescent unreality about that
great winged thing, so cumbersome, yet so fairy-like.

It came out of the smoke flying straight for B hangar. Too
late the pilot saw the trap. Poor devil. He was feeling for a
landing in thick smoke. Suddenly he had dropped right
through the smoke, and in the dazzling light the dark shadow
of a hangar loomed up in front of his cockpit.

The sudden frantic revving of the engines made the 'plane
buoyant. It lifted slightly. For a moment I thought he would
clear the hangar. But his under-carriage caught the edge of the
roof, and the great 'plane tipped slowly up on to its nose and
then over to its back. There was a splintering crash and it disappeared from sight as the roof of the hangar collapsed.

The next one was already coming in. Above us the burst of
machine-gun fire were becoming more and more persistent.
Somewhere up there in the cold light of the dawn a dog-fight
was in progress. The next 'plane was coming in to find its
landing now. It was crossing the landing ground, feeling its
way as the first one had done. Because I wanted a visual impression of the pit in that moment I glanced round it. All eyes
were fixed, fascinated, on the white glare of the searchlight,
waiting for the instant when the 'plane would become visible
as it dropped gently through the smoke. I imagine the gaze of
every one around the landing field was fascinatedly fixed on
the bright belly of the smoke above the hangars.

The Tannoy broke in upon our expectancy. "Ground defences south of B hangar to cover exits from the hangar. Cover
exits from B hangar. Off."

I hardly heard it. All my senses were concentrated on watching the 'plane that was coming in. No one in the pit stirred.
No one spoke.

One moment there was just the smoke made white by the
searchlight. The next, the 'plane was there. It looked just like
the other, monstrously big and all silvery. I felt rather than
heard the slight gasp as we saw it. It was dropping faster than
the other. The pilot never seemed to see the hangar. The great

'plane simply drifted straight into it. The wings crumpled, and as it fell in a shattered wreck to the ground we heard the crash of it. Several figures staggered out. They seemed dazed. There was a burst of machine-gun fire. And then another. The figures crumpled.

I suddenly realised that it was getting lighter. The fog of smoke above our heads was thinning out. The Hurricanes had finished laying the smoke. Another Ju. 52 was coming in. Above our heads the sounds of machine-gun fire had become almost constant, and behind the throb of the circling troop-carriers was the high-pitched drone of fighters diving and twisting and climbing. A pale light filtered into the pit. And in a moment I could see the eastern sky all flushed with the light of the sun, which had not yet risen above the horizon. The edge of the smoke, banked up in dark-brown billows, rolled away from the pit like a curtain, revealing a cold sky tinged with bluish green. To the east of us I could see a dozen or more big Junkers flying round and round in a circle, nose to tail for protection. It was not light enough yet to see the fighters, scrapping high overhead. But I could see one fighter diving on the formation of Junkers, letting rip with his guns and zooming away again.

"Look!" Langdon nudged my arm.

I swung back to the landing field. The breeze had freshened and the bank of smoke was rolling back fast. But it still covered two-thirds of the field. The light of the searchlight seemed fainter and farther away now that we were standing in daylight. And it showed another troop-carrier below the smoke. It had come through the smoke sooner than the others, and the pilot had time to see the danger. The roar of his engines as he revved seemed to shake the pit. But he scarcely lifted at all. Only his speed increased. He banked and his wing hit the the hangar. The whole scene looked unreal. It was like watching a show. The presence of the smoke seemed to put a barrier between ourselves, who were standing in daylight, and the 'plane and the hangars, which were in artificial darkness and lit by artificial light. Rather a similar effect to that of the footlights in a theatre. The 'plane crumpled up, much as the other had done. But there was a sudden explosion and a great sheet of flame was puffed up into the smoke. In an in-

stant the flames had spread to the hangar. The belly of the
smoke glowed red. It was a fantastic sight—the twisted, blazing wreckage and the flames licking up the battered side of the
hangar. I thought I heard screams. It may have been my imagination. But I knew men were dying in that inferno, dying a
horrible torturing death. The thought sickened me. I had not
become sufficiently imbued with the bestiality of war to feel
exultant, though I knew they were dying because they had
come to destroy us. It was either they or us. I knew that. But
it didn't prevent me from feeling a direct responsibility for
their death.

The next 'plane coming in was frightened by that red glow.
Its engines revved up and the sound began to come towards us.
Suddenly it appeared out of the smoke, its wings balanced at a
crazy angle as it banked. It was coming straight for us.

" 'Plane!" yelled Langdon. "On, on," came the voices of the
layers. And the barrel of the gun began to follow the target as
it banked round and away from us. Langdon waited till it
was side on to us and then ordered, "Fire!"

The gun cracked and before the flames of the charge had
ceased to spurt from the barrel, it seemed, the shell had exploded. The noise of it was almost as loud as the noise of the
gun. At that range it was impossible to miss. Langdon had
judged the fuse range nicely. The shell burst just in front of
the 'plane. The wings folded down and the whole 'plane
seemed to disintegrate. The fuselage split in half. I saw men
falling out. The wreckage strewed itself among the trees in
the valley.

The smoke had rolled back now and exposed the whole aerodrome. It lay on the south-western edge of the 'drome like a
low cloud. It was getting really light now and the high cloud
above us was tinged with a delicate pink. Against that lovely
colouring little dark dots darted in and out amongst each
other like flies.

All round the 'drome big cumbersome Ju. 52's circled and
circled incessantly like vultures waiting for their prey to die.
And amongst them the fighters droned like angry hornets. To
the north-east of us there were more over Mitchet.

What would they do now? They were full of troops, not
bombs—thank God! I half expected them to sheer off home-

ward now that their plan had failed. But they continued to circle. I wasn't sure whether they were undecided or whether they were waiting for something.

But we were not left long in doubt. Some twenty German fighters, who were still flying in formation well above the dog-fight, went into a dive. It was Langdon who first pointed them out to us. He had been searching the sky with his glasses.

They came right down to the north of us. Only when they were at about two thousand did they flatten out. Then they began to circle, and one by one they dived out of their new formation and came straight for the 'drome.

I had no doubt of their intention. Nor had Langdon. "Take cover!" he yelled. And we flattened ourselves in a bunch against the parapet nearest the approaching fighters. He crouched down too, but he kept his head just above the sand-bags so that he could see what was happening. There was a sharp burst of machine-gun fire, and a second later an Me. 109 shot over us. The Bofors pit to the north of us had taken the full force of the first attack. From the other side of the 'drome came the sound of a similar attack.

Then came the high-pitched drone of another German fighter. The staccato chatter of guns. The cinders on the floor of the pit kicked and little holes appeared in the sandbags op-posite where we lay. One of the sandbags above me fell on to my tin hat, covering me with sand. Zoom! The 'plane flashed overhead. All round the 'drome Lewis guns and Bren guns opened up, adding to the confusion.

"Layers on," Langdon shouted above the din. "Fuller am-munition. Chester number six. Remainder stay under cover."

I peeped over the parapet as the men sprang to their posts. A troop-carrier was just coming in to land. "Fuse one. Load. Fire!" The drone of another Messerschmitt approaching could be heard even above the noise of the gun. We must have fired at practically the same moment as the other three-inch. There were two bursts just in front of the 'plane, mixed up with streams of tracer shell from the Bofors. I saw it plunge. Then I ducked as the pit was sprayed again.

By the grace of God no one was hit, though Langdon got his face cut by a bit of flying cinder.

Three times this happened. Each time we destroyed a 'plane.

The fourth time I found myself laying. Red had been killed outright, a bullet through his head. This had happened as we destroyed the second Junkers. The third time it was Blah who was hit. He got a bullet through his arm. Fuller got one in the foot.

Three twin-engined 'planes appeared out of the north. At first we thought they were Me. 110's. But suddenly Langdon cried, "They're Blenheims."

And Blenheims they were, thrown in as fighters to make weight in the emergency. They came in at about two thousand feet. And high up we saw a squadron of Spitfires dive on the Messerschmitts that had been worrying us.

Then suddenly Junkers and Messerschmitts turned for home, the latter circling the troop-carriers to cover their retreat. It was all over in a few seconds. One moment the sky was full of Jerries and the din of battle. Then the sky emptied. The throb and drone of 'planes died away. A great quiet settled on the Station, in which the crackle of the flames at B hangar was the only sound. I leaned back against the gun. Peace at last. It was over.

I think I passed out then. I didn't faint. It was just that the reaction left my mind a blank. I wasn't conscious of sound or sight. I came to to find Langdon getting the casualties to the sick bay. And the Tannoy was announcing: "All clear! All clear! All ground defences and gun teams will remain at the alert. All clear! All clear!"

TOPICS FOR DISCUSSION

1. Do these account of what happens at an airdrome sound convincing—as if it were written by one who had seen it all? Any improbabilities? If so, what?

2. Read over the description of what Hanson saw in the Officer's room and then explain how Headquarters got its information, and sent out its orders. Could they send orders to fighter planes already in the air? How?

3. Some one who has read all of *Attack Alarm* should tell the story preceding the final chapter which we have here.

4. Mr. Innes did not mention the handsome uniforms, the marching, and the bands that we always associate with armies. Why?

5. Are soldiers in this story ever afraid? Would this book make a good motion picture? If you were planning the picture would you take the story exactly as it is, or would you play up the romance, glory, and courage?

6. Vayle in the novel is respected and liked by nearly everyone who knew him. In the picture would you make him a slinking villain, cruel, overbearing, hated? Why or why not?

BIBLIOGRAPHY

AIR YOUTH OF AMERICA—*Building and Flying Model Airplanes.* Appleton-Century, N. Y., 1941. 246 pp.
A book prepared for Air Youth of America.

ALLEN, Elmer L.—*New Model Airplanes.* Frederick A. Stokes Co., N. Y., 1937. 224 pp.
Detailed instructions with diagrams and measurements.

BENÉT, William Rose—*With Wings as Eagles,* Dodd, Mead & Co., N. Y., 1940.
Twenty-four poems about flying and fliers, all by Mr. Benét.

BLACK, Archibald—*The Story of Flying.* McGraw, Hill & Co., N. Y., 1940. 257 pp.
An interesting narrative of the development of aviation.

BOFF, Charles—*Boys' Book of Flying.* E. P. Dutton & Co., N. Y., 1937.
A story of the development of flying. Elementary.

BRIER, H. M.—*Sky Cruisers.* Random House, N. Y., 1942.
Fiction.

BRIER, H. M.—*Sky Freighters.* Random House, N. Y., 1942.
Fiction.

COLLINS, Francis A.—*Boys' Book of Model Aeroplanes.* Appleton-Century Co., N. Y., 1941. 262 pp.
An excellent practical book on construction of models.

DONAHUE, Arthur G.—*Tally-Ho! Yankee in a Spitfire.* Macmillan Co., N. Y., 1941.
The story of the author's experience as a British pilot in the fall and winter of 1940–1941. Really thrilling, but a modestly written account.

EDMUNDS, Ann C.—*Silent Flight.* Country Life Ltd., London, 1939. 83 pp.
A good account of constructing and flying gliders, models, and man-carrying sizes.

FLOHERTY, John J.—*'Board the Airliner.* Doubleday, Doran and Company, N. Y., 1939. 96 pp.
Very interesting stories about flying.

GANN, Ernest K.—*All American Aircraft.* Thomas Y. Crowell Co., N. Y., 1941. 122 pp.
Excellent pictures and brief descriptions of our commercial and military airplanes.

GARNETT, David—*A Rabbit in the Air.* Chatto & Windus, London, 1932. 117 pp.
Entries in the diary of a man made at the time he was learning to fly a plane.

GRAF, Nelly—*Air Stewardess.* Gramercy Pub. Co., N. Y., 256 pp.
Popular adventure and romance of an air stewardess giving all the facts about training and duties. Recommended for girls.

GUYTON, Boone T.—*Air Base*. McGraw-Hill Book Co., N. Y., 1941. 295 pp.
Accurate description and narrative of training for Naval air service at North Island base, San Diego. Very good. Well written, not technical. Good pictures.

HALL, Charles Gilbert—*Skyways*. Macmillan Co., N. Y., 1938. 141 pp.
An unusually good brief account of the development of flying. Well illustrated.

HAWKES, Frank—*Once to Every Pilot*. Stackpole, N. Y., 1936. 144 pp.
Popular narrative with pictures by a world-famous pilot.

HEFLIN, Alma—*Adventure was the Compass*. Little, Brown & Co., Boston, 1942.
Two young women decide to buy a plane and fly to Alaska for a vacation. Miss Heflin is a very capable pilot. The story is full of adventure but gaiety is its dominant tone.

INNES, Hammond—*Attack Alarm*. Macmillan Co., N. Y., 1942. 287 pp.
Fiction. A story of the air battle over Britain by a Lieutenant who was in it as a pilot. Exciting, accurate. Well written.

LANGWIESCHE, Wolfgang—*I'll Take the High Road*. Harcourt, Brace & Co., N. Y., 1939. 254 pp.
A narrative (not a novel) of the author's experiences in piloting an inexpensive small plane over a good deal of country. Real but amusing.

LENT, Henry B.—*Aviation Cadet*. Macmillan Co., N. Y., 1941. 175 pp.
In the form of an interesting story, a reliable account of cadet training at Pensacola.

LENT, Henry B.—*Flight 17*. Macmillan Co., N. Y., 1940. 96 pp.
In narrative form we have a complete story of a passenger-plane flight from New York to Chicago. Many illustrations.

LEYSON, Capt. Burr W.—*Aeronautical Occupations*. E. P. Dutton & Co., N. Y., 210 pp.
Information about the jobs connected with aviation. Authentic.

LEYSON, Capt. Burr W.—*American Wings*. E. P. Dutton & Co., N. Y.
Stories by a pilot who really knows how to write. Very interesting to young people. All types of flying service.

LEYSON, Capt. Burr W.—*Flight Training for the Army and Navy*. E. P. Dutton & Co., N. Y.
The routine of training and requirements for entrance.

LEYSON, Capt. Burr W.—*Wings of Defense*. E. P. Dutton & Co., N. Y., 1942. 210 pp.
A practical book of information about the several phases of aviation that a young man would like to know. Captain Leyson is an authority.

McDONALD, E. E., Jr.—*Youth Must Fly*. Harper & Brothers, N. Y., 1942. 221 pp.
A well-written book about the construction and use of gliders, written by a manufacturer of radios.

MATTOON, Charles S.—*How to Get a Job in Aviation*. Air Youth of America, Wash., D. C., 1942.

A practical and accurate handbook. It deals with many kinds of jobs—factory and ground—as well as with flying.

MERRILL, Dick, and DAWES, George—*How to be an Aviator*. Robt. M. McBride & Co., N. Y., 1942. 192 pp.

A practical book for young men ambitious to become aviators, by men who know the answers.

MILLER, BLAINE and DUPONT—*Bob Wakefield Naval Aviator*. Dodd, Mead & Co., N. Y., 1936. 285 pp.

Short stories about the experiences and adventures of a popular hero pilot, Bob Wakefield. A favorite for boys.

MILLER, BLAINE and DUPONT—*Bob Wakefield's Flight Log*. Dodd, Mead & Co., N. Y., 1940.

A second collection of the Bob Wakefield stories.

MORGAN, Deck—*Trans-Pacific Flight*. John H. Hopkins, Inc., N. Y., 1938. 247 pp.

About the wives and sweethearts of the men who make the commercial flights across the Pacific. Adult reading.

O'MALLEY, Patricia—*Wider Wings*. Greystone Press, N. Y., 1940. 273 pp.

Carol becomes chief hostess for an airline in the Central and South American business with the United States. Again, a pleasant story for girls.

O'MALLEY, Patricia—*Wings for Carol*. Greystone Press, N. Y., 1941. 320 pp.

A romance with Carol Rogers, an air hostess as heroine. Pleasant reading. Accurate as to facts about the duties of an air hostess. Miss O'Malley is intimately acquainted with her subject. Good reading for girls.

OTT, Lester—*Airplane Spotter*. Harcourt, Brace & Co., N. Y.

Aircraft identification for Army, Navy, and civilians. Detailed text, pictures and diagrams of the planes of the United States, Britain, Germany, Italy, and Japan.

PECKHAM, Betty—*Sky Hostess*. Thomas Nelson & Sons, N. Y., 84 pp. Narratives with pictures about the duties of the air hostesses. Very interesting for girls.

PLANCK, Charles E.—*Women with Wings*. Harper & Brothers, N. Y., 1941. 333 pp.

Excellent narrative account of the women who have been fliers as aviation developed. A good deal of biography. Good informal writing, occasionally slangy. News reporter style.

SAINT-EXUPÉRY, Antoine de—*Flight to Arras*. Reynal & Hitchcock, N. Y., 1942. 255 pp.

War flying, the author's experiences in the final days of the collapse of France in 1940. The experiences are packed in a single day, ending in a view of captured Arras. Saint-Exupéry has been called the Joseph Conrad of the air. This is a very tense book, beautifully written.

SAINT-EXUPÉRY, Antoine de—*Wind, Sand and Stars,* Reynal & Hitchcock, N. Y., 1939.

Narrative account of the experiences of the author as a passenger and air-mail carrier from Toulouse in Southern France across Spain, Morocco, and the desert to Dakar.

SEARS, W. R.—*The Airplane and its Component Parts*. John Wiley & Sons, N. Y., 1942. 75 pp.
Accurate information without being too technical. Pictures, drawings, and text.

DE SEVERSKY, Alexander P.—*Victory Through Air Power*. Simon & Shuster, N. Y., 1942. 355 pp.
One of the most important books yet written about air power in war. Adult. An excellent presentation of the case for the airplane in military organization. For adult readers.

SMITH, Henry Ladd—*Airways*. Alfred A. Knopf, Inc., N. Y., 1942. 430 pp.
An excellent history of commercial flying in the United States, from 1903 to 1942. Adult reading, but within the reach of high school students.

TEALE, Edwin W.—*The Book of Gliders*. E. P. Dutton & Co., N. Y. 379 pp.

THEISS, Lewis E.—*Flood Mappers Aloft*. W. A. Wilde & Co., 1937. The use of airplanes and photography in non-military map making.

TUNIS, John R.—*Million-Miler*. Julian Messner, Inc., N. Y., 1942. 253 pp.
The biography of Jack Zimmerman, the Ohio boy who became chief pilot for TWA (Transcontinental and Western Air, Inc.) and in his fifteen years as a pilot has spent 15,000 hours in the air and flown a million miles. Written by a professional writer of great skill.

WINSTON, Robert A.—*Dive Bomber*. Holiday House, N. Y., 1939. 191 pp.
In the form of a narrative, the book covers the details of learning to fly the Navy's fighting planes.

AIR MAGAZINES

Air Facts. Air Facts, Inc., 30 Rockefeller Plaza, N. Y.
A magazine for pilots.
Air News. Air News Pub. Co., 404 N. Wesley Ave., Mt. Morris, Ill.
The picture magazine of aviation.
Model Airplane News. Joy Publishing Co., Mt. Morris, Ill.
For amateurs.
New Horizons. Pan-American Airways, 135 E. 42 St. N. Y.
Magazine of the American Merchant Marine of the air.
U. S. Air Service. Air Service Publishing Co. Wash., D. C.